Responsorial Psalms

Compiled by Colin Mawby

kevin
mayhew

We hope you enjoy the music in this book. Further copies are available from your local Kevin Mayhew stockist.

In case of difficulty, or to request a catalogue, please contact the publisher direct by writing to:

The Sales Department
KEVIN MAYHEW LTD
Buxhall
Stowmarket
Suffolk IP14 3BW

Phone 01449 737978
Fax 01449 737834
E-mail info@kevinmayhewltd.com

First published in Great Britain in 2004 by Kevin Mayhew Ltd.

ISBN 1 84417 313 5
ISMN M 57024 378 5
Catalogue No: 1450335

0 1 2 3 4 5 6 7 8 9

Cover design by Angela Selfe

Music setter: Donald Thomson

Printed and bound in Great Britain

Foreword

The Psalms are not readings nor were they specifically composed as prayers, but as poems of praise.

Though sometimes they may be proclaimed like a reading, nevertheless, because of their literary character, they are rightly called in Hebrew *Tehillim,* that is, 'songs of praise', and in Greek *Psalmoi,* 'songs to be sung to the sound of the harp'. In all the psalms there is a certain musical quality which determines the correct way of praying them. Therefore, though a psalm may be recited without being sung, its musical character should not be overlooked. Whilst certainly offering a text to our mind, the psalm is more concerned with moving the spirits of those singing and listening, and indeed of those accompanying it with music.

Whoever sings the psalms properly, meditating as they pass from verse to verse, is always prepared to respond in their hearts to the movements of that Spirit who inspired the psalmists and is present to devout men and women ready to accept his grace. Thus the psalmody, though it commands the reverence due to the majesty of God, should be conducted in joy and a spirit of charity, as befits the freedom of the children of God, and is in harmony with divinely inspired poetry and song.

Whoever sings a psalm opens their heart to those emotions which inspired the psalm, each according to its literary type, whether it be a psalm of lament, confidence or thanksgiving.

THE GENERAL INTRODUCTION OF THE LITURGY
OF THE HOURS, NOS. 103, 104, 106

Performance Notes

The Psalms

Each psalm has a response and a simple tone both of which are designed to lie well within the range of cantors and congregations. An optional instrumental descant is given to be played on C or B♭ instruments – a flute will be ideal.

The psalm may be sung responsorially, for example at Mass, where the psalm provides a mediation for the following readings. The Cantor/ Choir sing the response which is repeated by the people. The Cantor/Choir sing the verses and the people sing the response at the end of each verse.

Alternatively, and more appropriately at morning and evening prayer, the Response may be sung at the beginning and end of the psalm only. The psalm may then be sung in the following ways:

A Cantor/Choir alternating with the congregation
two sides of a choir alternating
two sides of a congregation alternating
sung straight through by all.

If the Gloria is to be sung after the final verse of a psalm or canticle, it is pointed thus:

Glory to the Father and | to the Son
and to the | Holy Spirit;
as it was in | the beginning
is now and shall be for e | ver. Amen

The Gospel Acclamations

Except from Ash Wednesday to Maundy Thursday, they are sung as follows:

All	Alleluia
Cantor/Choir	sings the appropriate scriptural verse
All	Alleluia

From Ash Wednesday to Maundy Thursday the Alleluia is replaced by the response:

Praise to you, O Christ, King of eternal glory.

The musical settings of the Acclamations will be found on pages 207-214.
Any setting may be chosen for any text.

Composers of Psalm Tones

TB	Timothy Blinko
KD	Keith Duke
SL	Simon Lesley
CM	Colin Mawby
GN	Geoff Nobes

Contents

Responsorial Psalms

First Sunday of Advent

YEAR A

Responsorial Psalm Psalm 121:1-2, 4-5, 6-9. Response cf. v.1

Andrew Wright

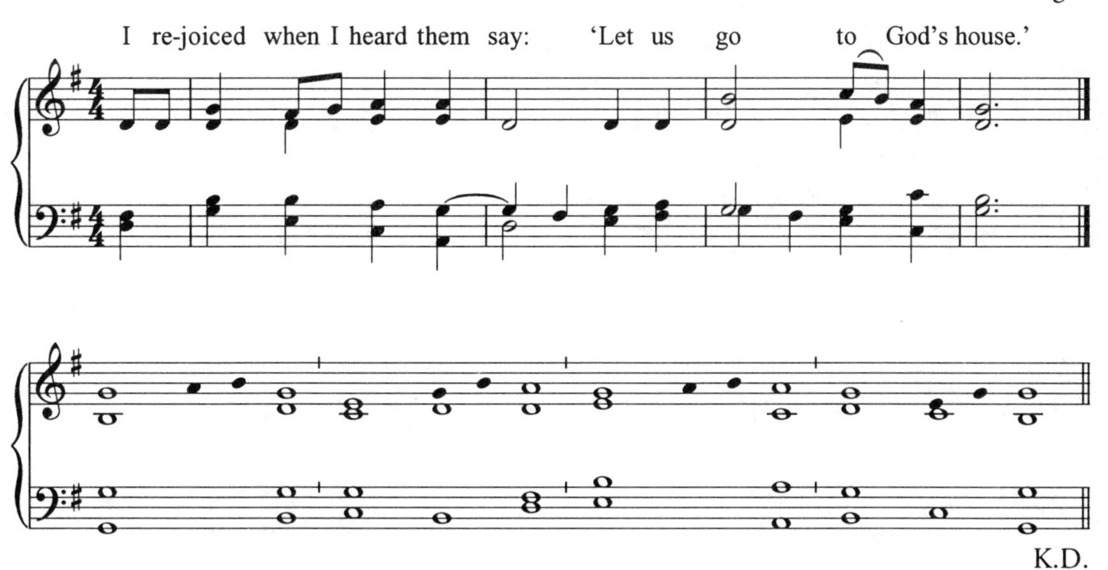

1. I rejoiced when I heard them say:
   'Let us go to God's house.'
   And now our feet are standing
   within your gates, O Jerusalem.

2. It is there that the tribes go up,
   the tribes of the Lord.
   For Israel's law it is,
   there to praise the Lord's name.

3. For the peace of Jerusalem pray:
   'Peace be to your homes!
   May peace reign in your walls,
   in your palaces, peace!'

4. For love of my brethren and friends
   I say: 'Peace upon you!'
   For love of the house of the Lord
   I will ask for your good.

Gospel Acclamation Psalm 84:8

Alleluia.
Let us see, O Lord, your mercy
and give us your saving help.
Alleluia.

First Sunday of Advent

YEAR B

Responsorial Psalm Psalm 79:2-3, 15-16, 18-19. Response v.4

Colin Mawby

God of hosts, bring us back; let your face shine on us and we shall be saved.

S.L.

1. O Shepherd of Israel, hear us,
   shine forth from your cherubim throne.
   O Lord, rouse up your might,
   O Lord, come to our help.

2. God of hosts, turn again, we implore,
   look down from heaven and see.
   Visit this vine and protect it,
   the vine your right hand has planted.

3. May your hand be on the one you have chosen,
   the one you have given your strength.
   And we shall never forsake you again:
   give us life that we may call upon your name.

Gospel Acclamation Psalm 84:8

Alleluia.
Let us see, O Lord, your mercy
and give us your saving help.
Alleluia.

C Instrument
B♭ Instrument

First Sunday of Advent

YEAR C

Responsorial Psalm Psalm 24:4-5, 8-9, 10, 14. Response v.1

Andrew Moore

To you, O Lord, I lift up my soul, I lift up my soul.

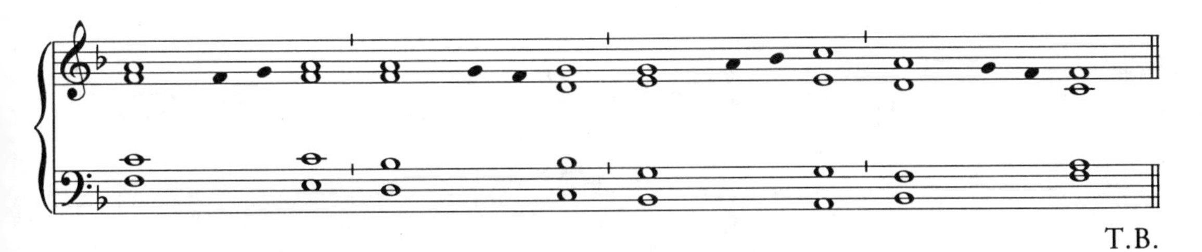

T.B.

1. Lord, make me know your ways.
   Lord, teach me your paths.
   Make me walk in your truth, and teach me:
   for you are God my saviour.

2. The Lord is good and upright.
   He shows the path to those who stray,
   he guides the humble in the right path;
   he teaches his way to the poor.

3. His ways are faithfulness and love
   for those who keep his covenant and will.
   The Lord's friendship is for those who revere him;
   to them he reveals his covenant.

Gospel Acclamation Psalm 84:8

Alleluia.
Let us see, O Lord, your mercy
and give us your saving help.
Alleluia.

Second Sunday of Advent

YEAR A

Responsorial Psalm Psalm 71:1-2, 7-8, 12-13, 17. Response cf. v.7

Alan Rees

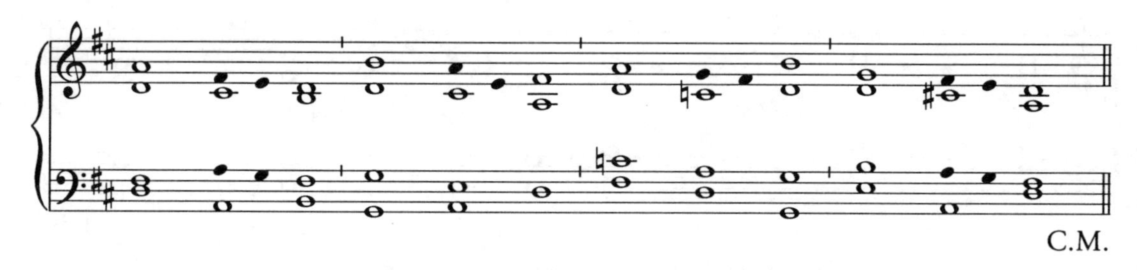

1. O God, give your judgement to the king,
to a king's son your justice,
that he may judge your people in justice
and your poor in right judgement.

2. In his days justice shall flourish
and peace till the moon fails.
He shall rule from sea to sea,
from the Great River to earth's bounds.

3. For he shall save the poor when they cry
and the needy who are helpless.
He will have pity on the weak
and save the lives of the poor.

4. May his name be blest for ever
and endure like the sun.
Every tribe shall be blest in him,
all nations bless his name.

Gospel Acclamation Luke 3:4, 6

Alleluia.
Prepare a way for the Lord and make his paths straight,
and all mankind shall see the salvation of our God.
Alleluia.

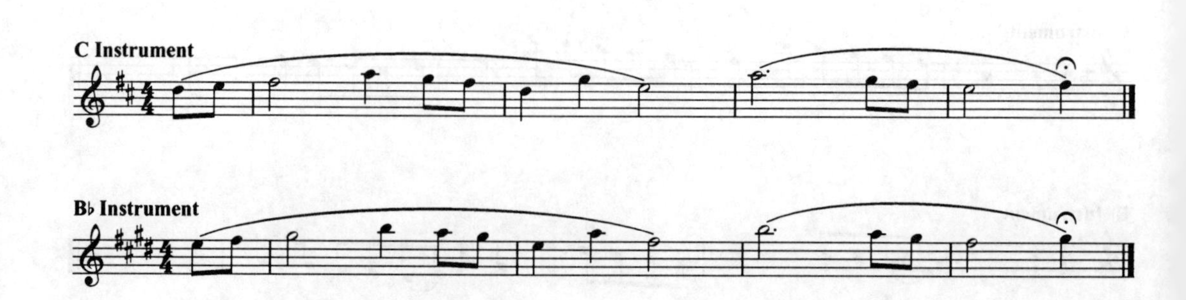

Second Sunday of Advent

YEAR B

Responsorial Psalm Psalm 84:9-14. Response v.8

Richard Lloyd

Let us see, O Lord, your mer - cy and give us your sav - ing help.

G.N.

1. I will hear what the Lord God has to say,
   a voice that speaks of peace.
   His help is near for those who fear him
   and his glory will dwell in our land.

2. Mercy and faithfulness have met;
   justice and peace have embraced.
   Faithfulness shall spring from the earth
   and justice look down from heaven.

3. The Lord will make us prosper
   and our earth shall yield its fruit.
   Justice shall march before him
   and peace shall follow his steps.

Gospel Acclamation Luke 3:4, 6

Alleluia.
Prepare a way for the Lord and make his paths straight,
and all mankind shall see the salvation of our God.
Alleluia.

C Instrument
B♭ Instrument

Second Sunday of Advent

YEAR C

Responsorial Psalm Psalm 125. Response v.3

John Bertalot

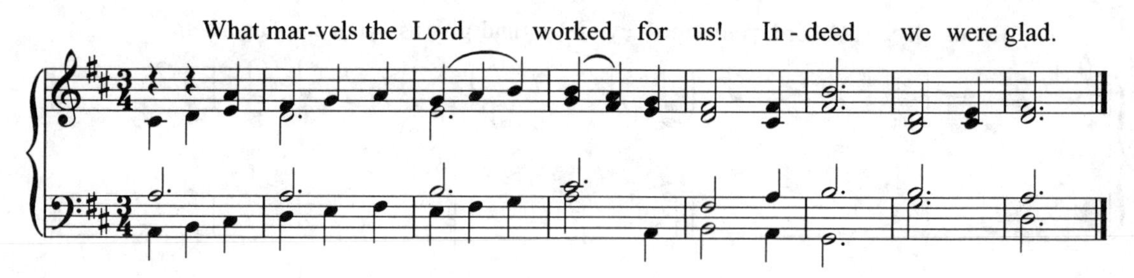

K.D.

1. When the Lord delivered Zion from bondage,
   it seemed like a dream.
   Then was our mouth filled with laughter,
   on our lips there were songs.

2. The heathens themselves said: 'What marvels
   the Lord worked for them!'
   What marvels the Lord worked for us!
   Indeed we were glad.

3. Deliver us, O Lord, from our bondage
   as streams in dry land.
   Those who are sowing in tears
   will sing when they reap.

4. They go out, they go out, full of tears
   carrying seed for the sowing:
   they come back, they come back, full of song,
   carrying their sheaves.

Gospel Acclamation Luke 3:4, 6

Alleluia.
Prepare a way for the Lord and make his paths straight,
and all mankind shall see the salvation of our God.
Alleluia.

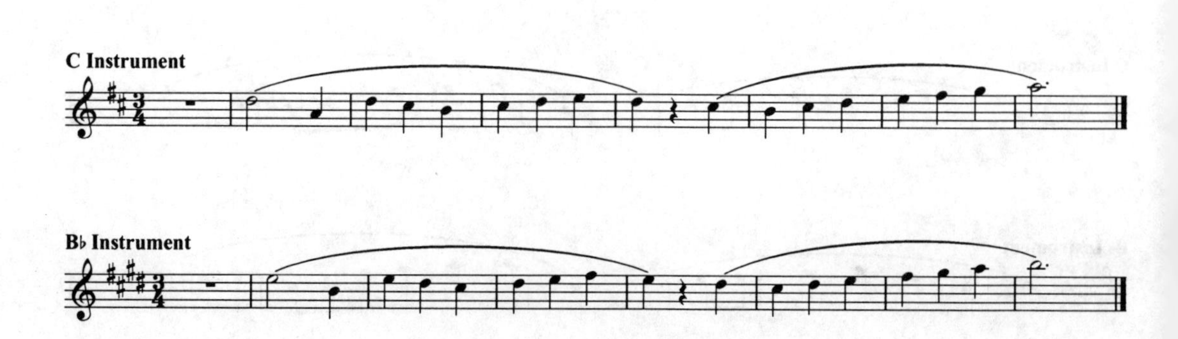

Third Sunday of Advent

YEAR A

Responsorial Psalm Psalm 145:6-10. Response cf. Isaiah 35:4

Andrew Moore

Come, Lord, and save us, come, Lord, and save us.

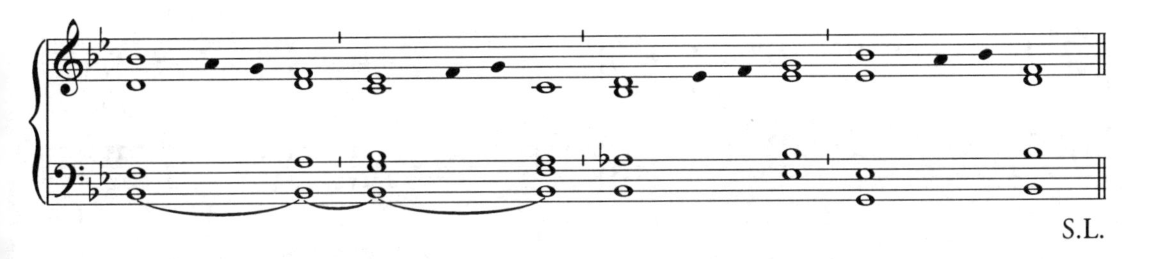

S.L.

1. It is the Lord who keeps faith for ever,
   who is just to those who are oppressed.
   It is he who gives bread to the hungry,
   the Lord, who sets prisoners free.

2. It is the Lord who gives sight to the blind,
   who raises up those who are bowed down,
   the Lord, who protects the stranger
   and upholds the widow and orphan.

3. It is the Lord who loves the just
   but thwarts the path of the wicked.
   the Lord will reign for ever,
   Zion's God, from age to age.

Gospel Acclamation Isaiah 61:1 (Luke 4:18)

Alleluia.
The spirit of the Lord has been given to me.
He has sent me to bring good news to the poor.
Alleluia.

Third Sunday of Advent

YEAR B

Responsorial Psalm Luke 1:46-50, 53-54. Response Isaiah 61:10

Gerry Fitzpatrick

My soul re - joi - ces in my God.

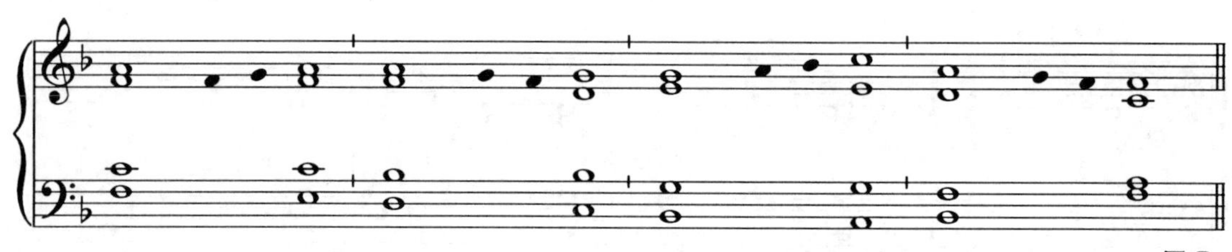

T.B.

1. My soul glorifies the Lord,
   my spirit rejoices in God, my saviour.
   He looks on his servant in her nothingness;
   henceforth all ages will call me blessed.

2. The Almighty works marvels for me.
   Holy is his name!
   His mercy is from age to age,
   on those who fear him.

3. He fills the starving with good things,
   sends the rich away empty.
   He protects Israel, his servant,
   remembering his mercy.

Gospel Acclamation Isaiah 61:1 (Luke 4:18)

Alleluia.
The spirit of the Lord has been given to me.
He has sent me to bring good news to the poor.
Alleluia.

C Instrument
B♭ Instrument

Third Sunday of Advent

YEAR C

Responsorial Psalm Isaiah 12:2-6. Response v.6

Andrew Wright

C.M.

1. Truly, God is my salvation,
   I trust, I shall not fear.
   For the Lord is my strength, my song,
   he became my saviour.

2. Give thanks to the Lord,
   give praise to his name!
   Make his mighty deeds known to the peoples!
   Declare the greatness of his name.

3. Sing a psalm to the Lord for he has done glorious deeds,
   make them known to all the earth!
   People of Zion, sing and shout for joy
   for great in your midst is the Holy One of Israel.

Gospel Acclamation Isaiah 61:1 (Luke 4:18)

Alleluia.
The spirit of the Lord has been given to me.
He has sent me to bring good news to the poor.
Alleluia.

C Instrument

B♭ Instrument

Fourth Sunday of Advent

YEAR A

Responsorial Psalm Psalm 23:1-6. Response cf. vv.7, 10

Alan Rees

G.N.

1. The Lord's is the earth and its fullness,
   the world and all its peoples.
   It is he who set it on the seas;
   on the waters he made it firm.

2. Who shall climb the mountain of the Lord?
   Who shall stand in his holy place?
   Those with clean hands and pure heart,
   who desire not worthless things.

3. They shall receive blessings from the Lord
   and reward from the God who saves them.
   Such are the ones who seek him,
   seek the face of the God of Jacob.

Gospel Acclamation Matthew 1:23

Alleluia.
The virgin will conceive and give birth to a son
and they will call him Emmanuel, a name which means 'God-is-with-us'.
Alleluia.

Fourth Sunday of Advent

YEAR B

Responsorial Psalm Psalm 88:2-5, 27, 29. Response cf. v.2

Richard Lloyd

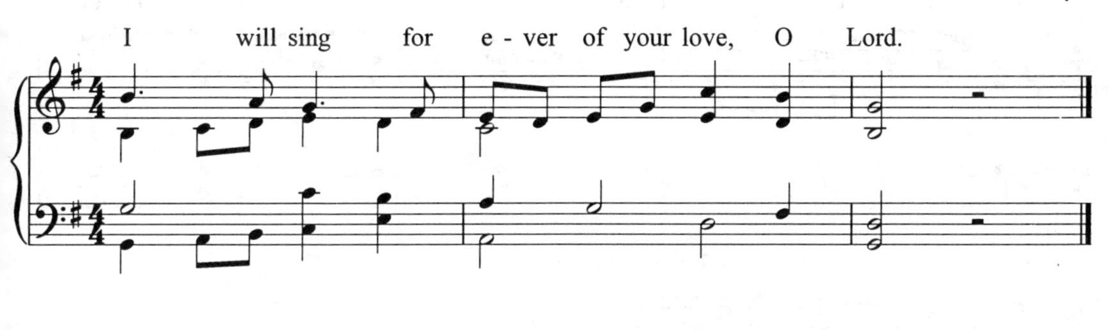

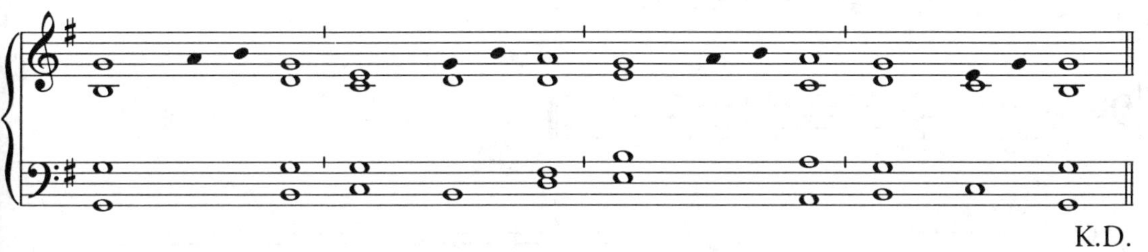

K.D.

1. I will sing for ever of your love, O Lord;
   through all ages my mouth will proclaim your truth.
   Of this I am sure, that your love lasts for ever,
   that your truth is firmly established as the heavens.

2. 'I have made a covenant with my chosen one;
   I have sworn to David my servant:
   I will establish your dynasty for ever
   and set up your throne through all ages.'

3. He will say to me: 'You are my father,
   my God, the rock who saves me.'
   I will keep my love for him always;
   for him my covenant shall endure.

Gospel Acclamation Luke 1:38

Alleluia.
I am the handmaid of the Lord:
let what you have said be done to me.
Alleluia.

Fourth Sunday of Advent

YEAR C

Responsorial Psalm Psalm 79: 2-3, 15-16, 18-19. Response v.4

Gerry Fitzpatrick

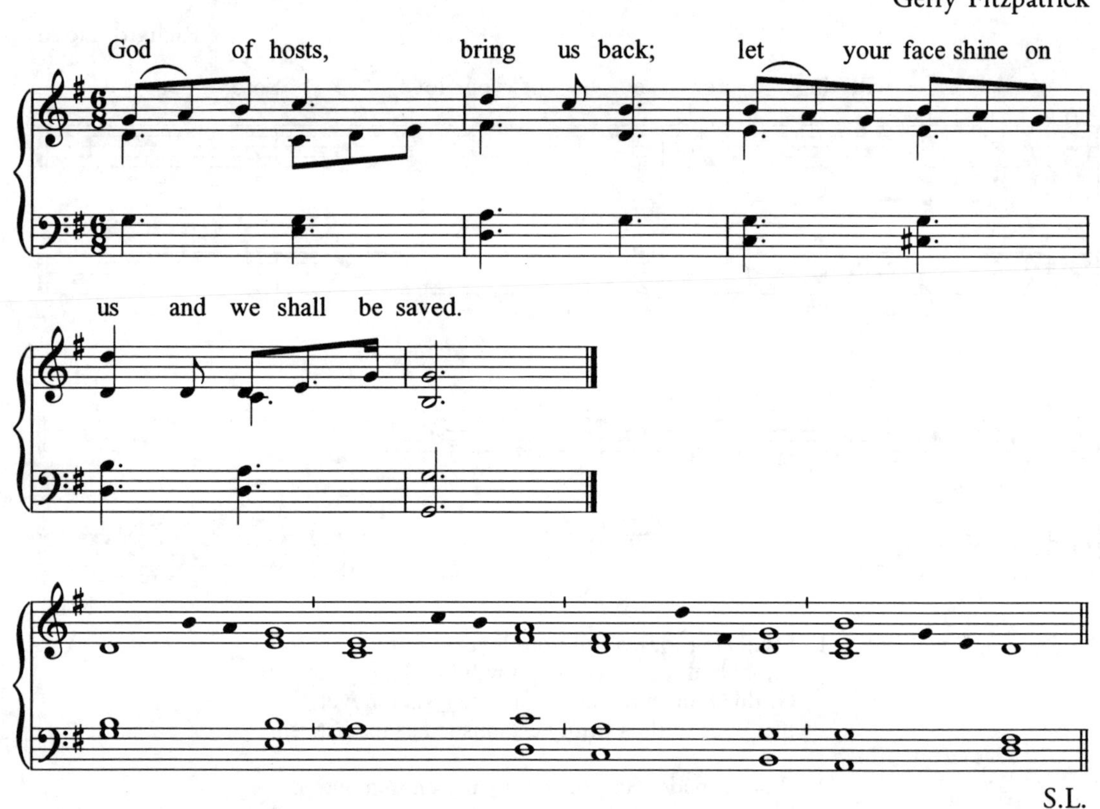

God of hosts, bring us back; let your face shine on
us and we shall be saved.
S.L.

1. O Shepherd of Israel, hear us,
shine forth from your cherubim throne.
O Lord, rouse up your might,
O Lord, come to our help.

2. God of hosts, turn again, we implore,
look down from heaven and see.
Visit this vine and protect it,
the vine your right hand has planted.

3. May your hand be on the one you have chosen,
the one you have given your strength.
And we shall never forsake you again:
give us life that we may call upon your name.

Gospel Acclamation Luke 1:38

Alleluia.
I am the handmaid of the Lord:
let what you have said be done to me.
Alleluia.

The Nativity of Our Lord – Midnight Mass

YEARS A, B AND C

Responsorial Psalm Psalm 95:1-3, 11-13. Response Luke 2:11

Colin Mawby

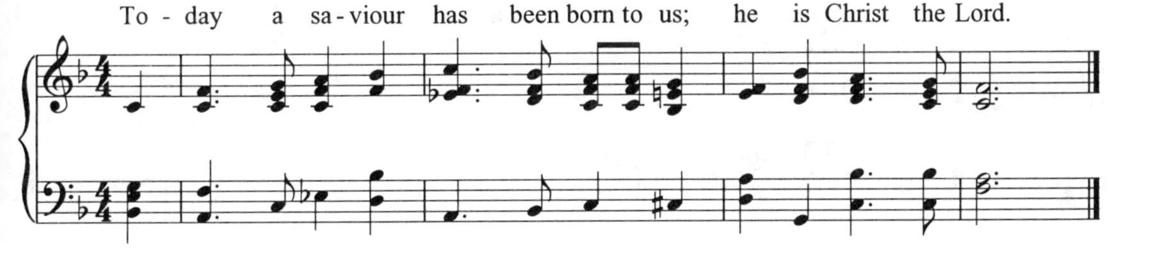

C.M.

1. O sing a new song to the Lord,
   sing to the Lord all the earth.
   O sing to the Lord, bless his name.
   Proclaim his help day by day,
   tell among the nations his glory
   and his wonders among all the peoples.

2. Let the heavens rejoice and earth be glad,
   let the sea and all within it thunder praise,
   let the land and all it bears rejoice,
   all the trees of the wood shout for joy
   at the presence of the Lord for he comes,
   he comes to rule the earth.

Gospel Acclamation Luke 2:10-11

Alleluia.
I bring you news of great joy:
today a saviour has been born to us, Christ the Lord.
Alleluia.

C Instrument

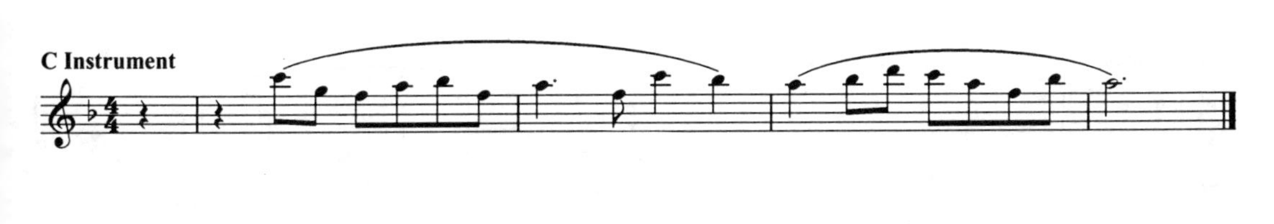

B♭ Instrument

The Nativity of Our Lord – Mass During the Day

YEARS A, B AND C

Responsorial Psalm Psalm 97:1-6. Response v.3

Alan Rees

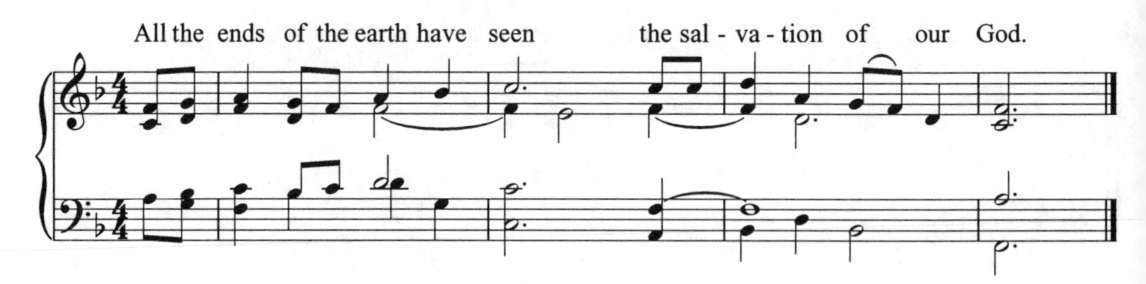

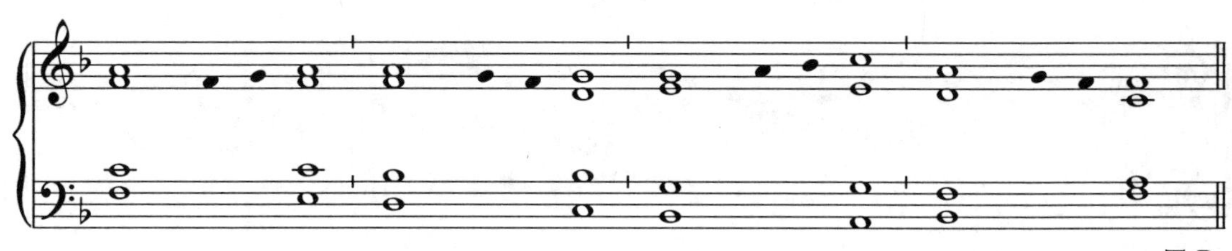

T.B.

1. Sing a new song to the Lord
   for he has worked wonders.
   His right hand and his holy arm
   have brought salvation.

2. The Lord has made known his salvation;
   has shown his justice to the nations.
   He has remembered his truth and love
   for the house of Israel.

3. All the ends of the earth have seen
   the salvation of our God.
   Shout to the Lord all the earth,
   ring out your joy.

4. Sing psalms to the Lord with the harp,
   with the sound of music.
   With trumpets and the sound of the horn
   acclaim the King, the Lord.

Gospel Acclamation

Alleluia.
Come, you nations, worship the Lord,
for today a great light has shone down upon the earth.
Alleluia.

Sunday in the Octave of Christmas

The Holy Family

YEARS A, B AND C

Responsorial Psalm Psalm 127:1-5. Response cf. v.1

Andrew Wright

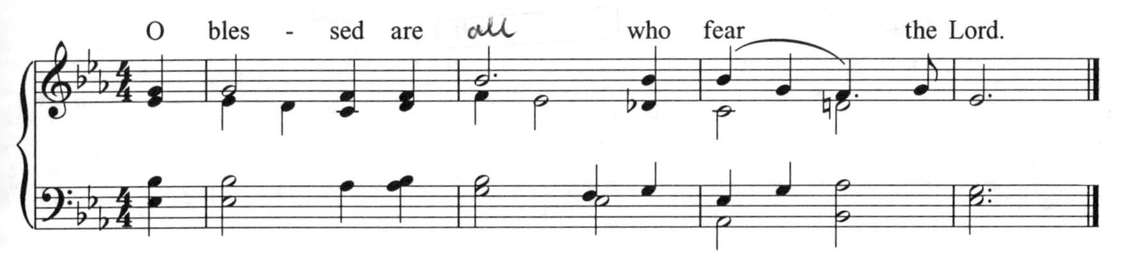

G.N.

Blessed are all who fear the Lord,
and walk in his ways!
By the labour of your hands you shall eat.
You will be blessed and prosper.

Your wife like a fruitful vine
in the heart of your house;
your children like shoots of the olive
around your table.

Indeed thus shall be blessed
the husband who fears the Lord.
May the Lord bless you from Sion/
all the days of your life!
May you see your children's children.

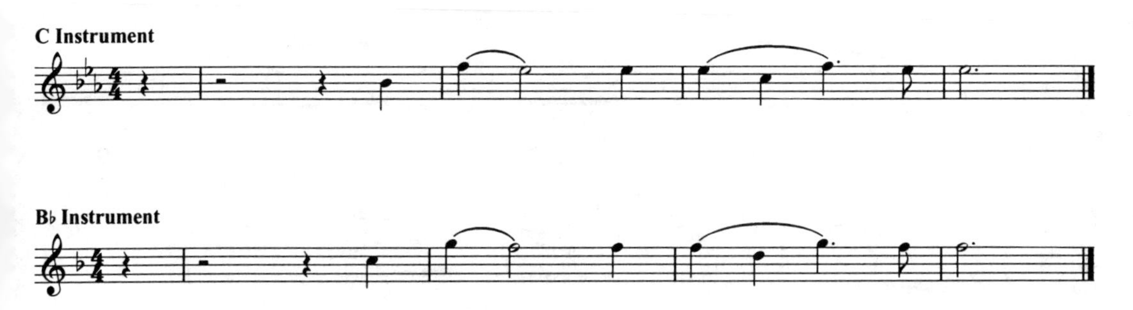

The Holy Family

YEAR B AD LIB

Responsorial Psalm Psalm 104:1-6, 8-9. Response vv.7, 8

Simon Lesley

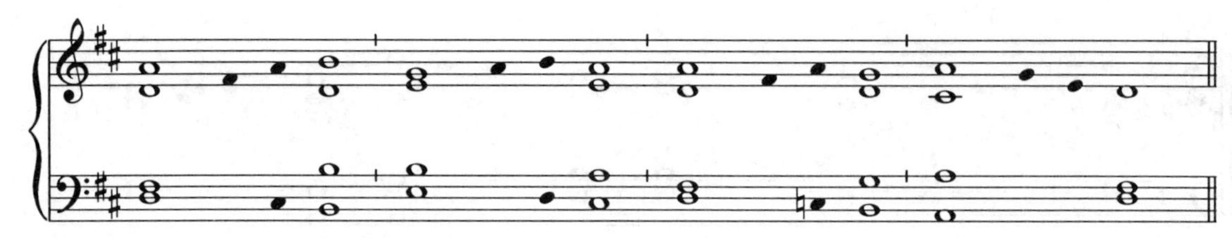

K.D.

1. Give thanks to the Lord, tell his name,
   make known his deeds among the peoples.
   O sing to him, sing his praise;
   tell all his wonderful works!

2. Be proud of his holy name,
   let the hearts that seek the Lord rejoice.
   Consider the Lord and his strength;
   constantly seek his face.

3. Remember the wonders he has done,
   his miracles, the judgements he spoke.
   O children of Abraham, his servant,
   O sons of the Jacob he chose.

4. He remembers his covenant for ever,
   his promise for a thousand generations,
   the covenant he made with Abraham,
   the oath he swore to Isaac.

Gospel Acclamation Hebrews 1:1-2

Alleluia.
At various times in the past
and in various different ways,
God spoke to our ancestors through the prophets;
but in our own time, the last days, he has spoken to us through his Son.
Alleluia.

Note: the tone should be sung twice.

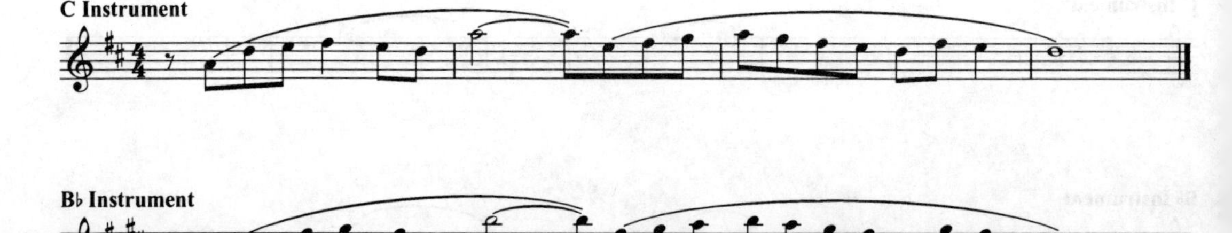

The Holy Family

YEAR C AD LIB

Responsorial Psalm Psalm 83:2-3, 5-6, 9-10. Response v.5

John Bertalot

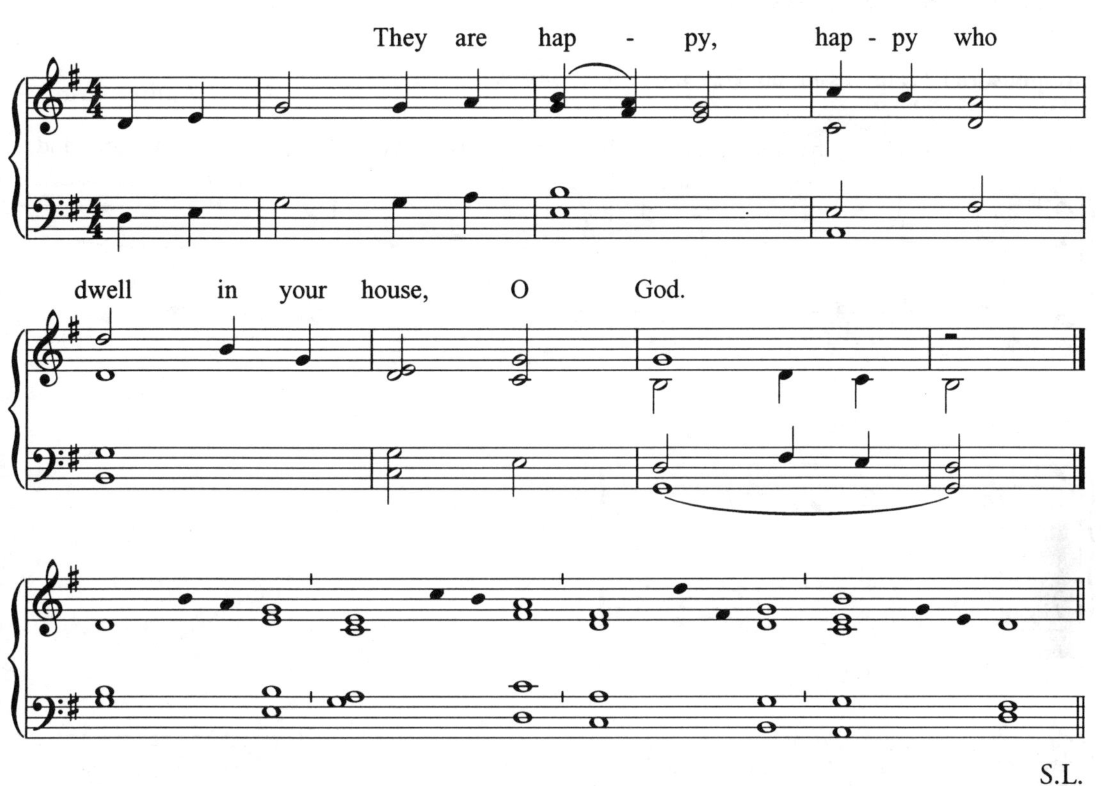

S.L.

1. How lovely <u>is</u> your dwelling place,
   Lord <u>God</u> of hosts.
   My soul is long<u>ing</u> and yearning,
   is yearning for the courts <u>of</u> the Lord.

2. They are happy, who dwell <u>in</u> your house,
   for ever sing<u>ing</u> your praise.
   They are happy, whose strength <u>is</u> in you;
   they walk with ever <u>grow</u>ing strength.

3. O Lord, God of hosts, <u>hear</u> my prayer,
   give ear, O <u>God</u> of Jacob.
   Turn your eyes, O <u>God</u>, our shield,
   look on the face of <u>your</u> anointed.

Gospel Acclamation cf. Acts 16:14

Alleluia.
Open our <u>heart</u>, O Lord,
to accept the words <u>of</u> your Son.
Alleluia.

1 January: Octave of Christmas

YEARS A, B AND C

Solemnity of Mary, Mother of God

Responsorial Psalm Psalm 66: 2-3, 5, 6, 8. Response v.2

Andrew Moore

T.B.

1. God, be gracious and bless us
   and let your face shed its light upon us.
   So will your ways be known upon earth
   and all nations learn your saving help.

2. Let the nations be glad and exult
   for you rule the world with justice.
   With fairness you rule the peoples,
   you guide the nations on earth.

3. Let the peoples praise you, O God;
   let all the peoples praise you.
   May God still give us his blessing
   till the ends of the earth revere him.

Gospel Acclamation Hebrews 1:1-2

Alleluia.
At various times in the past
and in various different ways,
God spoke to our ancestors through the prophets;
but in our own time, the last days, he has spoken to us through his Son.
Alleluia.

Note: the tone should be sung twice.

Second Sunday after Christmas YEARS A, B AND C

Responsorial Psalm Psalm 147:12-15, 19-20. Response John 1:14

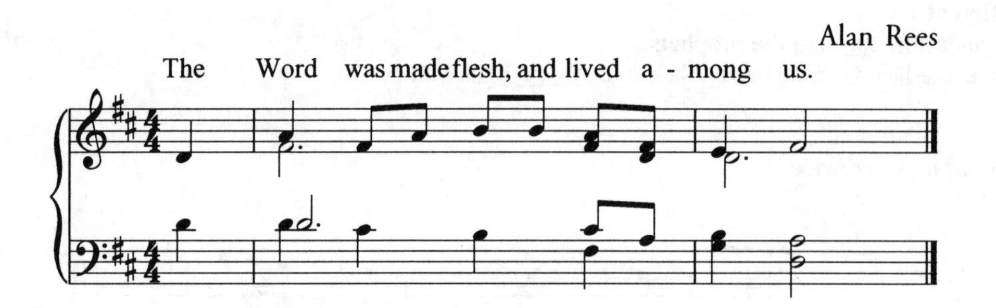

Alan Rees
The Word was made flesh, and lived a - mong us.

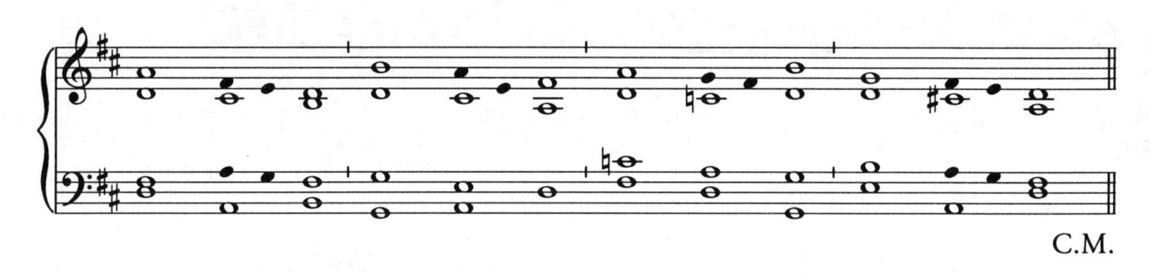

C.M.

1. O praise the Lord, Jerusalem!
   Zion, praise your God!
   He has strengthened the bars of your gates,
   he has blessed the children within you.

2. He established peace on your borders,
   he feeds you with finest wheat.
   He sends out his word to the earth
   and swiftly runs his command.

3. He makes his word known to Jacob,
   to Israel his laws and decrees.
   He has not dealt thus with other nations;
   he has not taught them his decrees.

Gospel Acclamation cf. 1 Timothy 3:16

Alleluia.
Glory be to you, O Christ, proclaimed to the pagans;
Glory be to you, O Christ, believed in by the world.
Alleluia.

6 January or the Sunday between 2 January and 8 January

The Epiphany of the Lord

YEARS A, B AND C

Responsorial Psalm Psalm 71:1-2, 7-8, 10-13. Response cf. v.11

John Bertalot

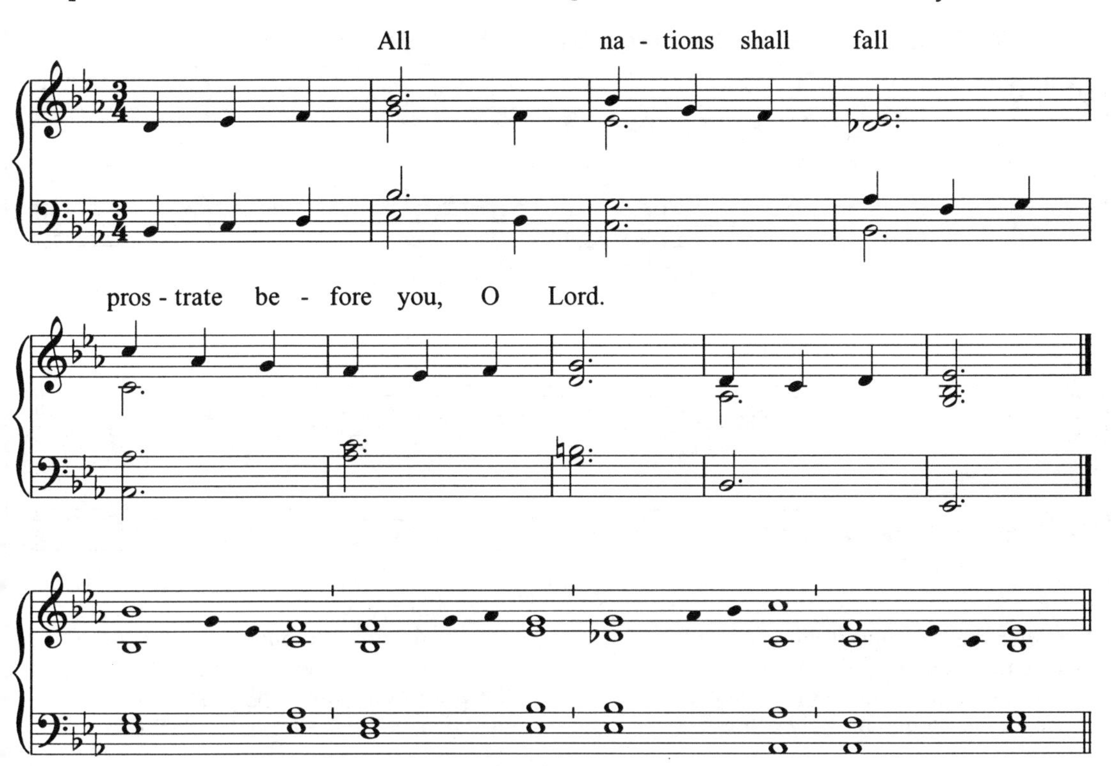

G.N.

1. O God, give your judgement to the king,
   to a king's son your justice,
   that he may judge your people in justice
   and your poor in right judgement.

2. In his days justice shall flourish
   and peace till the moon fails.
   He shall rule from sea to sea,
   from the Great River to earth's bounds.

3. The kings of Tarshish and the sea coasts
   shall pay him tribute.
   The kings of Sheba and Seba shall bring him gifts.
   Before him all kings shall fall prostrate,
   all nations shall serve him.

4. For he shall save the poor when they cry
   and the needy who are helpless.
   He will have pity on the weak
   and save the lives of the poor.

Gospel Acclamation Matthew 2:2

Alleluia.
We saw his star as it rose
and have come to pay homage to the Lord.
Alleluia.

The Baptism of the Lord

YEAR A

Responsorial Psalm Psalm 28:1-4, 9-10. Response v.11

Simon Lesley

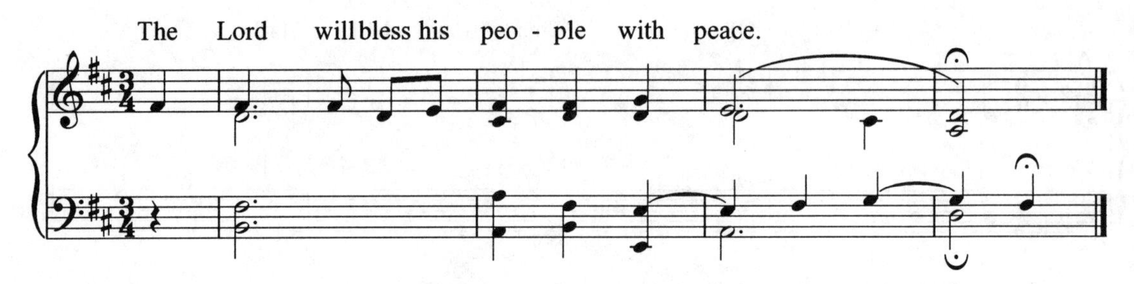

The Lord will bless his peo - ple with peace.

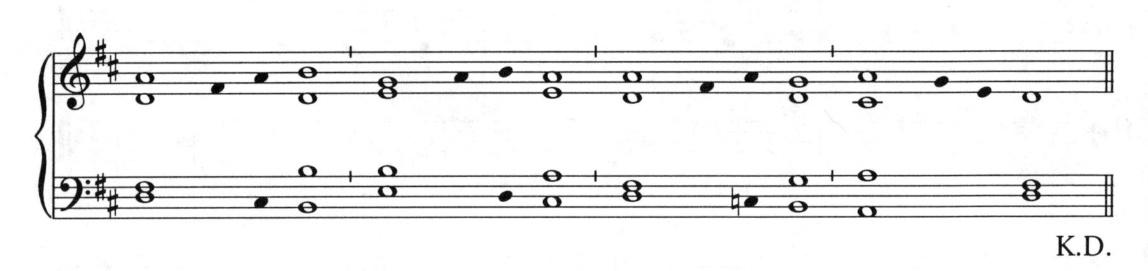

K.D.

1. O give the Lord you children of God,
   give the Lord glory and power;
   give the Lord the glory of his name.
   Adore the Lord in his holy court.

2. The Lord's voice resounding on the waters,
   the Lord on the immensity of waters;
   the voice of the Lord, full of power,
   the voice of the Lord, full of splendour.

3. The God of glory thunders.
   In his temple they all cry: 'Glory!'
   The Lord sat enthroned over the flood;
   the Lord sits as king for ever.

Gospel Acclamation cf. Mark 9:8

Alleluia.
The heavens opened and the Father's voice resounded:
'This is my Son, the Beloved. Listen to him.'
Alleluia.

C Instrument

B♭ Instrument

The Baptism of the Lord

YEAR B AD LIB

Responsorial Psalm Isaiah 12:2-6. Response v.6

John McCann

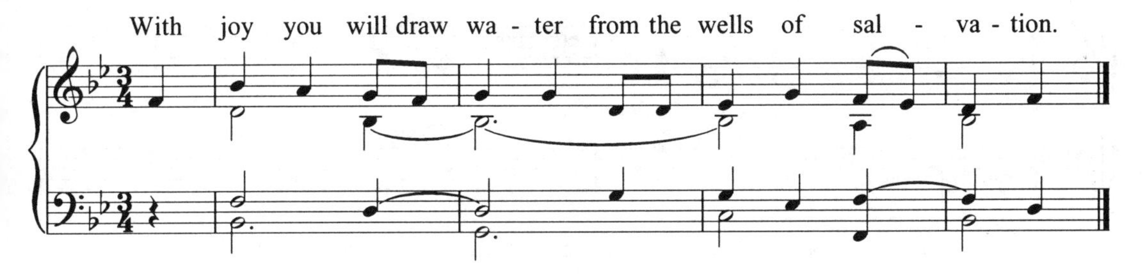
With joy you will draw wa - ter from the wells of sal - va - tion.

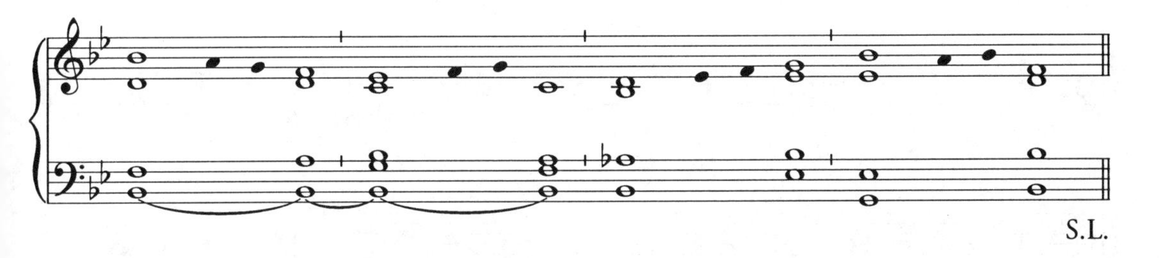

S.L.

1. Truly, God is my salvation
   I trust, I shall not fear
   for the Lord is my strength, my song,
   he became my saviour.

2. Give thanks to the Lord,
   give praise to his name!
   Make his mighty deeds known to the peoples!
   Declare the greatness of his name.

3. Sing a psalm to the Lord for he has done glorious deeds,
   make them known to all the earth!
   People of Zion, sing and shout for joy
   for great in your midst is the Holy One of Israel.

Gospel Acclamation cf. John 1:29

Alleluia.
John saw Jesus coming towards him, and said:
This is the Lamb of God who takes away the sin of the world.
Alleluia.

C Instrument
B♭ Instrument

The Baptism of the Lord

YEAR C AD LIB

Responsorial Psalm Psalm 103:1-2, 3-4, 24-25, 27-30. Response v.1

John Bertalot

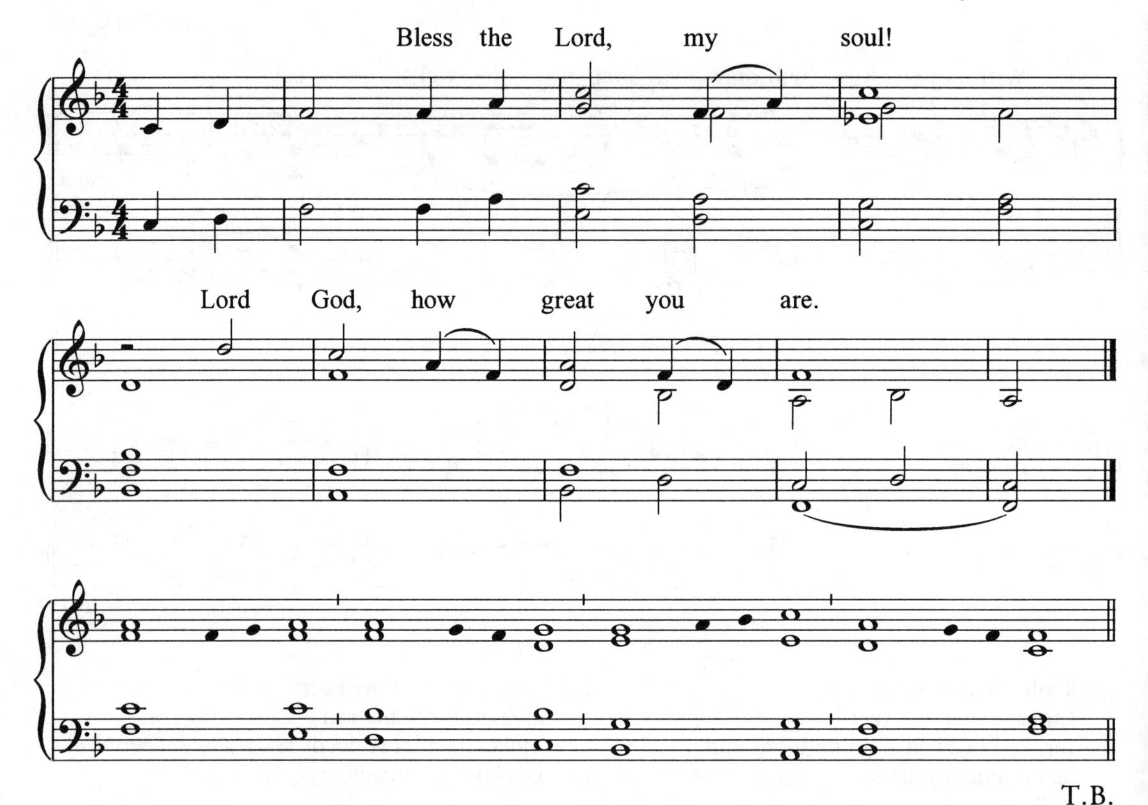

T.B.

1. Lord God, how great you are,
   clothed in majesty and glory,
   wrapped in light as in a robe!
   You stretch out the heavens like a tent.

2. The earth is full of your riches.
   There is the sea, vast and wide,
   with its moving swarms past counting,
   living things great and small.

3. All of these look to you
   to give them their food in due season.
   You give it, they gather it up:
   you open your hand, they have their fill.

4. You take back your spirit, they die,
   returning to the dust from which they came.
   You send forth your spirit, they are created;
   and you renew the face of the earth.

Gospel Acclamation cf. Luke 3:16

Alleluia.
Someone is coming, said John, someone greater than I.
He will baptise you with the Holy Spirit and with fire.
Alleluia.

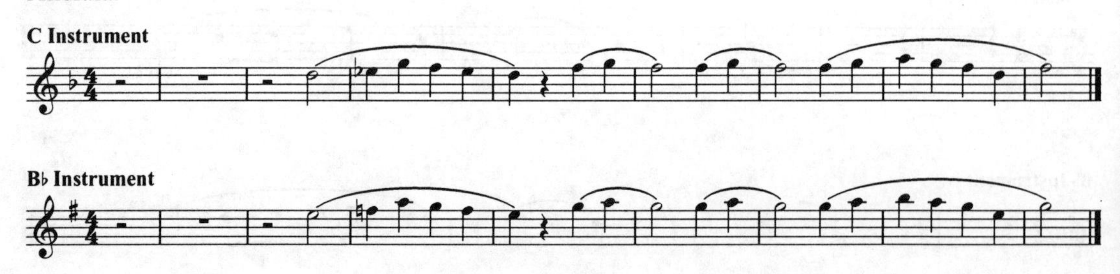

Ash Wednesday

YEARS A, B AND C

Responsorial Psalm Psalm 50:3-6, 12-14, 17. Response cf. v.3

Colin Mawby

Have mer - cy on us, Lord, for we have sinned.

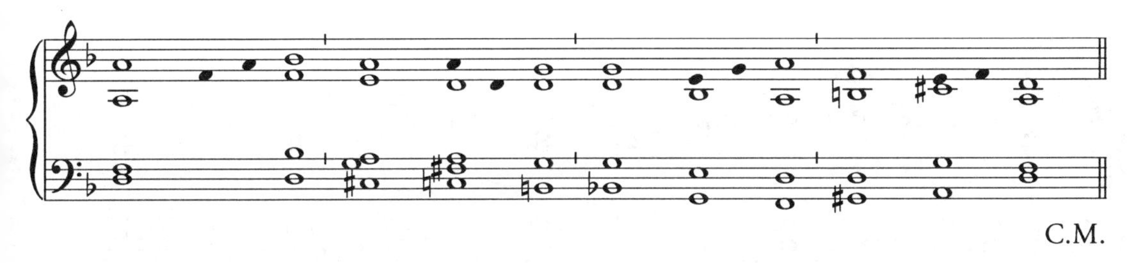
C.M.

1. Have mercy on me, God, in your kindness.
   In your compassion blot out my offence.
   O wash me more and more from my guilt
   and cleanse me from my sin.

2. My offences truly I know them;
   my sin is always before me.
   Against you, you alone, have I sinned;
   what is evil in your sight I have done.

3. A pure heart create for me, O God,
   put a steadfast spirit within me.
   Do not cast me away from your presence,
   nor deprive me of your holy spirit.

4. Give me again the joy of your help;
   with a spirit of fervour sustain me.
   O Lord, open my lips
   and my mouth shall declare your praise.

Gospel Acclamation Psalm 50:12, 14

One of the responses on pages 213 and 214 should be sung before and after this text.

A pure heart create for me, O God,
and give me again the joy of your help.

or cf. Psalm 94:8

Harden not your hearts today,
but listen to the voice of the Lord.

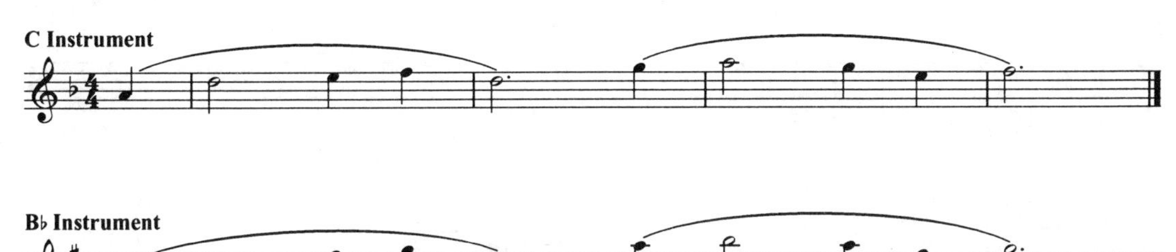
C Instrument
B♭ Instrument

First Sunday of Lent

YEAR A

Responsorial Psalm Psalm 50:3-6, 12-14, 17. Response cf. v.3

Andrew Wright

Have mer - cy on us, Lord, for we have sinned.

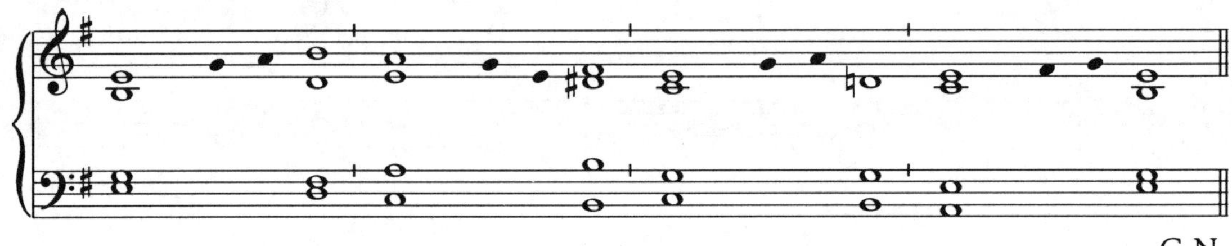

G.N.

1. Have mercy on me, God, in your kindness.
   In your compassion blot out my offence.
   O wash me more and more from my guilt
   and cleanse me from my sin.

2. My offences truly I know them;
   my sin is always before me.
   Against you, you alone, have I sinned;
   what is evil in your sight I have done.

3. A pure heart create for me, O God,
   put a steadfast spirit within me.
   Do not cast me away from your presence,
   nor deprive me of your holy spirit.

4. Give me again the joy of your help;
   with a spirit of fervour sustain me.
   O Lord, open my lips
   and my mouth shall declare your praise.

Gospel Acclamation Matthew 4:4

One of the responses on pages 213 and 214 should be sung before and after this text.

Man does not live on bread alone,
but on every word that comes from the mouth of God.

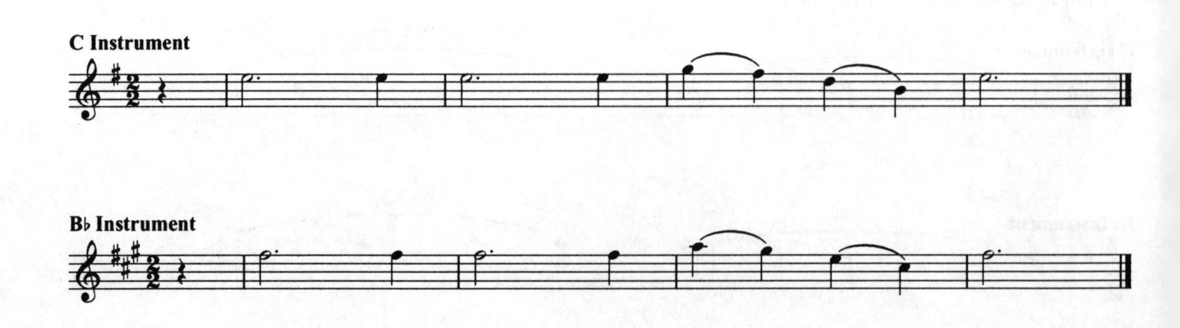
C Instrument
B♭ Instrument

First Sunday of Lent

YEAR B

Responsorial Psalm Psalm 24:4-9. Response cf. v.10

Colin Mawby

1. Lord, make me know your ways.
   Lord, teach me your paths.
   Make me walk in your truth, and teach me:
   for you are God my saviour.

2. Remember your mercy, Lord,
   and the love you have shown from of old.
   In your love remember me,
   because of your goodness, O Lord.

3. The Lord is good and upright.
   He shows the path to those who stray,
   he guides the humble in the right path;
   he teaches his way to the poor.

Gospel Acclamation Matthew 4:4

One of the responses on pages 213 and 214 should be sung before and after this text.

Man does not live on bread alone,
but on every word that comes from the mouth of God.

First Sunday of Lent

YEAR C

Responsorial Psalm Psalm 90:1-2, 10-15. Response v.15

Richard Lloyd

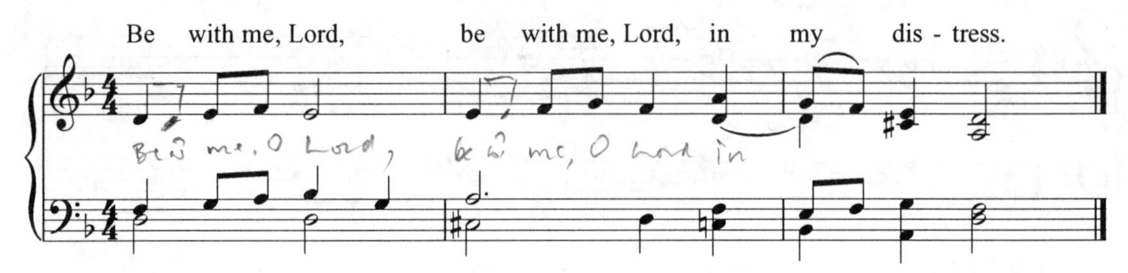

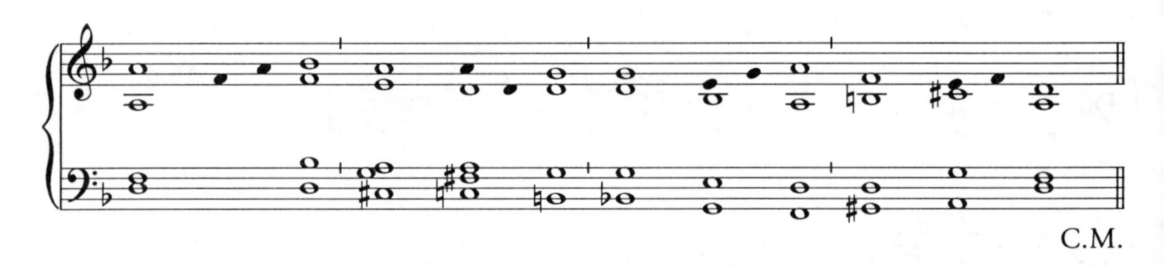

1. He who dwells in the shelter of the Most High
   and abides in the shade of the Almighty,
   says to the Lord: 'My refuge,
   my stronghold, my God in whom I trust!'

2. Upon you no evil shall fall,
   no plague approach where you dwell.
   For you has he commanded his angels,
   to keep you in all your ways.

3. They shall bear you upon their hands
   lest you strike your foot against a stone.
   On the lion and the viper you will tread
   and trample the young lion and the dragon.

4. His love he set on me, so I will rescue him;
   protect him for he knows my name.
   When he calls I shall answer: 'I am with you.'
   I will save him in distress and give him glory.

Gospel Acclamation Matthew 4:4

One of the responses on pages 213 and 214 should be sung before and after this text.

Man does not live on bread alone,
but on every word that comes from the mouth of God.

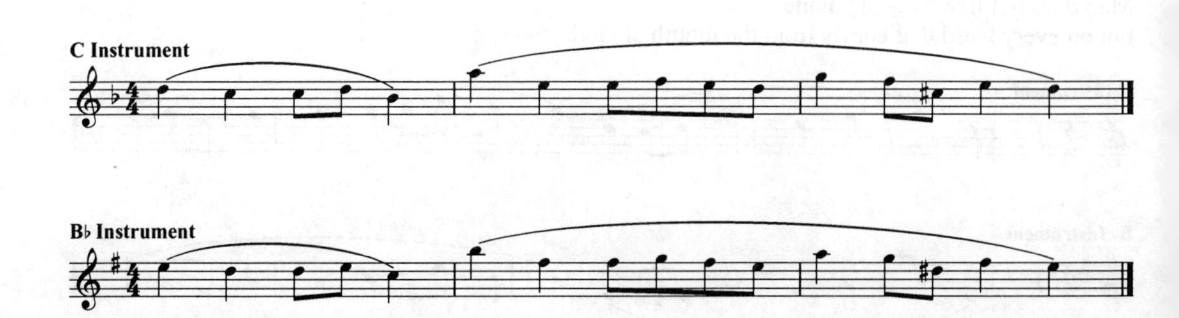

Second Sunday of Lent

YEAR A

Responsorial Psalm Psalm 32:4-5, 18-20, 22. Response v.22

Gerry Fitzpatrick

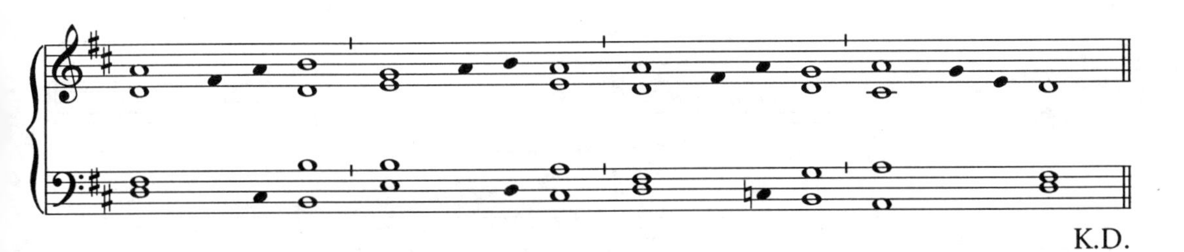

K.D.

1. The word of the Lord is faithful
   and all his works to be trusted.
   The Lord loves justice and right
   and fills the earth with his love.

2. The Lord looks on those who revere him,
   on those who hope in his love,
   to rescue their souls from death,
   to keep them alive in famine.

3. Our soul is waiting for the Lord.
   The Lord is our help and our shield.
   May your love be upon us, O Lord,
   as we place all our hope in you.

Gospel Acclamation Matthew 17:5

One of the responses on pages 213 and 214 should be sung before and after this text.

From the bright cloud the Father's voice was heard:
'This is my Son, the Beloved. Listen to him.'

Second Sunday of Lent

YEAR B

Responsorial Psalm Psalm 115:10, 15-19. Response Psalm 114:9

John Bertalot

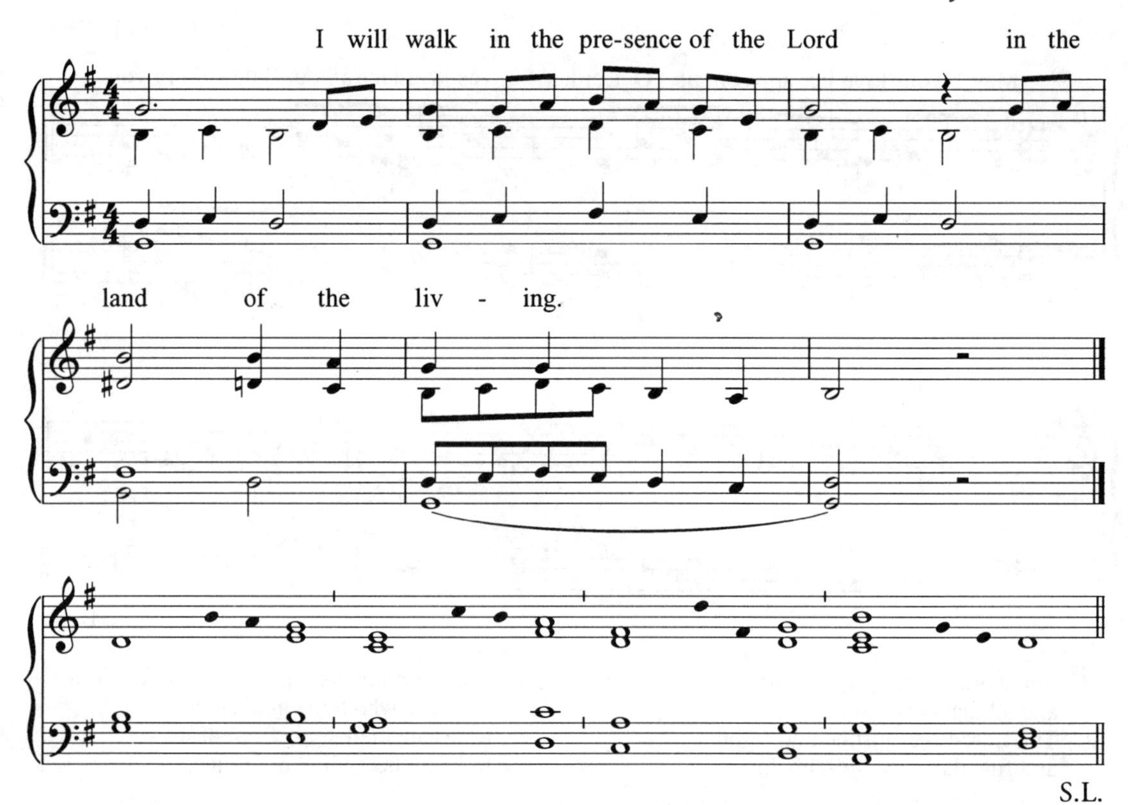
I will walk in the pre-sence of the Lord in the
land of the liv - ing.
S.L.

1. I trusted, even when I said:
   'I am sorely afflicted.'
   O precious in the eyes of the Lord
   is the death of his faithful.

2. Your servant, Lord, your servant am I;
   you have loosened my bonds.
   A thanksgiving sacrifice I make:
   I will call on the Lord's name.

3. My vows to the Lord I will fulfil
   before all his people,
   in the courts of the house of the Lord,
   in your midst, O Jerusalem.

Gospel Acclamation Matthew 17:5

One of the responses on pages 213 and 214 should be sung before and after this text.

From the bright cloud the Father's voice was heard:
'This is my Son, the Beloved. Listen to him.'

C Instrument
B♭ Instrument

Second Sunday of Lent

YEAR C

Responsorial Psalm Psalm 26:1, 7-9, 13-14. Response v.1

Simon Lesley

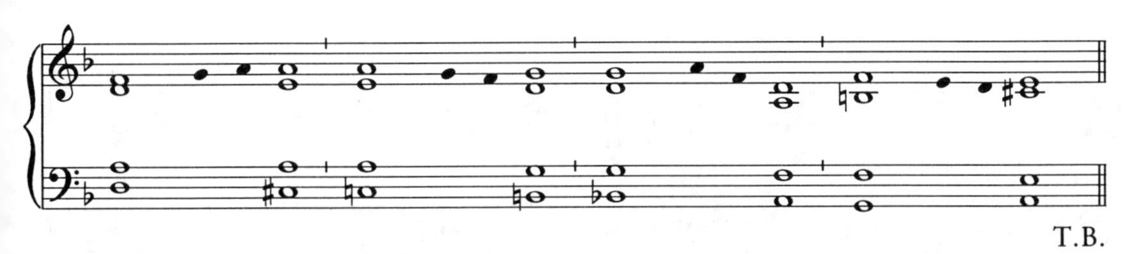

1. The Lord is my light and my help;
   whom shall I fear?
   The Lord is the stronghold of my life;
   before whom shall I shrink?

2. O Lord, hear my voice when I call;
   have mercy and answer.
   Of you my heart has spoken:
   'Seek his face.'

3. It is your face, O Lord, that I seek;
   hide not your face.
   Dismiss not your servant in anger;
   you have been my help.

4. I am sure I shall see the Lord's goodness
   in the land of the living.
   Hope in him, hold firm and take heart.
   Hope in the Lord!

Gospel Acclamation Matthew 17:5

One of the responses on pages 213 and 214 should be sung before and after this text.

From the bright cloud the Father's voice was heard:
'This is my Son, the Beloved. Listen to him.'

Third Sunday of Lent

YEAR A

Responsorial Psalm Psalm 94:1-2, 6-9. Response v.8

Andrew Moore

O that to-day you would lis-ten to his voice: 'Har-den not your hearts.'

C.M.

1. Come, ring out our joy to the Lord;
   hail the rock who saves us.
   Let us come before him, giving thanks,
   with songs let us hail the Lord.

2. Come in; let us bow and bend low;
   let us kneel before the God who made us
   for he is our God, and we the people who
   belong to his pasture,
   the flock that is led by his hand.

3. O that today you would listen to his voice!
   'Harden not your hearts as at Meribah,
   as on that day at Massah in the desert, when
   your fathers put me to the test;
   when they tried me, though they saw my work.

Gospel Acclamation cf. John 4:42, 15

One of the responses on pages 213 and 214 should be sung before and after this text.

Lord, you are really the saviour of the world;
give me the living water, so that I may never get thirsty.

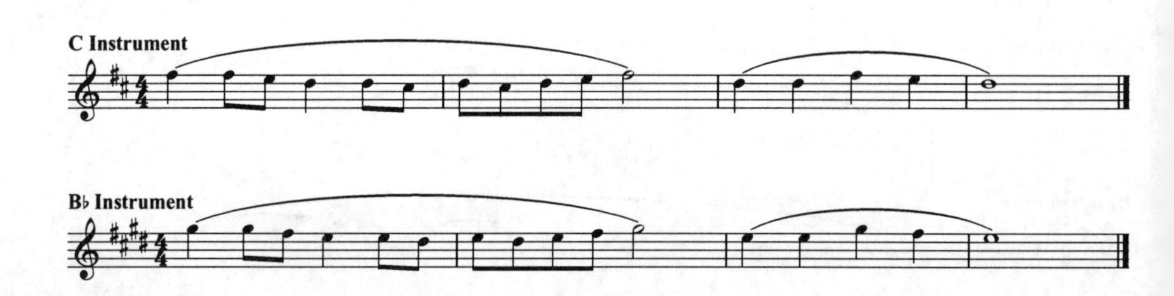

Third Sunday of Lent

YEAR B

Responsorial Psalm Psalm 18:8-11. Response John 6:68

Gerry Fitzpatrick

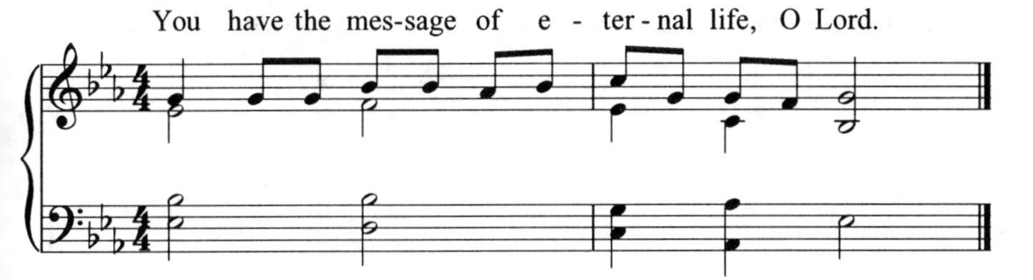

G.N.

1. The law of the Lord is perfect,
   it revives the soul.
   The rule of the Lord is to be trusted,
   it gives wisdom to the simple.

2. The precepts of the Lord are right,
   they gladden the heart.
   The command of the Lord is clear,
   it gives light to the eyes.

3. The fear of the Lord is holy,
   abiding for ever.
   The decrees of the Lord are truth
   and all of them just.

4. They are more to be desired than gold,
   than the purest of gold
   and sweeter are they than honey,
   than honey from the comb.

Gospel Acclamation John 11:25-26

One of the responses on pages 213 and 214 should be sung before and after this text.

I am the resurrection and the life, says the Lord,
whoever believes in me will never die.

C Instrument

B♭ Instrument

Third Sunday of Lent

YEAR C

Responsorial Psalm Psalm 102:1-4, 6-8, 11. Response v.8

Alan Rees

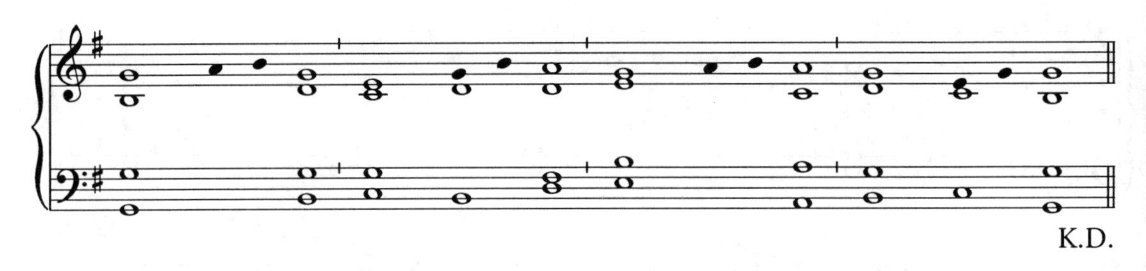

1. My soul, give thanks to the Lord,
   all my being, bless his holy name.
   My soul give thanks to the Lord
   and never forget all his blessings.

2. It is he who forgives all your guilt,
   who heals every one of your ills,
   who redeems your life from the grave,
   who crowns you with love and compassion.

3. The Lord does deeds of justice,
   gives judgement for all who are oppressed.
   He made known his ways to Moses
   and his deeds to Israel's sons.

4. The Lord is compassion and love,
   slow to anger and rich in mercy,
   for as the heavens are high above the earth
   so strong is his love for those who fear him.

Gospel Acclamation Matthew 4:17

One of the responses on pages 213 and 214 should be sung before and after this text.

Repent, says the Lord,
for the kingdom of heaven is close at hand.

Fourth Sunday of Lent

YEAR A

Responsorial Psalm Psalm 22. Response v.1

John McCann

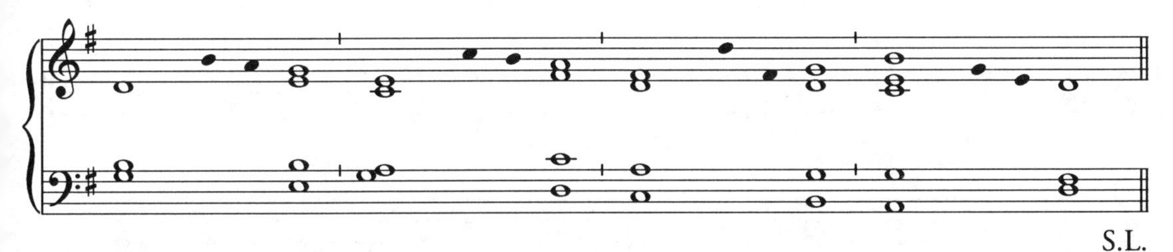

S.L.

1. The Lord is my shepherd;
   there is nothing I shall want.
   Fresh and green are the pastures
   where he gives me repose.

2. Near restful waters he leads me,
   to revive my drooping spirit.
   He guides me along the right path;
   he is true to his name.

3. If I should walk in the valley of darkness
   no evil would I fear.
   You are there with your crook and your staff;
   with these you give me comfort.

4. You have prepared a banquet for me
   in the sight of my foes.
   My head you have anointed with oil;
   my cup is overflowing.

5. Surely goodness and kindness shall follow me
   all the days of my life.
   In the Lord's own house shall I dwell
   for ever and ever.

Note: verse 3 may be omitted.

Gospel Acclamation John 8:12

One of the responses on pages 213 and 214 should be sung before and after this text.

I am the light of the world, says the Lord;
anyone who follows me will have the light of life.

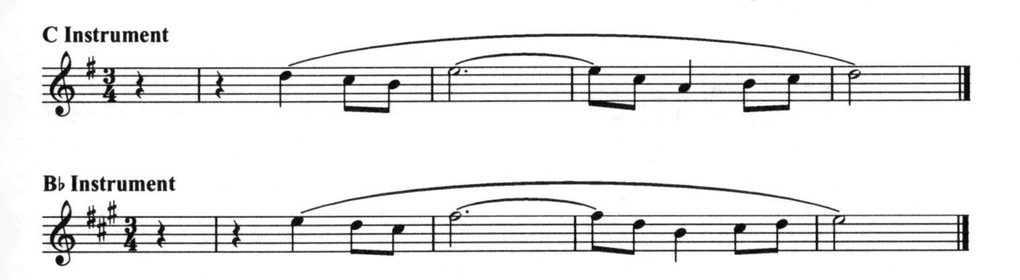

Fourth Sunday of Lent

YEAR B

Responsorial Psalm Psalm 136. Response v.6

John Bertalot

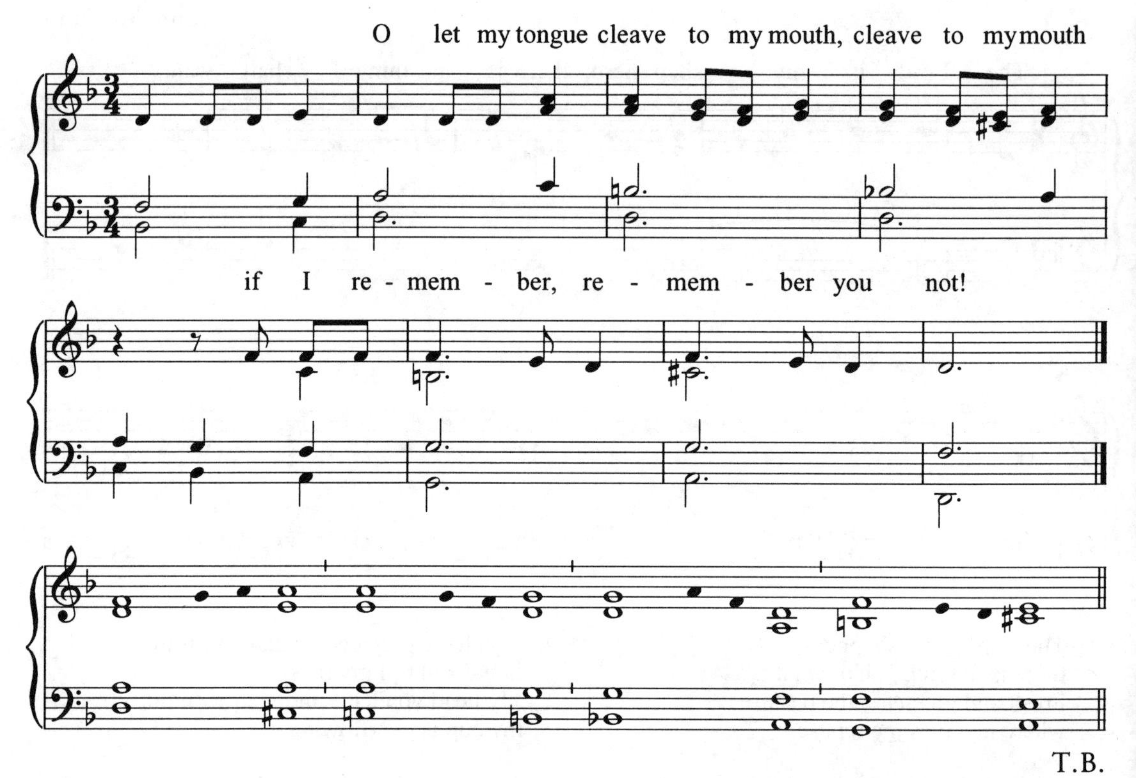

1. By the rivers of Babylon there we sat and wept,
remembering Zion;
on the poplars that grew there
we hung up our harps.

2. For it was there that they asked us our captors, for songs,
our oppressors, for joy.
'Sing to us,' they said,
'one of Zion's songs.'

3. O how could we sing the song of the Lord on alien soil?
If I forget you, Jerusalem,
let my right hand wither!

4. O let my tongue cleave to my mouth
if I remember you not,
if I prize not Jerusalem
above all my joys!

Gospel Acclamation John 3:16

One of the responses on pages 213 and 214 should be sung before and after this text.

God loved the world so much that he gave his only Son;
everyone who believes in him has eternal life.

Fourth Sunday of Lent

YEAR C

Responsorial Psalm Psalm 33:2-7. Response v.9

Richard Lloyd

Taste, O taste and see that the Lord is good.
C.M.

1. I will bless the Lord at all times,
   his praise always on my lips;
   in the Lord my soul shall make its boast.
   The humble shall hear and be glad.

2. Glorify the Lord with me.
   Together let us praise his name.
   I sought the Lord and he answered me;
   from all my terrors he set me free.

3. Look towards him and be radiant;
   let your faces not be abashed.
   This poor man called; the Lord heard him
   and rescued him from all his distress.

Gospel Acclamation Luke 15:18
One of the responses on pages 213 and 214 should be sung before and after this text.

I will leave this place and go to my father and say:
'Father, I have sinned against heaven and against you.'

Fifth Sunday of Lent

YEAR A

Responsorial Psalm Psalm 129. Response v.7

Andrew Wright

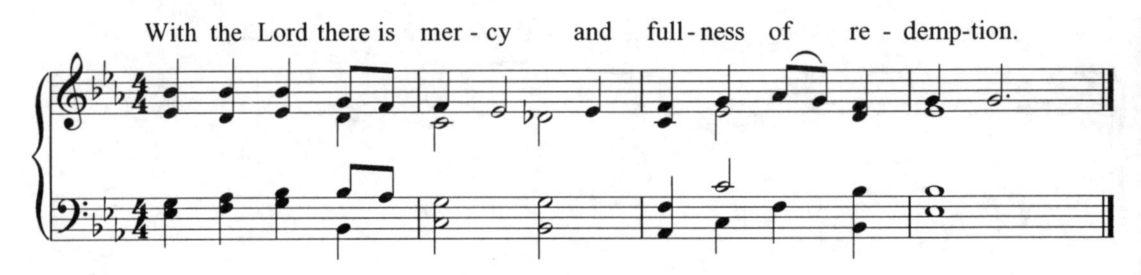

G.N.

1. Out of the depths I cry to you, O Lord,
   Lord, hear my voice!
   O let your ears be attentive
   to the voice of my pleading.

2. If you, O Lord, should mark our guilt,
   Lord, who would survive?
   But with you is found forgiveness:
   for this we revere you.

3. My soul is waiting for the Lord,
   I count on his word.
   My soul is longing for the Lord
   more than watchman for daybreak.

4. Because with the Lord there is mercy
   and fullness of redemption,
   Israel indeed he will redeem
   from all its iniquity.

Gospel Acclamation John 11:25, 26
One of the responses on pages 213 and 214 should be sung before and after this text.

I am the resurrection and the life, says the Lord;
whoever believes in me will never die.

Fifth Sunday of Lent

YEAR B

Responsorial Psalm Psalm 50:3-4, 12-15. Response v.12

Simon Lesley

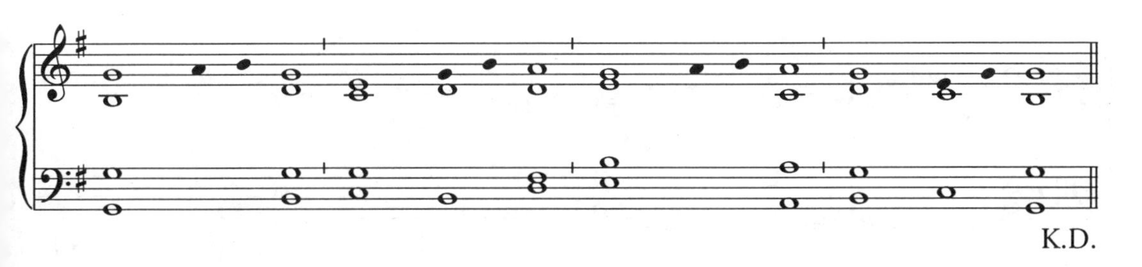

1. Have mercy on me, God, in your kindness.
   In your compassion blot out my offence.
   O wash me more and more from my guilt
   and cleanse me from my sin.

2. A pure heart create for me, O God,
   put a steadfast spirit within me.
   Do not cast me away from your presence,
   nor deprive me of your holy spirit.

3. Give me again the joy of your help;
   with a spirit of fervour sustain me,
   that I may teach transgressors your ways
   and sinners may return to you.

Gospel Acclamation John 12:26

One of the responses on pages 213 and 214 should be sung before and after this text.

If a man serves me, says the Lord, he must follow me,
wherever I am, my servant will be there too.

Fifth Sunday of Lent

YEAR C

Responsorial Psalm Psalm 125. Response v.3

Alan Rees

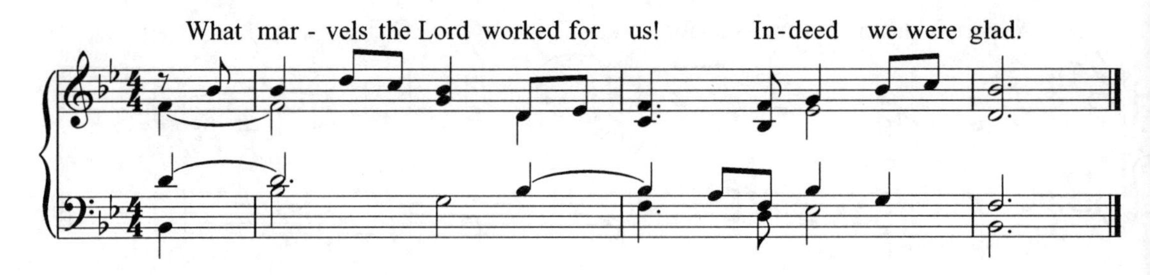

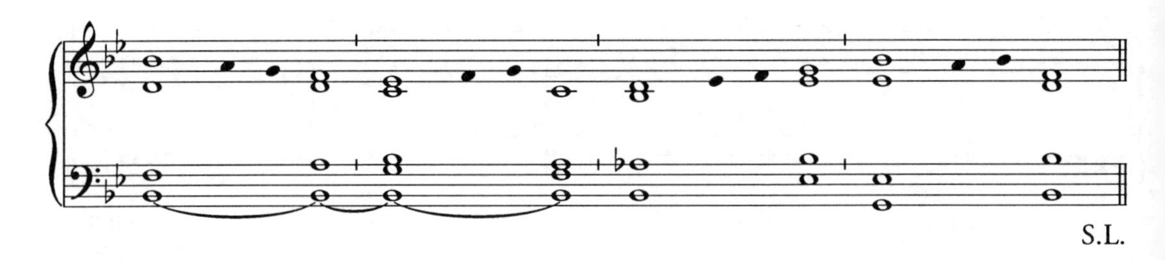

S.L.

1. When the Lord delivered Zion from bondage,
   it seemed like a dream.
   Then was our mouth filled with laughter,
   on our lips there were songs.

2. The heathens themselves said: 'What marvels
   the Lord worked for them!'
   What marvels the Lord worked for us!
   Indeed we were glad.

3. Deliver us, O Lord, from our bondage
   as streams in dry land.
   Those who are sowing in tears
   will sing when they reap.

4. They go out, they go out, full of tears,
   carrying seed for the sowing;
   they come back, they come back, full of song,
   carrying their sheaves.

Gospel Acclamation Amos 5:14

One of the responses on pages 213 and 214 should be sung before and after this text.

Seek good and not evil so that you may live,
and that the Lord God of hosts may really be with you.

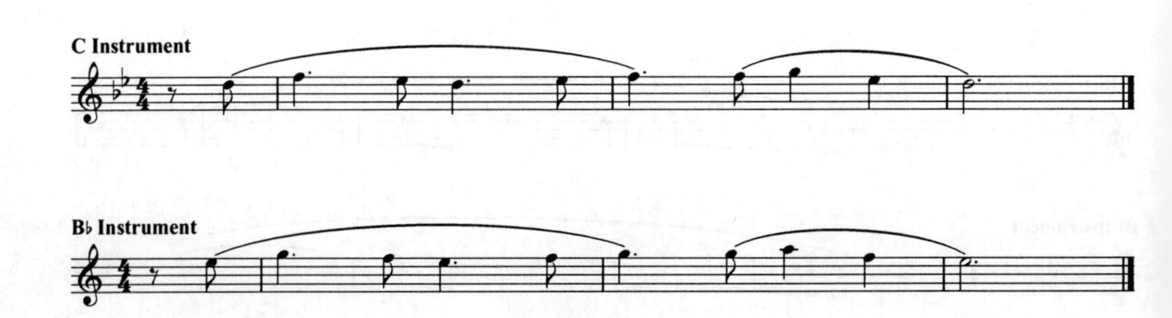

Passion Sunday

YEARS A, B AND C

Responsorial Psalm Psalm 21:8-9, 17-20, 23-34. Response v.2

Keith Duke

T.B.

1. All who see me deride me.
   They curl their lips, they toss their heads.
   'He trusted in the Lord, let him save him;
   let him release him if this is his friend.'

2. Many dogs have surrounded me,
   a band of the wicked beset me.
   They tear holes in my hands and my feet.
   I can count every one of my bones.

3. They divide my clothing among them.
   They cast lots for my robe.
   O Lord, do not leave me alone,
   my strength, make haste to help me!

4. I will tell of your name to my brethren
   and praise you where they are assembled.
   'You who fear the Lord give him praise;
   all sons of Jacob, give him glory.'

Gospel Acclamation Philippians 2:8-9

One of the responses on pages 213 and 214 should be sung before and after this text.

Christ was humbler yet, even to accepting death, death on a cross.
But God raised him high and gave him the name which is above all names.

Holy Thursday – Evening Mass of the Lord's Supper

YEARS A, B AND C

Responsorial Psalm Psalm 115:12-13, 15-18. Response cf. 1 Corinthians 10:16 — John McCann

The bles-sing cup that we bless is a com-mun-ion with the blood of Christ.

C.M.

1. How can I repay the Lord
   for his goodness to me?
   The cup of salvation I will raise;
   I will call on the Lord's name.

2. O precious in the eyes of the Lord
   is the death of his faithful.
   Your servant, Lord, your servant am I;
   you have loosened my bonds.

3. A thanksgiving sacrifice I make:
   I will call on the Lord's name.
   My vows to the Lord I will fulfil
   before all his people.

Gospel Acclamation John 13:34

One of the responses on pages 213 and 214 should be sung before and after this text.

I give you a new commandment:
love one another just as I have loved you, says the Lord.

Good Friday – Celebration of the Lord's Passion

YEARS A, B AND C

Responsorial Psalm Psalm 30:2, 6, 12-13, 15-17, 25. Response Luke 23:46

Gerry Fitzpatrick

Fa - ther, in - to your hands I com - mend my spi-rit.

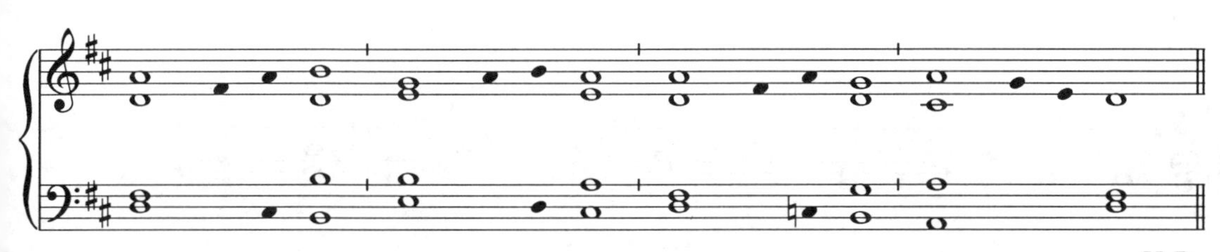

K.D.

1. In you, O Lord, I take refuge.
   Let me never be put to shame.
   In your justice, set me free.
   It is you who will redeem me, Lord.

2. In the face of all my foes
   I am a reproach,
   an object of scorn to my neighbours
   and of fear to my friends.

3. Those who see me in the street
   run far away from me.
   I am like the dead, forgotten by all,
   like a thing thrown away.

4. But as for me, I trust in you, Lord,
   I say: 'You are my God.'
   My life is in your hands, deliver me
   from the hands of those who hate me.

5. Let your face shine on your servant.
   Save me in your love.
   Be strong, let your heart take courage,
   all who hope in the Lord.

Gospel Acclamation Philippians 2:8-9

One of the responses on pages 213 and 214 should be sung before and after this text.

Christ was humbler yet, even to accepting death, death on a cross.
But God raised him high and gave him the name which is above all names.

Easter Sunday – The Easter Vigil

YEARS A, B AND C

After the first Reading

Responsorial Psalm Psalm 103:1-2, 5-6, 10, 12-14, 24, 35. Response cf. v.30

Richard Lloyd

Send forth your Spi-rit, O Lord, and re-new the face of the earth.

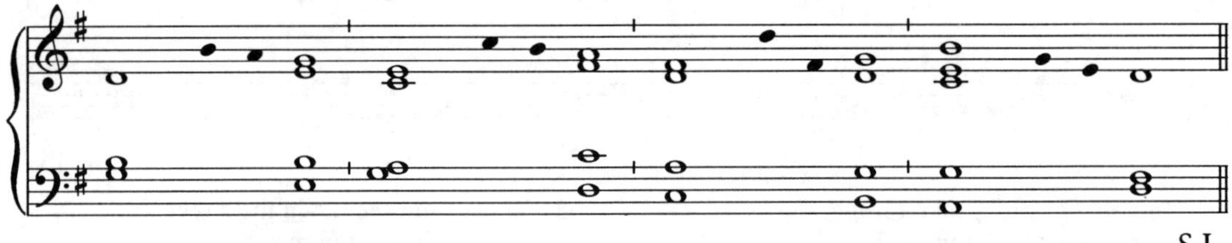

S.L.

1. Bless the Lord, my soul!
   Lord God, how great you are,
   clothed in majesty and glory,
   wrapped in light as in a robe!

2. You founded the earth on its base,
   to stand firm from age to age.
   You wrapped it with the ocean like a cloak:
   the waters stood higher than the mountains.

3. You make springs gush forth in the valleys:
   they flow in between the hills.
   On their banks dwell the birds of heaven;
   from the branches they sing their song.

4. From your dwelling you water the hills;
   earth drinks its fill of your gift.
   You make the grass grow for the cattle
   and the plants to serve our needs.

5. How many are your works, O Lord!
   In wisdom you have made them all.
   The earth is full of your riches.
   Bless the Lord, my soul!

C Instrument
B♭ Instrument

After the second Reading

Responsorial Psalm Psalm 15:5, 8-11. Response v.1

John Bertalot

Pre - serve me, God, I take ref - uge in you.

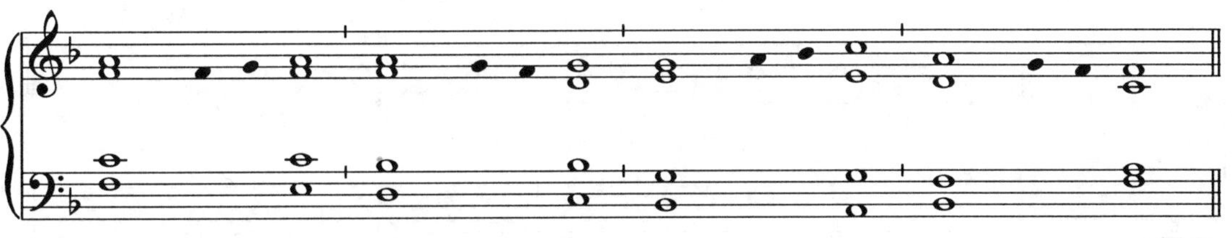

T.B.

1. O Lord, it is you who are my portion and cup;
   it is you yourself who are my prize.
   I keep the Lord ever in my sight:
   since he is at my right hand, I shall stand firm.

2. And so my heart rejoices, my soul is glad;
   even my body shall rest in safety.
   For you will not leave my soul among the dead,
   nor let your beloved know decay.

3. O Lord, you will show me
   the path of life,
   the fullness of joy in your presence,
   at your right hand happiness for ever.

C Instrument
B♭ Instrument

After the third Reading

Responsorial Psalm Exodus 15:1-6, 17-18. Response v.1

Andrew Moore

* *Omit in verses 1 and 2*

C.M.

1. I will sing to the Lord, glorious his triumph!
Horse and rider he has thrown into the sea!
The Lord is my strength, my song, my salvation.
This is my God and I extol him,
my father's God and I give him praise.

2. The Lord is a warrior!
The Lord is his name.
The chariots of Pharaoh he hurled into the sea,
the flower of his army is drowned in the sea.
The deeps hide them; they sank like a stone.

3. Your right hand, Lord, glorious in its power,
your right hand, Lord, has shattered the enemy.
In the greatness of your glory you crushed the foe.
You will lead your people and plant them on your mountain,
the sanctuary, Lord, which your hands have made.
The Lord will reign for ever and ever.

After the fourth Reading

Responsorial Psalm Psalm 29:2, 4-6, 11-13. Response v.2

John McCann

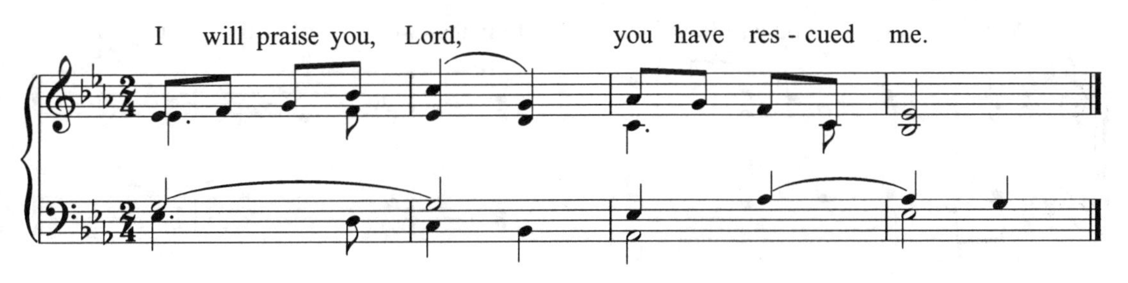

1. I will praise you, Lord, you have rescued me
   and have not let my enemies rejoice over me.
   O Lord, you have raised my soul from the dead,
   restored me to life from those who sink into the grave.

2. Sing psalms to the Lord, you who love him,
   give thanks to his holy name.
   His anger lasts but a moment; his favour through life.
   At night there are tears, but joy comes with dawn.

3. The Lord listened and had pity.
   The Lord came to my help.
   For me you have changed my mourning into dancing,
   O Lord my God, I will thank you for ever.

After the fifth Reading

Responsorial Psalm Isaiah 12:2-6. Response v.3

Alan Rees

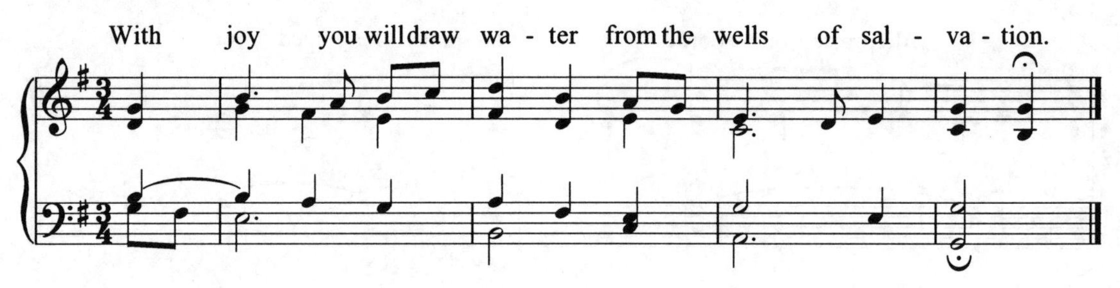
With joy you will draw wa - ter from the wells of sal - va - tion.

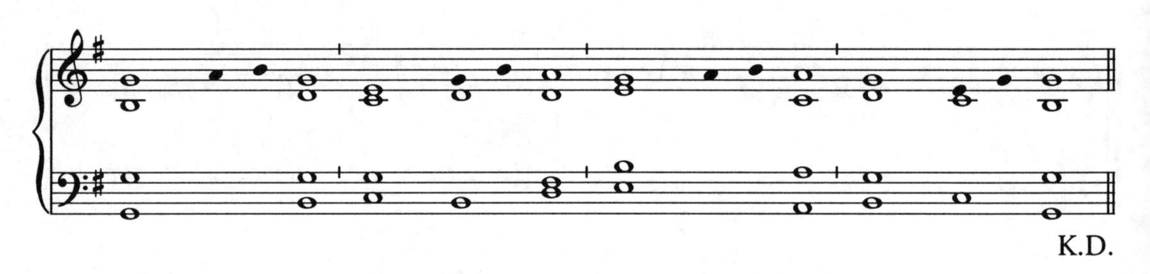

K.D.

1. Truly God is my salvation,
   I trust, I shall not fear.
   For the Lord is my strength, my song,
   he became my saviour.

2. Give thanks to the Lord,
   give praise to his name!
   Make his mighty deeds known to the peoples,
   declare the greatness of his name.

3. Sing a psalm to the Lord for he has done glorious deeds,
   make them known to all the earth!
   People of Zion, sing and shout for joy
   for great in your midst is the Holy One of Israel.

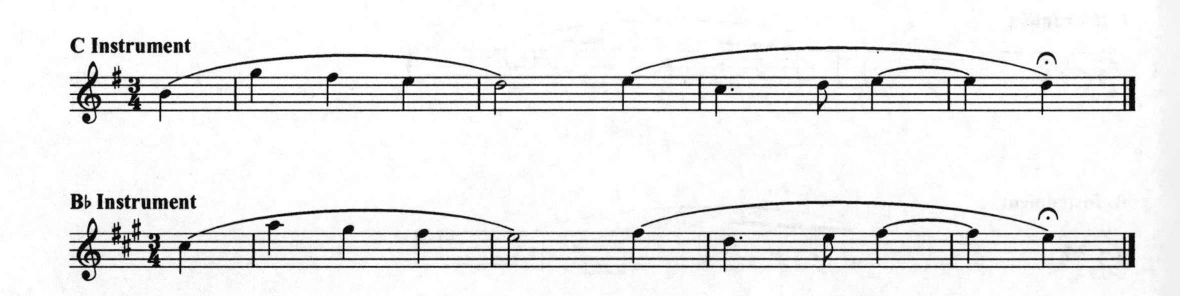
C Instrument
B♭ Instrument

After the sixth Reading

Responsorial Psalm Psalm 18:8-11. Response John 6:69

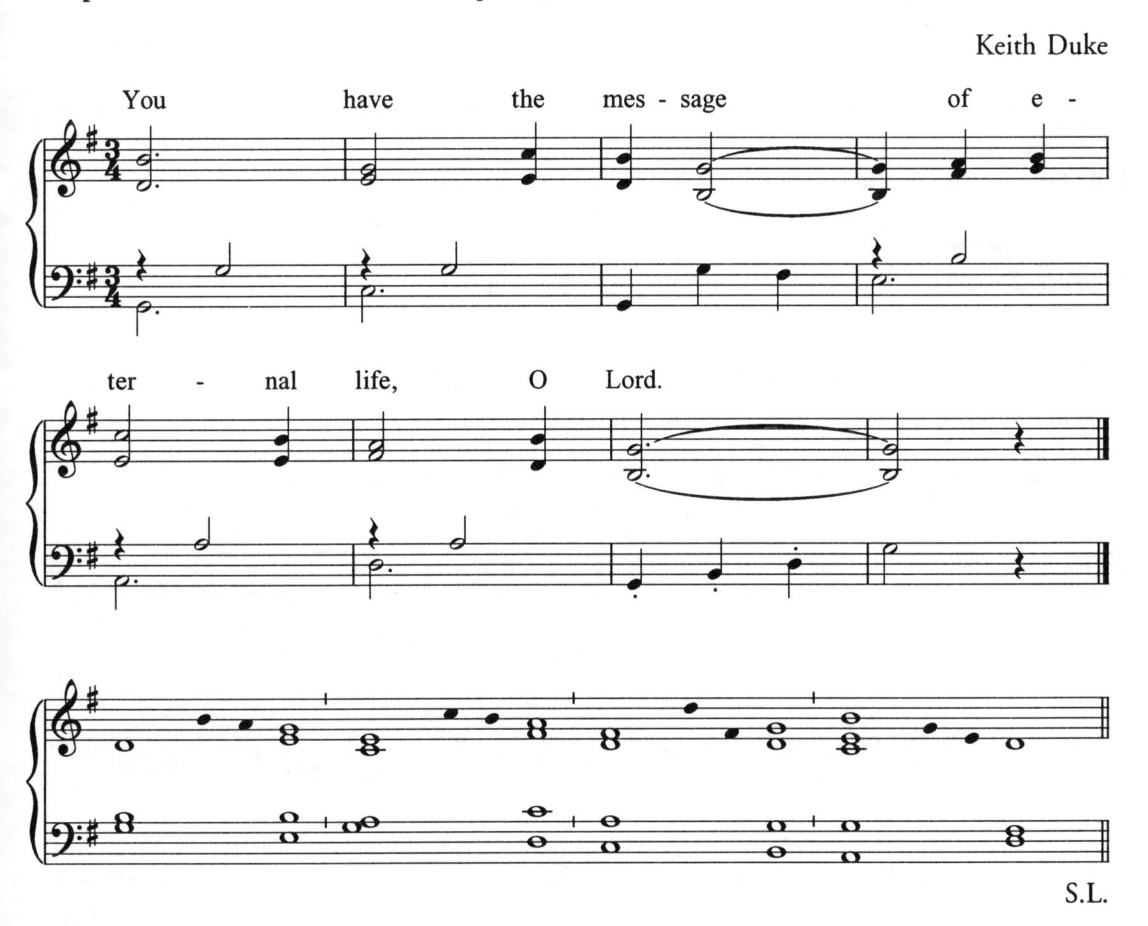

1. The law of the Lord is perfect,
   it revives the soul.
   The rule of the Lord is to be trusted,
   it gives wisdom to the simple.

2. The precepts of the Lord are right,
   they gladden the heart.
   The command of the Lord is clear,
   it gives light to the eyes.

3. The fear of the Lord is holy,
   abiding for ever.
   The decrees of the Lord are truth
   and all of them just.

4. They are more to be desired than gold,
   than the purest of gold
   and sweeter are they than honey,
   than honey from the comb.

After the seventh Reading

Responsorial Psalm Psalm 41:3, 5. 42:3, 4. Response Psalm 41:2

Geoff Nobes

Like the deer that yearns for run - ning streams, so my soul is yearn - ing for you, my God.

T.B.

1. My soul is thirsting for God,
   the God of my life;
   when can I enter and see
   the face of God?

2. These things will I remember as I pour
   out my soul:
   how I would lead the rejoicing crowd into
   the house of God,
   amid cries of gladness and thanksgiving,
   the throng wild with joy.

3. O send forth your light and your truth;
   let these be my guide.
   Let them bring me to your holy mountain
   to the place where you dwell.

4. And I will come to the altar of God,
   the God of my joy.
   My redeemer, I will thank you on the harp,
   O God, my God.

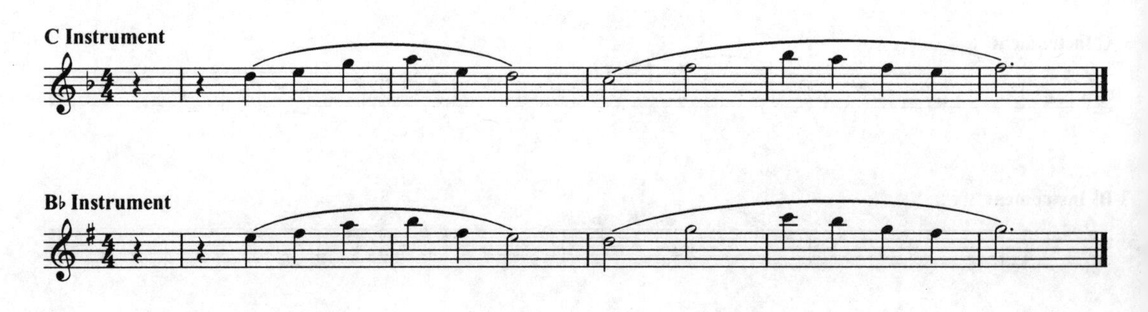

If a Baptism takes place, the Psalm which follows the fifth Reading is used, or the one that follows here.

Responsorial Psalm Psalm 50:12-15, 18, 19. Response v.12

Richard Lloyd
A pure heart cre - ate for me, O God.
C.M.

1. A pure heart create for me, O God,
   put a steadfast spirit within me.
   Do not cast me away from your presence,
   nor deprive me of your holy spirit.

2. Give me again the joy of your help;
   with a spirit of fervour sustain me,
   that I may teach transgressors your ways
   and sinners may return to you.

3. For in sacrifice you take no delight,
   burnt offering from me you would refuse,
   my sacrifice, a contrite spirit.
   A humbled, contrite heart you will not spurn.

C Instrument
B♭ Instrument

Easter Sunday – The Mass of Easter Night

YEARS A, B AND C

Responsorial Psalm Psalm 117:1-2, 16-17, 22-23

Andrew Wright

Al - le - lu - ia, al - le - lu - ia, al - le - lu - ia.

G.N.

1. Give thanks to the Lord for he is good,
   for his love has no end.
   Let the family of Israel say:
   'His love has no end.'

2. The Lord's right hand has triumphed;
   his right hand raised me up.
   I shall not die, I shall live
   and recount his deeds.

3. The stone which the builders rejected
   has become the corner stone.
   This is the work of the Lord,
   a marvel in our eyes.

C Instrument
B♭ Instrument

Easter Sunday – Mass of the Day

YEARS A, B AND C

Responsorial Psalm Psalm 117:1-2, 16-17, 22-23. Response v.24 — Andrew Moore

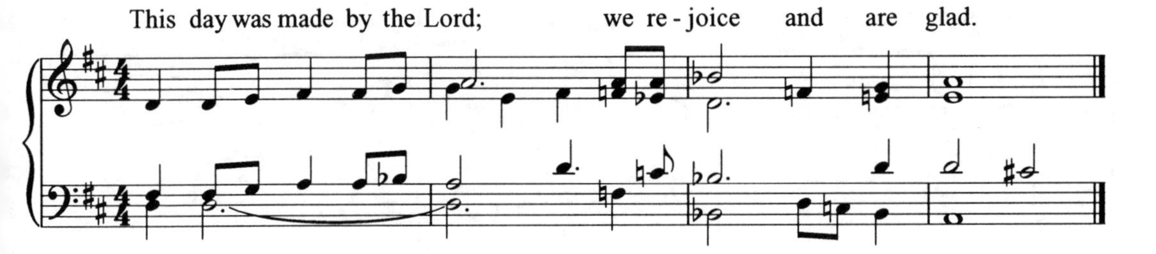

This day was made by the Lord; we re - joice and are glad.

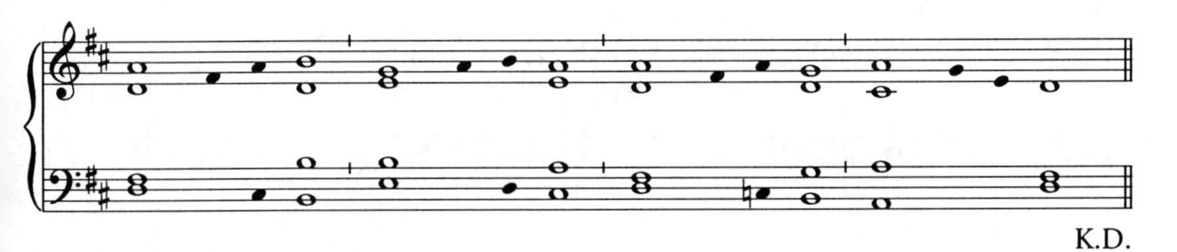

K.D.

1. Give thanks to the Lord for he is good,
   for his love has no end.
   Let the family of Israel say:
   'His love has no end.'

2. The Lord's right hand has triumphed;
   his right hand raised me up.
   I shall not die, I shall live
   and recount his deeds.

3. The stone which the builders rejected
   has become the corner stone.
   This is the work of the Lord,
   a marvel in our eyes.

Gospel Acclamation 1 Corinthians 5:7-8

Alleluia.
Christ, our passover, has been sacrificed;
let us celebrate the feast then, in the Lord.
Alleluia.

C Instrument
B♭ Instrument

Second Sunday of Easter

YEAR A

Responsorial Psalm Psalm 117:2-4, 13-15, 22-24. Response v.1

John McCann

Give thanks to the Lord for he is good, for his love has no end.
C.M.

1. Let the sons of Israel say:
   'His love has no end.'
   Let the sons of Aaron say:
   'His love has no end.'
   Let those who fear the Lord say:
   'His love has no end.'

2. I was thrust down, thrust down and falling
   but the Lord was my helper.
   The Lord is my strength and my song:
   he was my saviour.
   There are shouts of joy and victory
   in the tents of the just.

3. The stone which the builders rejected
   has become the corner stone.
   This is the work of the Lord,
   a marvel in our eyes.
   This day was made by the Lord;
   we rejoice and are glad.

Gospel Acclamation John 20:29

Alleluia.
Jesus said: 'You believe because you can see me.
Happy are those who have not seen and yet believe.'
Alleluia.

C Instrument
B♭ Instrument

Second Sunday of Easter

YEAR B

Responsorial Psalm Psalm 117:2-4, 15-18, 22-24. Response v.1

Simon Lesley

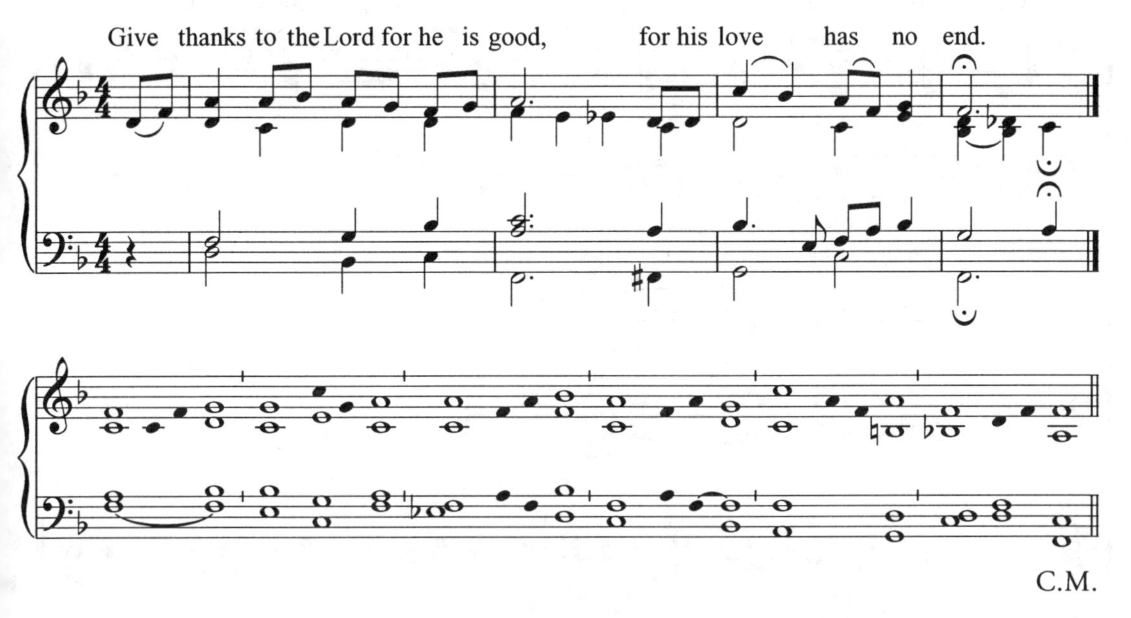
Give thanks to the Lord for he is good, for his love has no end.
C.M.

1. Let the sons of Israel say:
   'His love has no end.'
   Let the sons of Aaron say:
   'His love has no end.'
   Let those who fear the Lord say:
   'His love has no end.'

2. The Lord's right hand has triumphed;
   his right hand raised me up.
   I shall not die, I shall live
   and recount his deeds.
   I was punished, I was punished by the Lord,
   but not doomed to die.

3. The stone which the builders rejected
   has become the corner stone.
   This is the work of the Lord,
   a marvel in our eyes.
   This day was made by the Lord;
   we rejoice and are glad.

Gospel Acclamation John 20:29

Alleluia.
Jesus said: 'You believe because you can see me.
Happy are those who have not seen and yet believe.'
Alleluia.

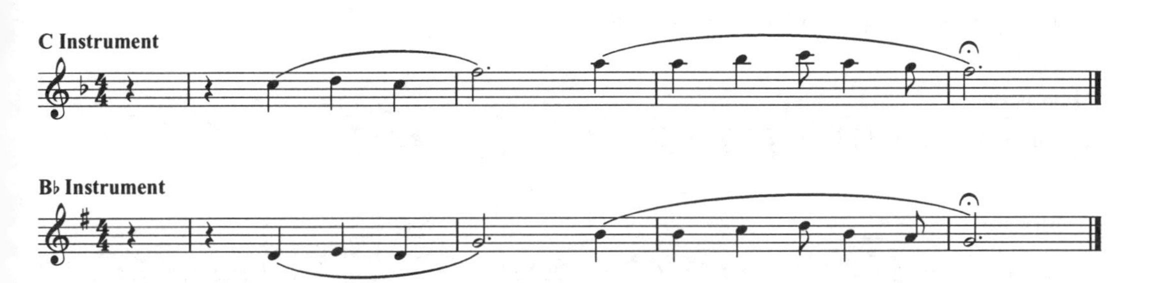
C Instrument
B♭ Instrument

Second Sunday of Easter

YEAR C

Responsorial Psalm Psalm 117:2-4, 22-27. Response v.1

Keith Duke

Give thanks to the Lord for he is good, for his love
has no end.
C.M.

1. Let the sons of Israel say:
   'His love has no end.'
   Let the sons of Aaron say:
   'His love has no end.'
   Let those who fear the Lord say:
   'His love has no end.'

2. The stone which the builders rejected
   has become the corner stone.
   This is the work of the Lord,
   a marvel in our eyes.
   This day was made by the Lord;
   we rejoice and are glad.

3. O Lord, grant us salvation;
   O Lord, grant success.
   Blessed in the name of the Lord
   is he who comes.
   We bless you from the house of the Lord;
   the Lord God is our light.

Gospel Acclamation John 20:29

Alleluia.
Jesus said: 'You believe because you can see me.
Happy are those who have not seen and yet believe.'
Alleluia.

C Instrument
B♭ Instrument

Third Sunday of Easter

YEAR A

Responsorial Psalm Psalm 15:1-2, 5, 7-11. Response v.11

Geoff Nobes

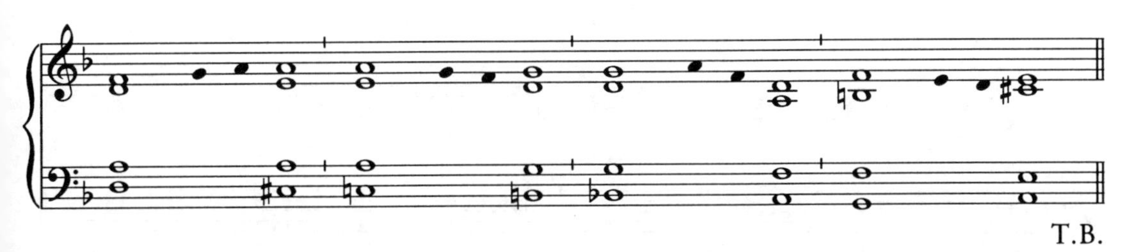

1. Preserve me, God, I take refuge in you.
   I say to the Lord: 'You are my God.
   O Lord, it is you who are my portion and cup;
   it is you yourself who are my prize.'

2. I will bless the Lord who gives me counsel,
   who even at night directs my heart.
   I keep the Lord ever in my sight:
   since he is at my right hand, I shall stand firm.

3. And so my heart rejoices, my soul is glad;
   even my body shall rest in safety.
   For you will not leave my soul among the dead,
   nor let your beloved know decay.

4. O Lord, you will show me
   the path of life,
   the fullness of joy in your presence,
   at your right hand happiness for ever.

Gospel Acclamation cf. Luke 24:32

Alleluia.
Lord Jesus, explain the scriptures to us.
Make our hearts burn within us as you talk to us.
Alleluia.

Third Sunday of Easter

YEAR B

Responsorial Psalm Psalm 4:2, 4, 7, 9. Response v.7

Gerry Fitzpatrick

G.N.

1. When I call, answer me, O God of justice;
   from anguish you release me, have mercy and hear me!
   It is the Lord who grants favours to those whom he loves;
   the Lord hears me whenever I call him.

2. 'What can bring us happiness?' many say.
   Lift up the light of your face on us, O Lord.
   I will lie down in peace and sleep comes at once,
   for you alone, Lord, make me dwell in safety.

Gospel Acclamation cf. Luke 24:32

Alleluia.
Lord Jesus, explain the scriptures to us.
Make our hearts burn within us as you talk to us.
Alleluia.

Third Sunday of Easter

YEAR C

Responsorial Psalm Psalm 29:2, 4-6, 11-13. Response v.2

Alan Rees

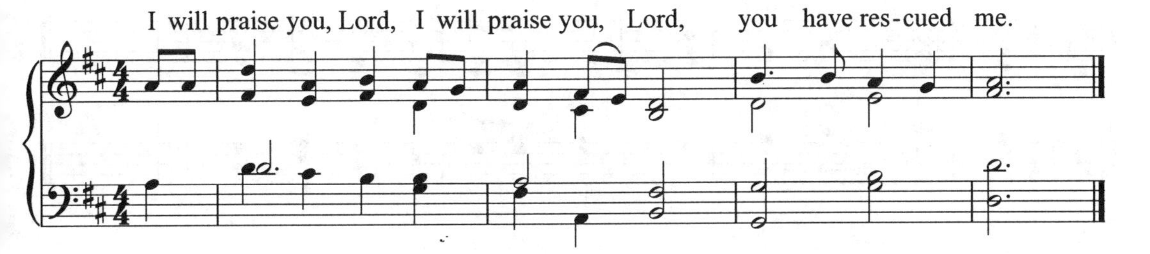

K.D.

1. I will praise you, Lord, you have rescued me
   and have not let my enemies rejoice over me.
   O Lord, you have raised my soul from the dead,
   restored me to life from those who sink into the grave.

2. Sing psalms to the Lord, you who love him,
   give thanks to his holy name.
   His anger lasts but a moment; his favour through life.
   At night there are tears, but joy comes with dawn.

3. The Lord listened and had pity.
   The Lord came to my help.
   For me you have changed my mourning into dancing;
   O Lord my God, I will thank you for ever.

Gospel Acclamation cf. Luke 24:32

Alleluia.
Lord Jesus, explain the scriptures to us.
Make our hearts burn within us as you talk to us.
Alleluia.

Fourth Sunday of Easter

YEAR A

Responsorial Psalm Psalm 22:1-6. Response v.1

Colin Mawby

1. The Lord is my shepherd;
   there is nothing I shall want.
   Fresh and green are the pastures
   where he gives me repose.

2. Near restful waters he leads me
   to revive my drooping spirit.
   He guides me along the right path;
   he is true to his name.

3. If I should walk in the valley of darkness
   no evil would I fear.
   You are there with your crook and your staff;
   with these you give me comfort.

4. You have prepared a banquet for me
   in the sight of my foes.
   My head you have anointed with oil;
   my cup is overflowing.

5. Surely goodness and kindness shall follow me
   all the days of my life.
   In the Lord's own house shall I dwell for
   ever and ever.

Note: verse 3 may be omitted.

Gospel Acclamation John 10:14

Alleluia.
I am the good shepherd, says the Lord;
I know my own sheep and my own know me.
Alleluia.

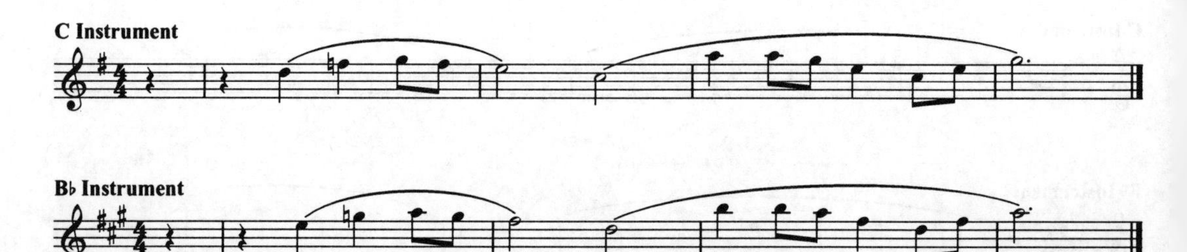

Fourth Sunday of Easter

YEAR B

Responsorial Psalm Psalm 117:1, 8-9, 21-23, 26, 28-29. Response v.22

Colin Mawby

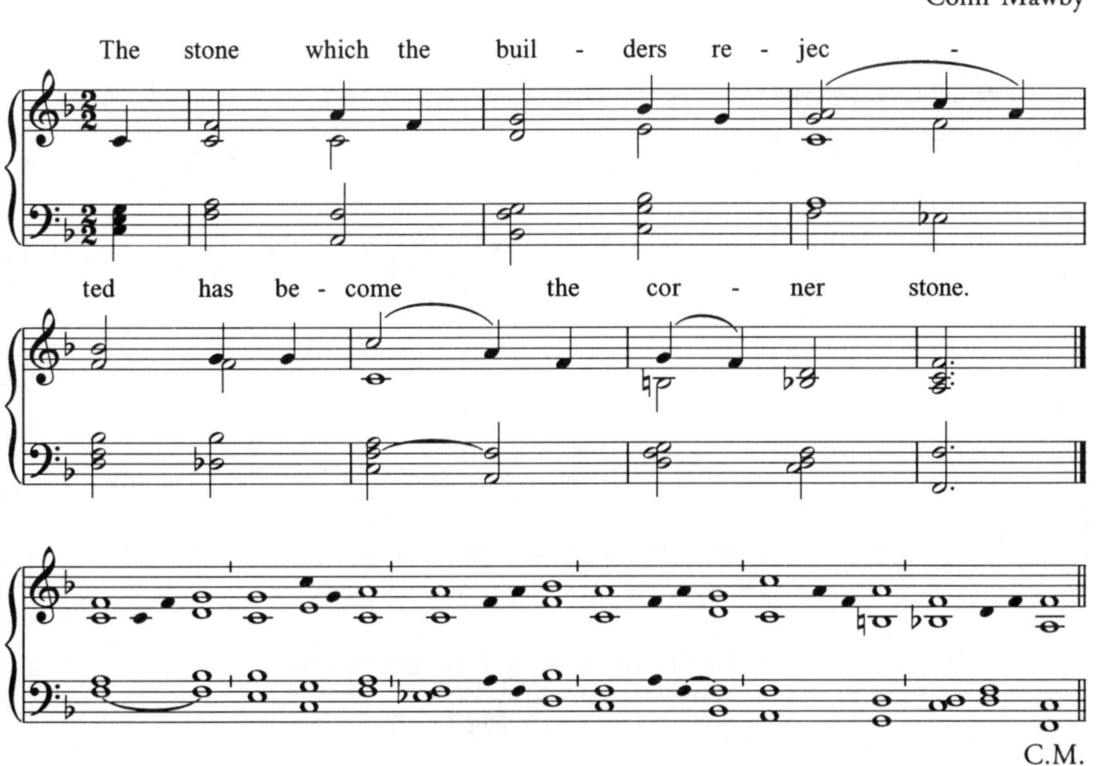

1. Give thanks to the Lord for he is good,
   for his love has no end.
   It is better to take refuge in the Lord
   than to trust in mortals;
   it is better to take refuge in the Lord
   than to trust in rulers.

2. I will thank you for you have given answer
   and you are my saviour.
   The stone which the builders rejected
   has become the corner stone.
   This is the work of the Lord,
   a marvel in our eyes.

3. Blessed in the name of the Lord is he who comes.
   We bless you from the house of the Lord;
   I will thank you for you have given answer
   and you are my saviour.
   Give thanks to the Lord for he is good;
   for his love has no end.

Gospel Acclamation John 10:14

Alleluia.
I am the good shepherd, says the Lord;
I know my own sheep and my own know me.
Alleluia.

Fourth Sunday of Easter

YEAR C

Responsorial Psalm Psalm 99:1-3, 5. Response v.3

Andrew Moore

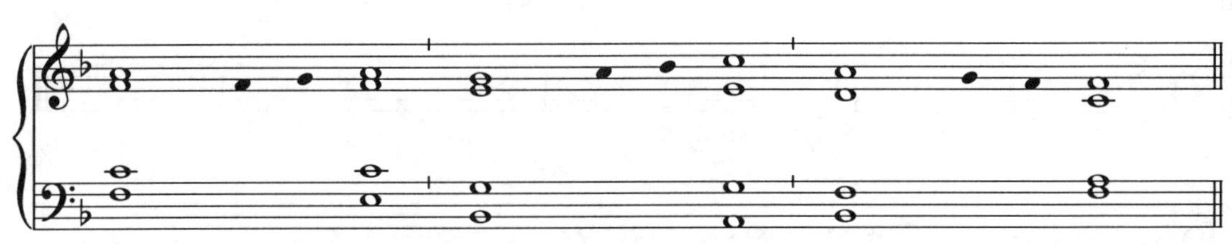

T.B.

1. Cry out with joy to the Lord, all the earth.
   Serve the Lord with gladness.
   Come before him, singing for joy.

2. Know that he, the Lord, is God.
   He made us, we belong to him,
   we are his people, the sheep of his flock.

3. Indeed, how good is the Lord,
   eternal his merciful love.
   He is faithful from age to age.

Gospel Acclamation John 10:14

Alleluia.
I am the good shepherd, says the Lord;
I know my own sheep and my own know me.
Alleluia.

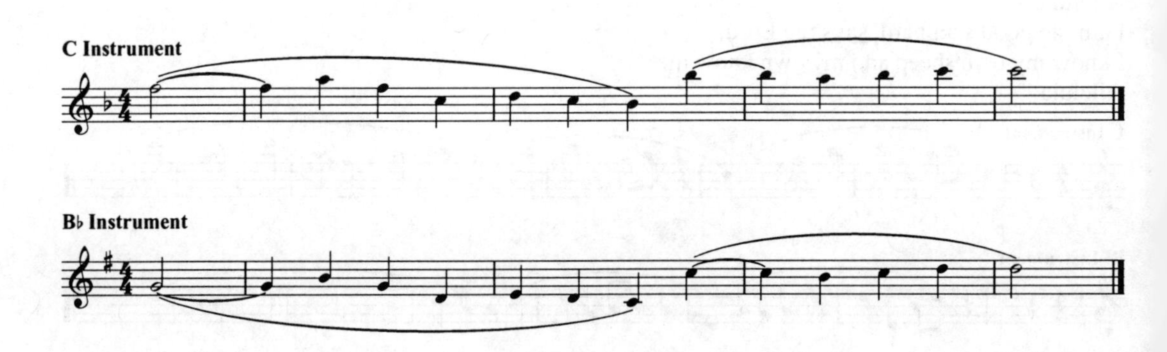

Fifth Sunday of Easter

YEAR A

Responsorial Psalm Psalm 32:1-2, 4-5, 18-19. Response v.22

Simon Lesley

May your love be up - on us, O Lord, as we
place all our hope in you.
G.N.

1. Ring out your joy to the Lord, O you just;
   for praise is fitting for loyal hearts.
   Give thanks to the Lord upon the harp,
   with a ten-stringed lute sing him songs.

2. For the word of the Lord is faithful
   and all his works to be trusted.
   The Lord loves justice and right
   and fills the earth with his love.

3. The Lord looks on those who revere him,
   on those who hope in his love,
   to rescue their souls from death,
   to keep them alive in famine.

Gospel Acclamation John 14:6

Alleluia.
Jesus said: 'I am the Way, the Truth and the Life.
No one can come to the Father except through me.
Alleluia.

C Instrument
B♭ Instrument

Fifth Sunday of Easter

YEAR B

Responsorial Psalm Psalm 21:26-28, 30-32. Response v.26

Keith Duke

You are my praise, O Lord, in the great as - sem - bly.

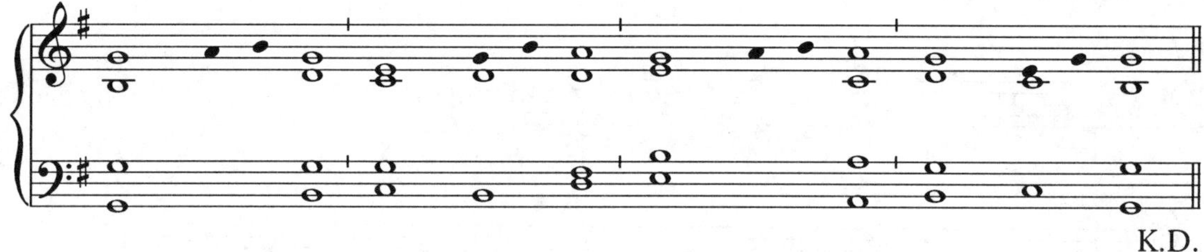

K.D.

1. My vows I will pay before those who fear him.
   The poor shall eat and shall have their fill.
   They shall praise the Lord, those who seek him.
   May their hearts live for ever and ever!

2. All the earth shall remember and return to the Lord,
   all families of the nations worship before him.
   They shall worship him, all the mighty of the earth;
   before him shall bow all who go down to the dust.

3. And my soul shall live for him, my children serve him.
   They shall tell of the Lord to generations yet to come,
   declare his faithfulness to peoples yet unborn:
   'These things the Lord has done.'

Gospel Acclamation John 15:4-5

Alleluia.
Make your home in me, as I make mine in you.
Whoever remains in me bears fruit in plenty.
Alleluia.

Fifth Sunday of Easter

YEAR C

Responsorial Psalm Psalm 144:8-13. Response cf. v.1

Geoff Nobes

I will bless your name for e - ver, O God my King.

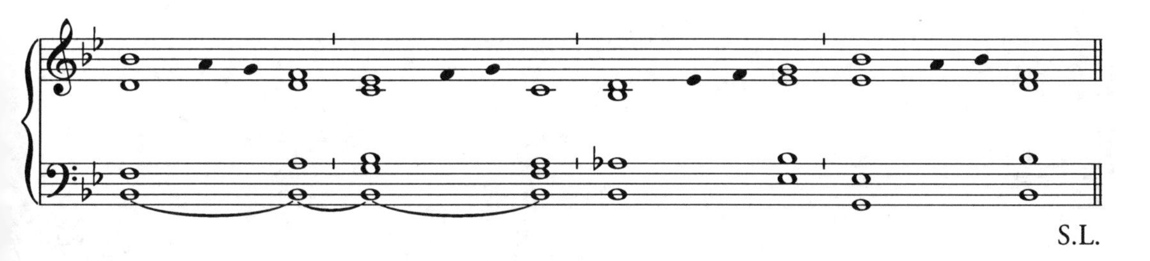

S.L.

1. The Lord is kind and full of compassion,
   slow to anger, abounding in love.
   How good is the Lord to all,
   compassionate to all his creatures.

2. All your creatures shall thank you, O Lord,
   and your friends shall repeat their blessing.
   They shall speak of the glory of your reign
   and declare your might, O God.

3. They will make known to all your mighty deeds
   and the glorious splendour of your reign.
   Yours is an everlasting kingdom;
   your rule lasts from age to age.

Gospel Acclamation John 13:34

Alleluia.
Jesus said: 'I give you a new commandment:
love one another, just as I have loved you.'
Alleluia.

C Instrument
B♭ Instrument

Sixth Sunday of Easter

YEAR A

Responsorial Psalm Psalm 65:1-7, 16, 20. Response v.1

John McCann

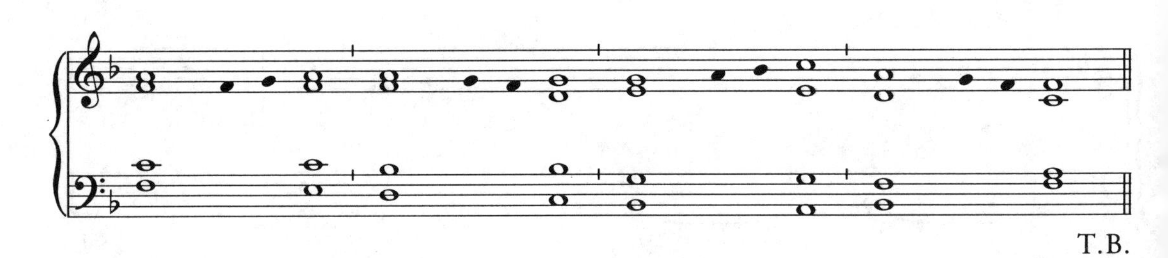

T.B.

1. Cry out with joy to God all the earth,
   O sing to the glory of his name.
   O render him glorious praise,
   say to God: 'How tremendous your deeds!'

2. 'Before you all the earth shall bow;
   shall sing to you, sing to your name!'
   Come and see the works of God,
   tremendous his deeds among men.

3. He turned the sea into dry land,
   they passed through the river dry-shod.
   Let our joy then be in him;
   he rules for ever by his might.

4. Come and hear, all who fear God.
   I will tell what he did for my soul:
   blessed be God who did not reject my prayer
   nor withhold his love from me.

Gospel Acclamation John 14:23

Alleluia.
Jesus said: 'If anyone loves me they will keep my word,
and my Father will love them and we shall come to them.'
Alleluia.

C Instrument

B♭ Instrument

Sixth Sunday of Easter

YEAR B

Responsorial Psalm Psalm 97:1-4. Response cf. v.2

Gerry Fitzpatrick

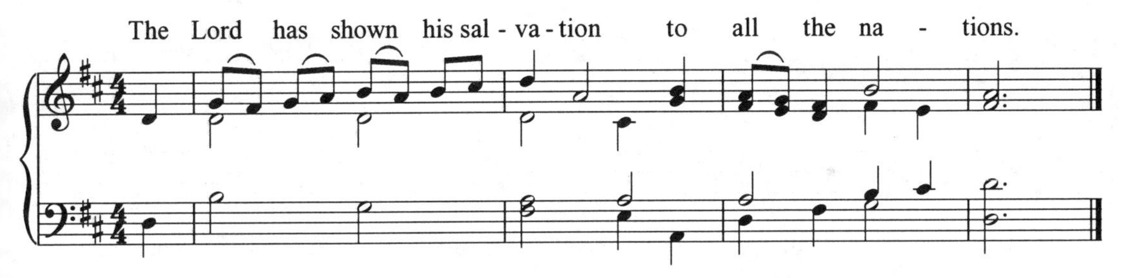

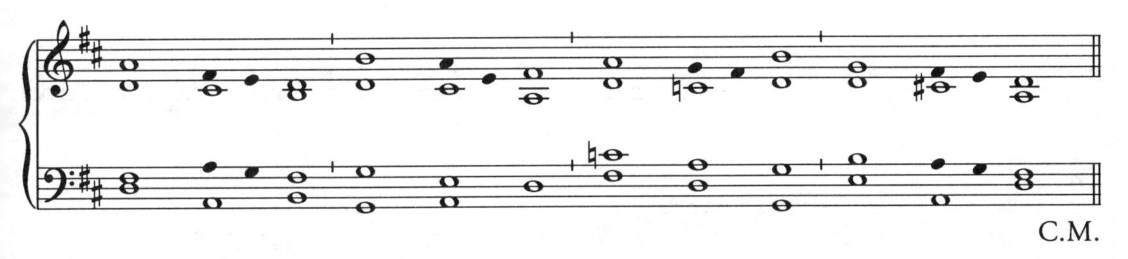

1. Sing a new song to the Lord
   for he has worked wonders.
   His right hand and his holy arm
   have brought salvation.

2. The Lord has made known his salvation;
   has shown his justice to the nations.
   He has remembered his truth and love
   for the house of Israel.

3. All the ends of the earth have seen
   the salvation of our God.
   Shout to the Lord all the earth,
   ring out your joy.

Gospel Acclamation John 14:23

Alleluia.
Jesus said: 'If anyone loves me they will keep my word,
and my Father will love them and we shall come to them.'
Alleluia.

Sixth Sunday of Easter

YEAR C

Responsorial Psalm Psalm 66:2-3, 5-6, 8. Response v.4

John Bertalot

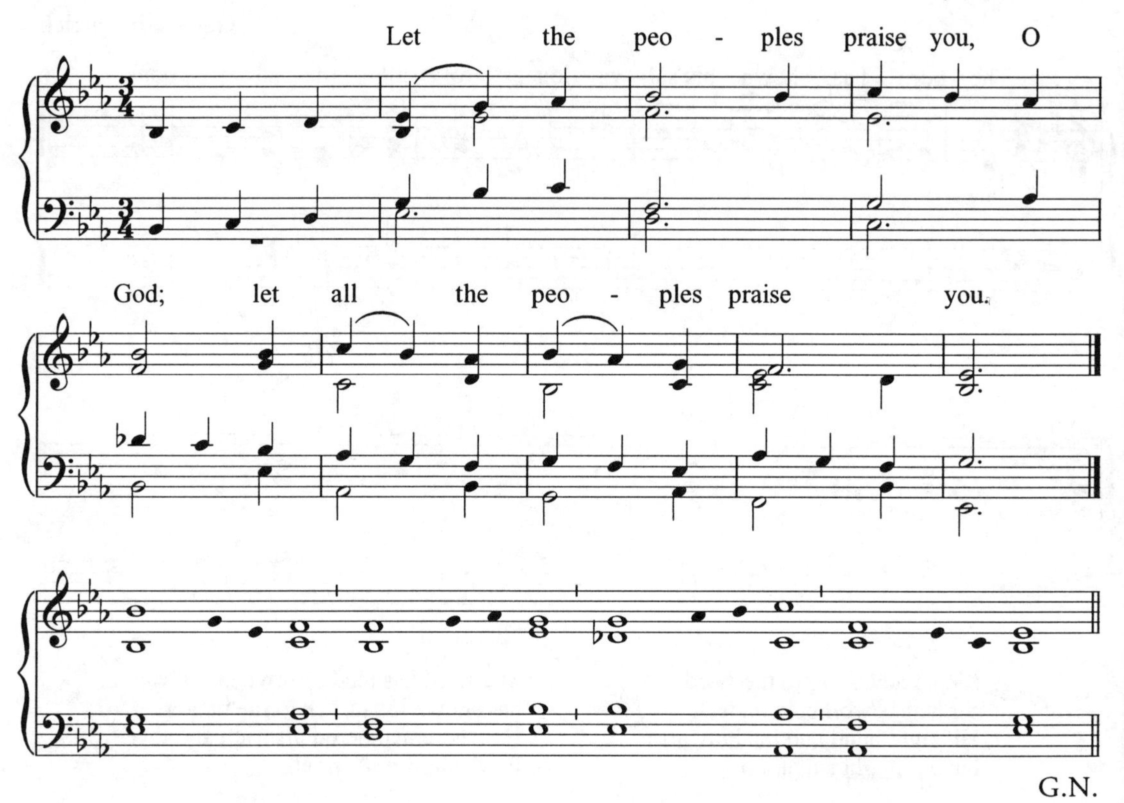

1. O God, be gracious and bless us
   and let your face shed its light upon us.
   So will your ways be known upon earth,
   and all nations learn your saving help.

2. Let the nations be glad and exult
   for you rule the world with justice.
   With fairness you rule the peoples,
   you guide the nations on earth.

3. Let the peoples praise you, O God;
   let all the peoples praise you.
   May God still give us his blessing
   till the ends of the earth revere him.

Gospel Acclamation John 14:23

Alleluia.
Jesus said: 'If anyone loves me they will keep my word,
and my Father will love them and we shall come to them.'
Alleluia.

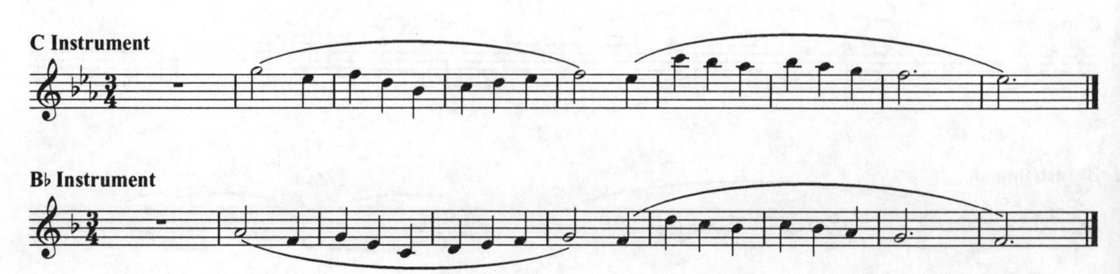

The Ascension of the Lord

YEARS A, B AND C

Responsorial Psalm Psalm 46:2-3, 6-9. Response v.6

Colin Mawby

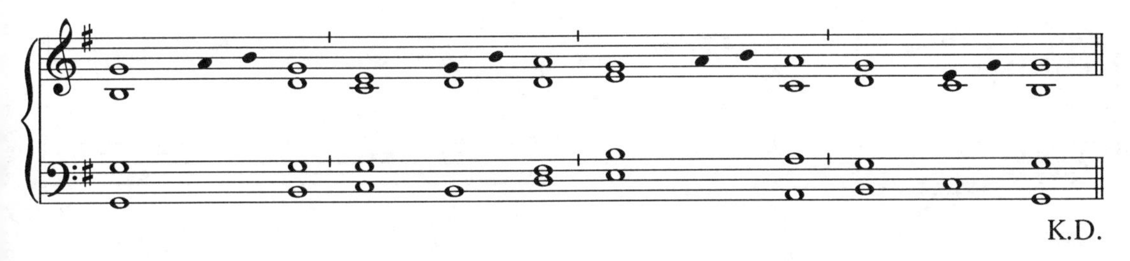

K.D.

1. All peoples, clap your hands,
   cry to God with shouts of joy!
   For the Lord, the Most High, we must fear,
   great king over all the earth.

2. God goes up with shouts of joy;
   the Lord goes up with trumpet blast.
   Sing praise for God, sing praise,
   sing praise to our king, sing praise.

3. God is king of all the earth.
   Sing praise with all your skill.
   God is king over the nations;
   God reigns on his holy throne.

Gospel Acclamation Matthew 28:19, 20

Alleluia.
Go, make disciples of all the nations;
I am with you always; yes, to the end of time.
Alleluia.

Seventh Sunday of Easter

YEAR A

Responsorial Psalm Psalm 26:1, 4, 7-8. Response v.13

Andrew Wright

I am sure I shall see the Lord's good-ness in the land of the liv-ing.

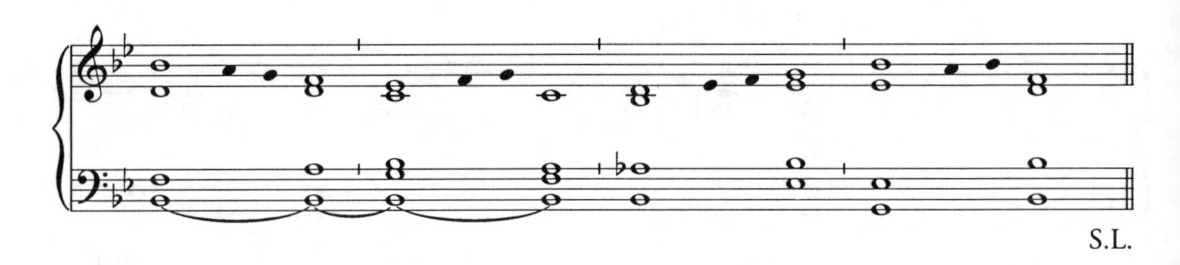

S.L.

1. The Lord is my light and my help;
   whom shall I fear?
   The Lord is the stronghold of my life;
   before whom shall I shrink?

2. There is one thing I ask of the Lord,
   for this I long,
   to live in the house of the Lord,
   all the days of my life.

3. O Lord, hear my voice when I call;
   have mercy and answer.
   Of you my heart has spoken;
   'Seek his face.'

Gospel Acclamation cf. John 14:18

Alleluia.
I will not leave you orphans, says the Lord;
I will come back to you, and your hearts will be full of joy.
Alleluia.

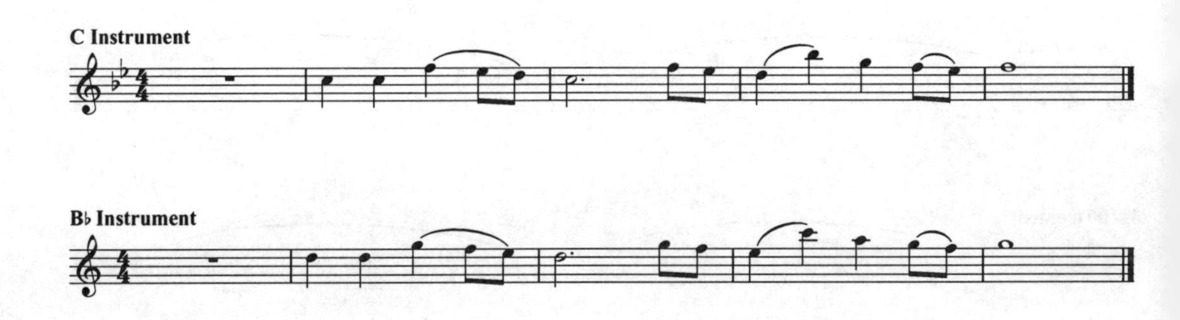
C Instrument
B♭ Instrument

Seventh Sunday of Easter

YEAR B

Responsorial Psalm Psalm 102:1-2, 11-12, 19-20. Response v.19

Alan Rees

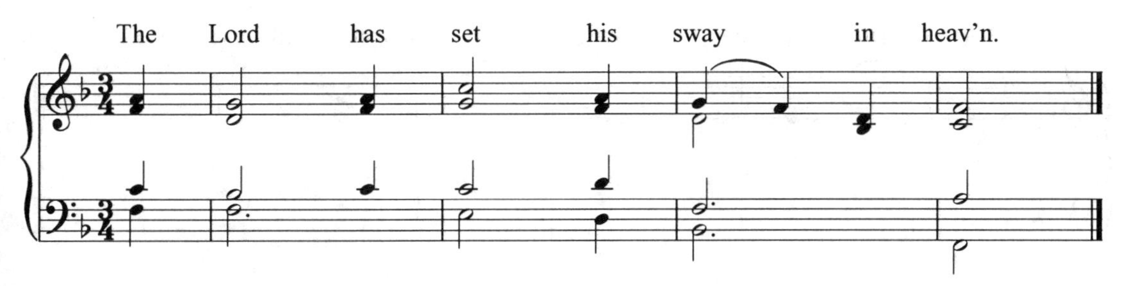

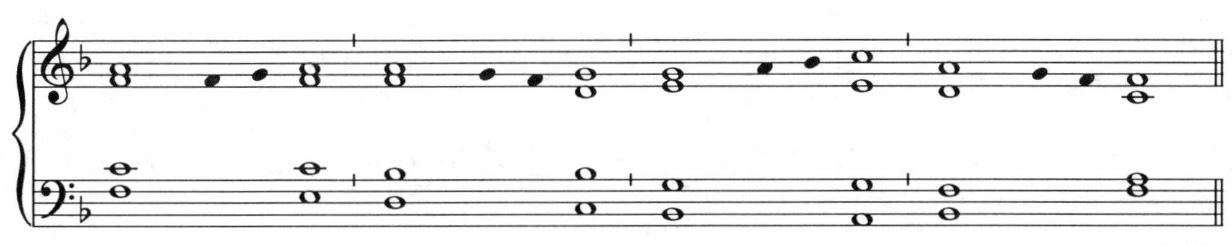

T.B.

1. My soul, give thanks to the Lord;
   all my being, bless his holy name.
   My soul, give thanks to the Lord
   and never forget all his blessings.

2. For as the heavens are high above the earth
   so strong is his love for those who fear him.
   As far as the east is from the west
   so far does he remove our sins.

3. The Lord has set his sway in heaven
   and his kingdom is ruling over all.
   Give thanks to the Lord, all his angels,
   mighty in power, fulfilling his word.

Gospel Acclamation cf. John 14:18

Alleluia.
I will not leave you orphans, says the Lord;
I will come back to you, and your hearts will be full of joy.
Alleluia.

Seventh Sunday of Easter

YEAR C

Responsorial Psalm Psalm 96:1-2, 6-7, 9. Response vv.1, 9

Richard Lloyd

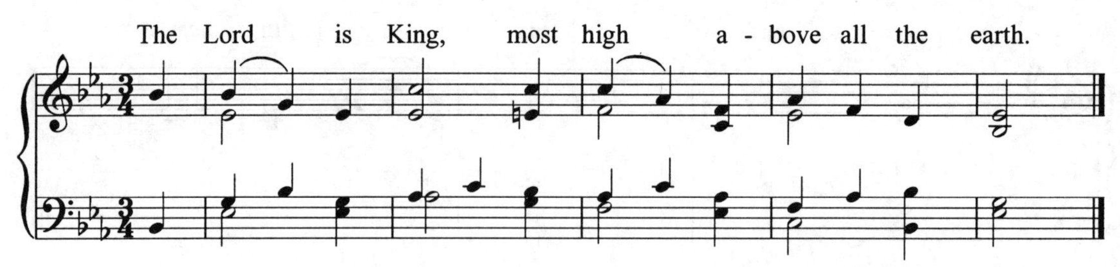
The Lord is King, most high a - bove all the earth.

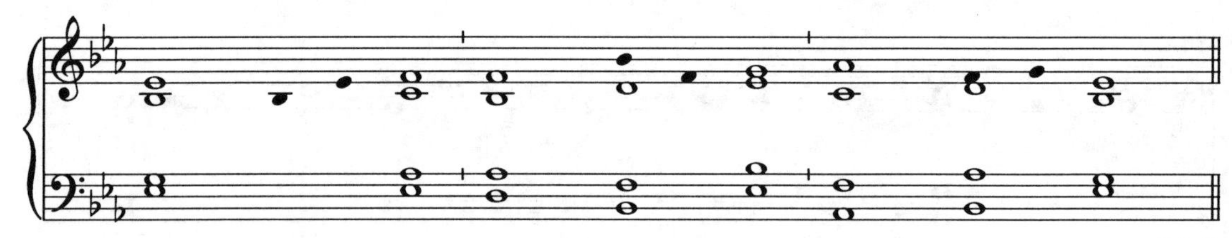

C.M.

1. The Lord is King, let earth rejoice,
   the many coastlands be glad.
   His throne is justice and right.

2. The skies proclaim his justice;
   all peoples see his glory.
   All you spirits, worship him.

3. For you indeed are the Lord
   most high above all the earth
   exalted far above all spirits.

Gospel Acclamation cf. John 14:18

Alleluia.
I will not leave you orphans, says the Lord;
I will come back to you, and your hearts will be full of joy.
Alleluia.

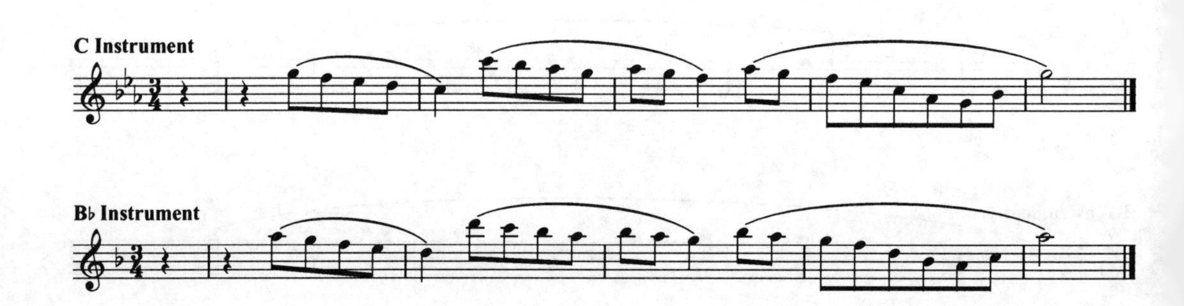
C Instrument
B♭ Instrument

Pentecost Sunday

YEARS A, B AND C

Responsorial Psalm Psalm 103:1, 24, 29-31, 34. Response cf. v.30

Keith Duke

K.D.

1. Bless the Lord, my soul!
   Lord God, how great you are.
   How many are your works, O Lord!
   The earth is full of your riches.

2. You take back your spirit, they die,
   returning to the dust from which they came.
   You send forth your spirit, they are created;
   and you renew the face of the earth.

3. May the glory of the Lord last for ever!
   May the Lord rejoice in his works!
   May my thoughts be pleasing to him.
   I find my joy in the Lord.

Gospel Acclamation

Alleluia.
Come, Holy Spirit, fill the hearts of your faithful
and kindle in them the fire of your love.
Alleluia.

Sunday after Pentecost

YEAR A

The Most Holy Trinity

Responsorial Psalm Daniel 3:52-56. Response v.22

This Psalm is sung as a Litany. The Response is given out and repeated by all and is then repeated at the end of each line.

Colin Mawby

K.D.

1. You are blest, Lord God of our fathers.
To you glory and praise for evermore.
Blest your glorious holy name.
To you glory and praise for evermore.

2. You are blest in the temple of your glory.
To you glory and praise for evermore.
You are blest on the throne of your kingdom.
To you glory and praise for evermore.

3. You are blest who gaze into the depths.
To you glory and praise for evermore.
You are blest in the firmament of heaven.
To you glory and praise for evermore.

Gospel Acclamation cf. Revelation 1:8

Alleluia.
Glory be to the Father, and to the Son, and to the Holy Spirit,
the God who is, who was, and who is to come.
Alleluia.

Sunday after Pentecost

The Most Holy Trinity

YEAR B

Responsorial Psalm Psalm 32:4-6, 9, 18-20, 22. Response v.12

John McCann

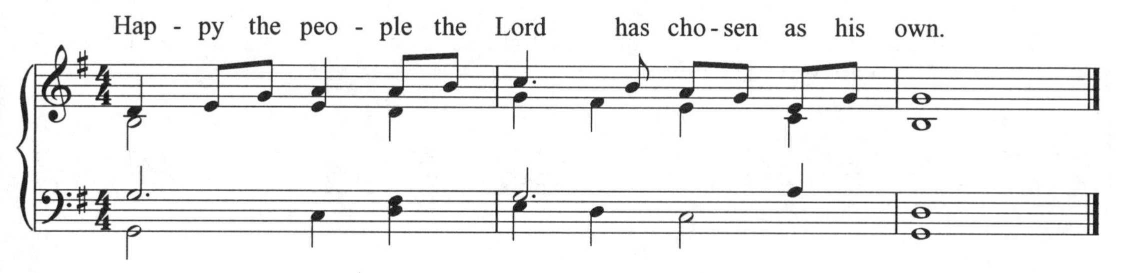
Hap - py the peo - ple the Lord has cho - sen as his own.

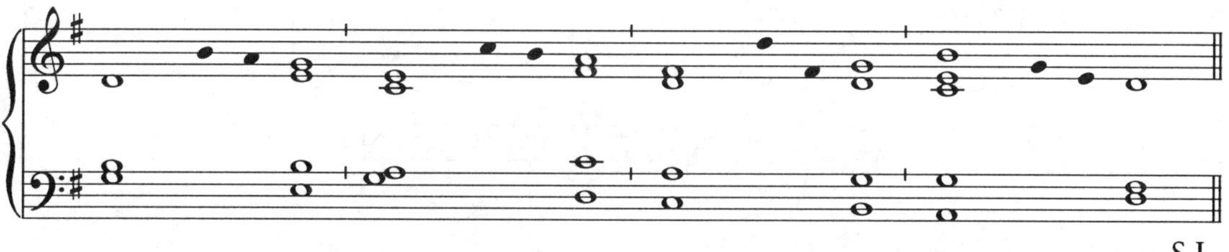

S.L.

1. The word of the Lord is faithful
   and all his works to be trusted.
   The Lord loves justice and right
   and fills the earth with his love.

2. By his word the heavens were made,
   by the breath of his mouth all the stars.
   He spoke; and they came to be.
   He commanded; they sprang into being.

3. The Lord looks on those who revere him,
   on those who hope in his love,
   to rescue their souls from death,
   to keep them alive in famine.

4. Our soul is waiting for the Lord.
   The Lord is our help and our shield.
   May your love be upon us, O Lord,
   as we place all our hope in you.

Gospel Acclamation cf. Revelation 1:8

Alleluia.
Glory be to the Father, and to the Son, and to the Holy Spirit,
the God who is, who was, and who is to come.
Alleluia.

C Instrument
B♭ Instrument

Sunday after Pentecost
The Most Holy Trinity

YEAR C

Responsorial Psalm Psalm 8:4-9. Response v.2

Geoff Nobes

How great is your name, O Lord, our God, through all the earth.

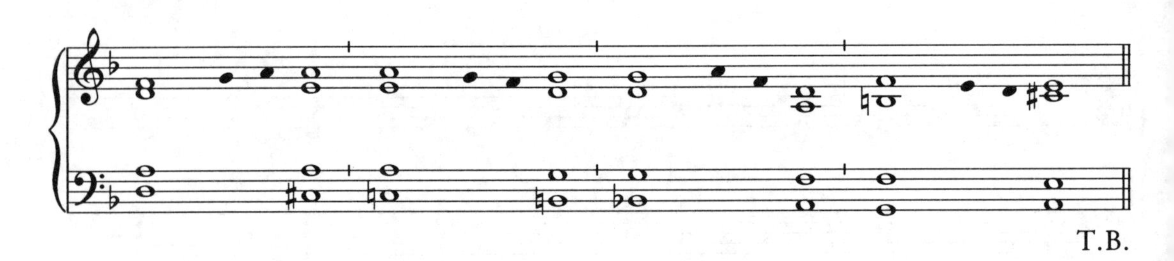

T.B.

1. When I see the heavens, the work of your hands,
   the moon and the stars which you arranged,
   what are we that you should keep us in mind,
   mortals that you care for us?

2. Yet you have made us little less than gods;
   with glory and honour you crowned us,
   gave us power over the works of your hand,
   put all things under our feet.

3. All of them, sheep and cattle,
   yes, even the savage beasts,
   birds of the air, and fish
   that make their way through the waters.

Gospel Acclamation cf. Revelation 1:8

Alleluia.
Glory be to the Father, and to the Son, and to the Holy Spirit,
the God who is, who was, and who is to come.
Alleluia.

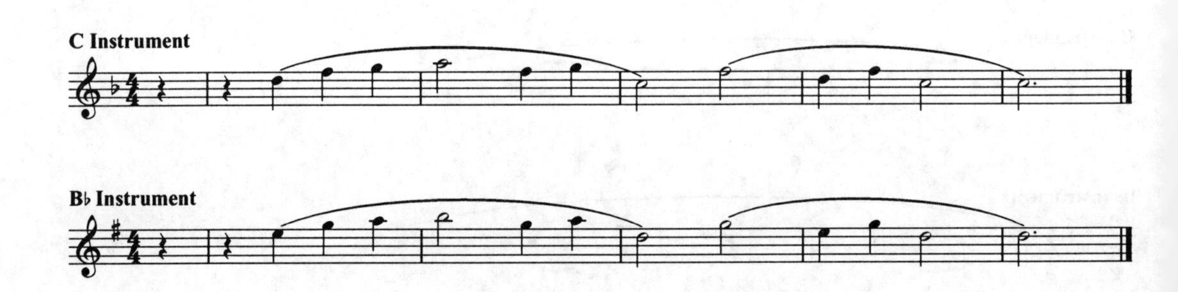

Thursday after Trinity Sunday

YEAR A

The Body and Blood of Christ

Responsorial Psalm Psalm 147:12-15, 19-20. Response v.12

Simon Lesley

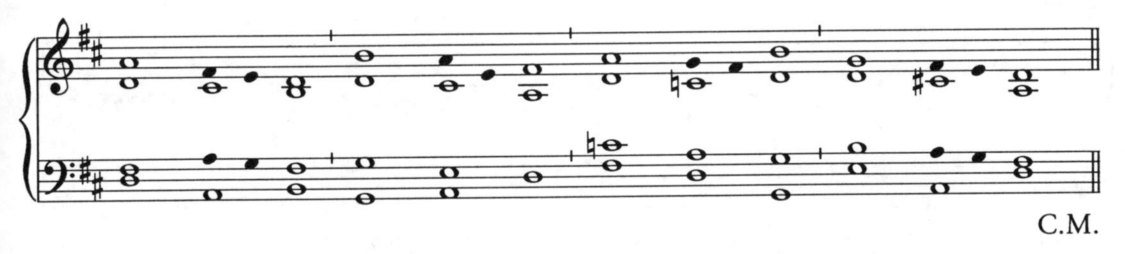

1. O praise the Lord, Jerusalem!
   Zion, praise your God!
   He has strengthened the bars of your gates,
   he has blessed the children within you.

2. He established peace on your borders,
   he feeds you with finest wheat.
   He sends out his word to the earth
   and swiftly runs his command.

3. He makes his word known to Jacob,
   to Israel his laws and decrees.
   He has not dealt thus with other nations;
   he has not taught them his decrees.

Gospel Acclamation John 6:51-52

Alleluia.
I am the living bread which has come down from heaven, says the Lord.
Anyone who eats this bread will live for ever.
Alleluia.

Thursday after Trinity Sunday
The Body and Blood of Christ

Responsorial Psalm Psalm 115:12-13, 15-18. Response v.13

John McCann

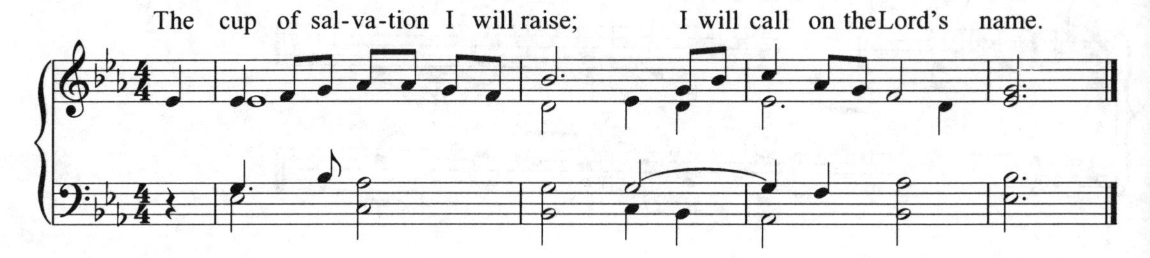

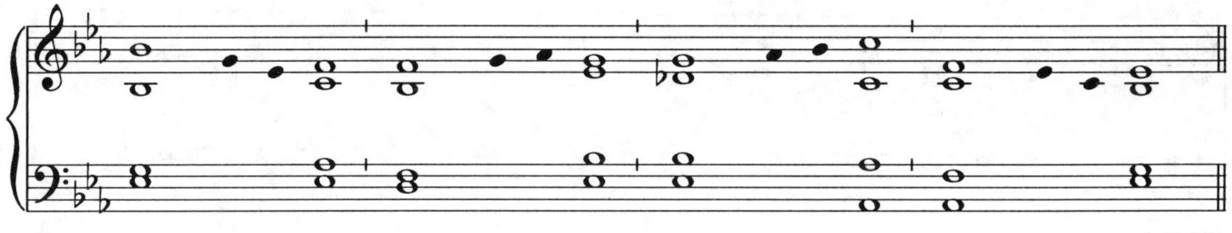

G.N.

1. How can I repay the Lord
   for his goodness to me?
   The cup of salvation I will raise;
   I will call on the Lord's name.

2. O precious in the eyes of the Lord
   is the death of his faithful.
   Your servant, Lord, your servant am I;
   you have loosened my bonds.

3. A thanksgiving sacrifice I make:
   I will call on the Lord's name.
   My vows to the Lord I will fulfil
   before all his people.

Gospel Acclamation John 6:51-52

Alleluia.
I am the living bread which has come down from heaven, says the Lord.
Anyone who eats this bread will live for ever.
Alleluia.

Thursday after Trinity Sunday

The Body and Blood of Christ

YEAR C

Responsorial Psalm Psalm 109:1-4. Response v.4

Richard Lloyd

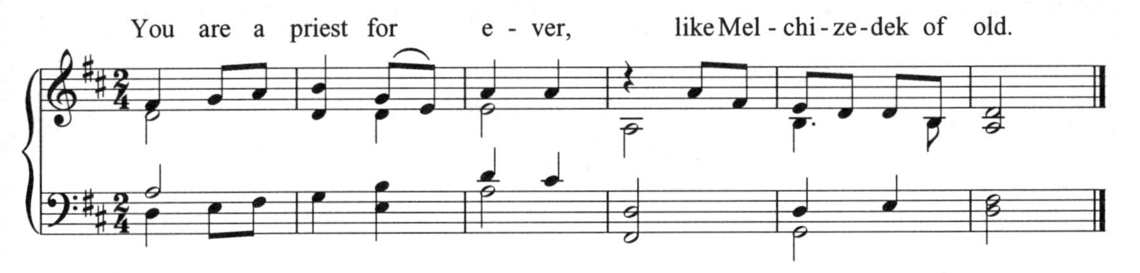

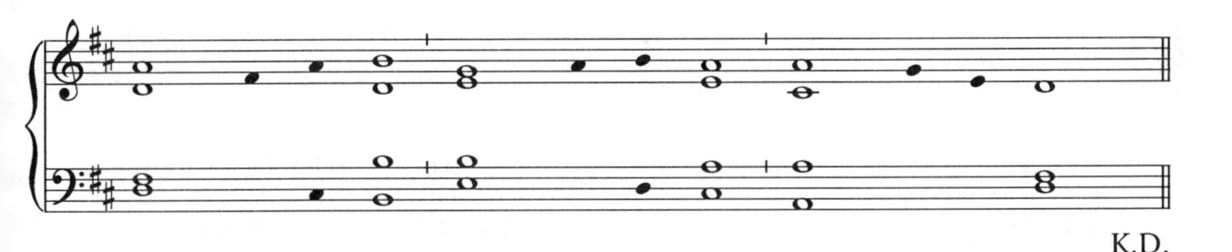

1. The Lord's revelation to my Master:
   'Sit on my right:
   I will put your foes beneath your feet.'

2. The Lord will send from Zion
   your sceptre of power:
   rule in the midst of all your foes.

3. A prince from the day of your birth
   on the holy mountains;
   from the womb before the daybreak I begot you.

4. The Lord has sworn an oath he will not change.
   'You are a priest for ever,
   a priest like Melchizedek of old.'

Gospel Acclamation John 6:51-52

Alleluia.
I am the living bread which has come down from heaven, says the Lord.
Anyone who eats this bread will live for ever.
Alleluia.

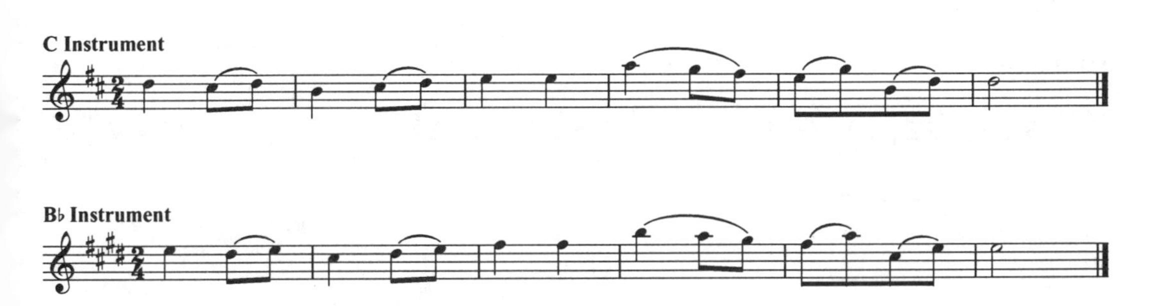

Second Sunday in Ordinary Time

YEAR A

Responsorial Psalm Psalm 39:2, 4, 7-10. Response vv.8, 9

Colin Mawby

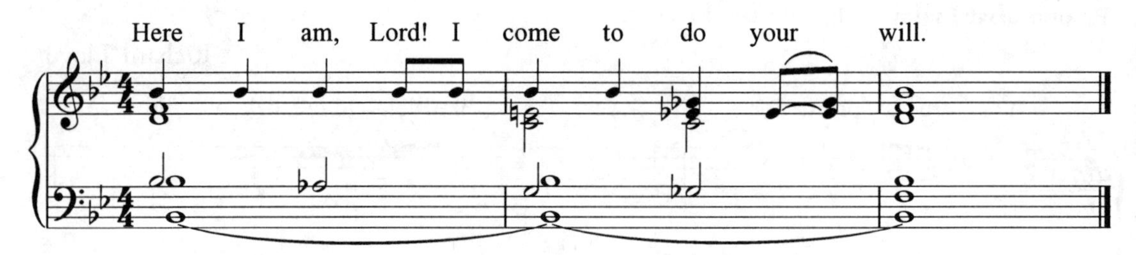
Here I am, Lord! I come to do your will.

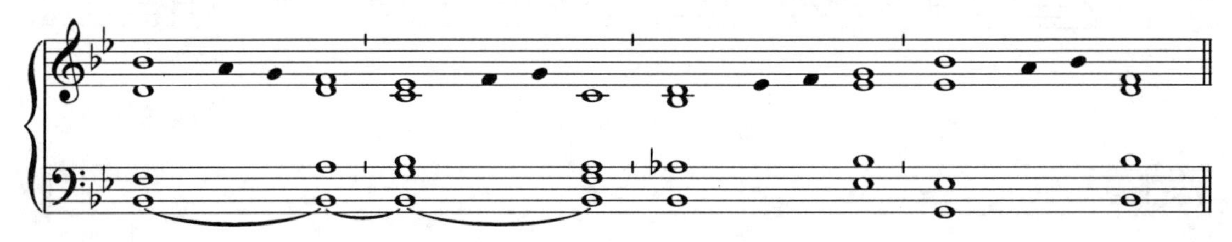

S.L.

1. I waited, I waited for the Lord and he stooped down to me; he heard my cry. He put a new song into my mouth, praise of our God.

2. You do not ask for sacrifice and offerings, but an open ear. You do not ask for holocaust and victim. Instead, here am I.

3. In the scroll of the book it stands written that I should do your will. My God, I delight in your law in the depth of my heart.

4. Your justice I have proclaimed in the great assembly. My lips I have not sealed; you know it, O Lord.

Gospel Acclamation Luke 19:38

Alleluia.
Blessings on the King who comes, in the name of the Lord!
Peace in heaven and glory in the highest heavens!
Alleluia.

or John 1:14, 12

Alleluia.
The Word was made flesh and lived among us;
to all who did accept him he gave power to become children of God.
Alleluia.

C Instrument
B♭ Instrument

Third Sunday in Ordinary Time

YEAR A

Responsorial Psalm Psalm 26:1, 4, 13-14. Response v.1

Keith Duke

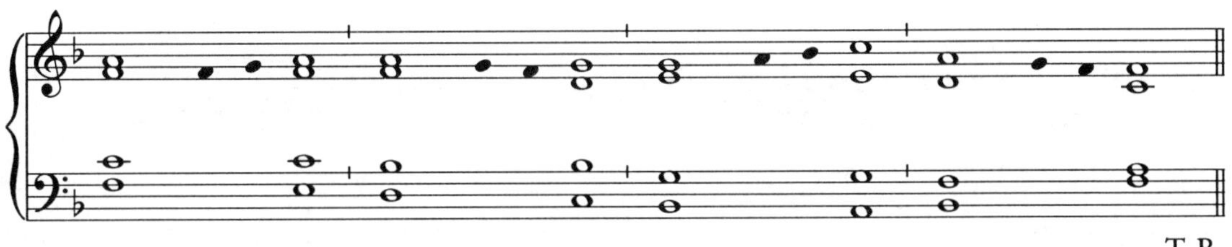

T.B.

1. The Lord is my light and my help;
   whom shall I fear?
   The Lord is the stronghold of my life;
   before whom shall I shrink?

2. There is one thing I ask of the Lord,
   for this I long,
   to live in the house of the Lord,
   all the days of my life.

3. I am sure I shall see the Lord's goodness
   in the land of the living.
   Hope in him, hold firm and take heart.
   Hope in the Lord!

Gospel Acclamation Matthew 4:23

Alleluia.
Jesus proclaimed the Good News of the kingdom,
and cured all kinds of sickness among the people.
Alleluia.

Fourth Sunday in Ordinary Time

YEAR A

Responsorial Psalm Psalm 145:7-10. Response Matthew 5:3

Colin Mawby

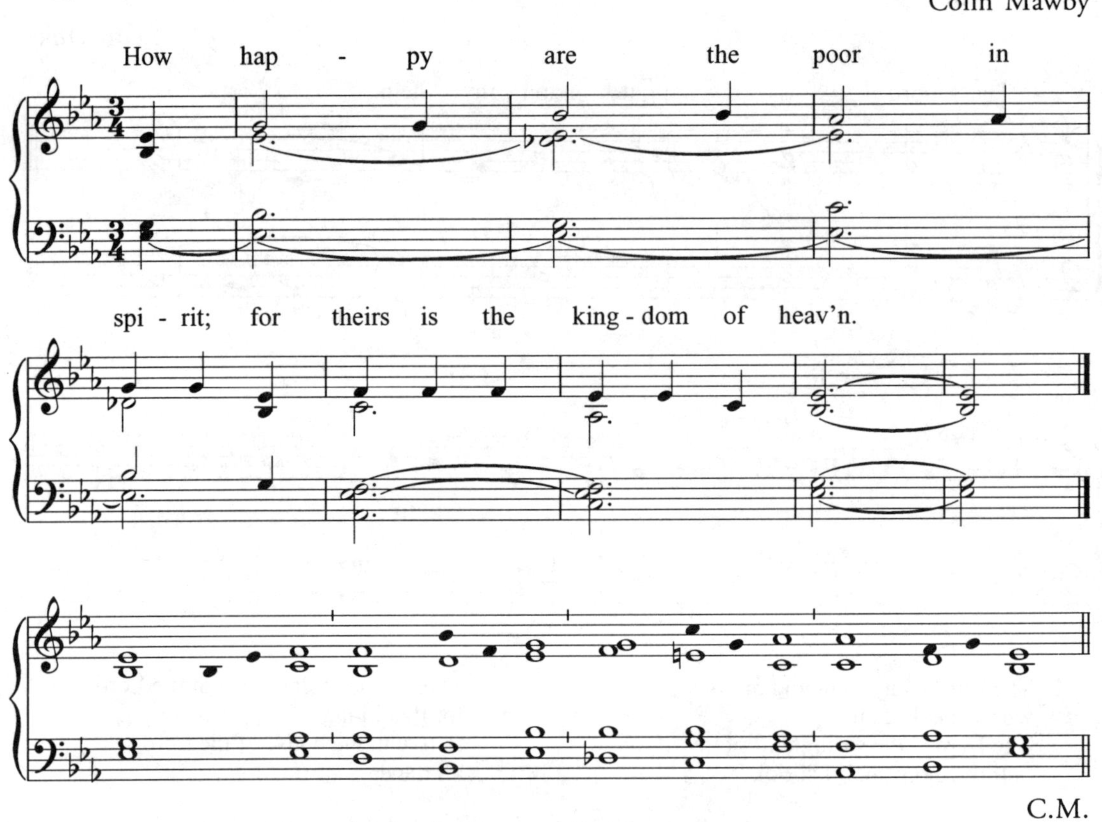

1. It is the Lord who keeps faith for ever,
   who is just to those who are oppressed.
   It is he who gives bread to the hungry,
   the Lord, who sets prisoners free.

2. It is the Lord who gives sight to the blind,
   who raises up those who are bowed down,
   the Lord, who protects the stranger
   and upholds the widow and orphan.

3. It is the Lord who loves the just
   but thwarts the path of the wicked.
   The Lord will reign for ever,
   Zion's God, from age to age.

Gospel Acclamation Matthew 11:25

Alleluia.
Blessed are you, Father, Lord of Hea<u>ven</u> and earth,
for revealing the mysteries of the kingdom <u>to</u> mere children.
Alleluia.

or Matthew 5:12

Alleluia.
Rejoice <u>and</u> be glad:
your reward will be <u>great</u> in heaven.
Alleluia.

Fifth Sunday in Ordinary Time

YEAR A

Responsorial Psalm Psalm 111:4-9. Response v.4

Colin Mawby

The good will be a light, a light in the dark - ness.

G.N.

1. They are a light in the darkness for the upright:
   they are generous, merciful and just.
   The good take pity and lend,
   they conduct their affairs with honour.

2. The just will never waver:
   they will be remembered for ever.
   They have no fear of evil news;
   with a firm heart they trust in the Lord.

3. With a steadfast heart they will not fear;
   open-handed, they give to the poor;
   their justice stands firm for ever.
   Their heads will be raised in glory.

Gospel Acclamation John 8:12

Alleluia.
I am the light of the world, says the Lord,
anyone who follows me will have the light of life.
Alleluia.

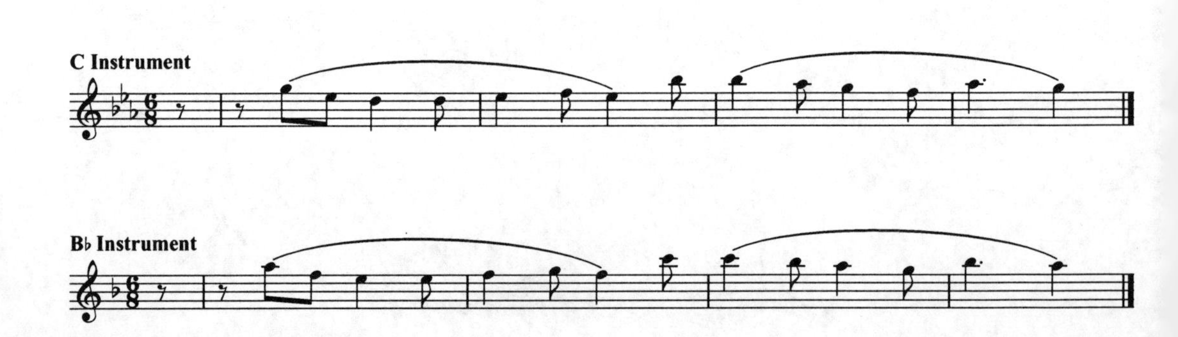
C Instrument
B♭ Instrument

Sixth Sunday in Ordinary Time

YEAR A

Responsorial Psalm Psalm 118:1-2, 4-5, 17-18, 33-34. Response v.1

1. They are happy whose life is blameless,
   who follow God's law!
   They are happy those who do his will,
   seeking him with all their hearts.

2. You have laid down your precepts
   to be obeyed with care.
   May my footsteps be firm
   to obey your statutes.

3. Bless your servant and I shall live
   and obey your word.
   Open my eyes that I may consider
   the wonders of your law.

4. Teach me the demands of your statutes
   and I will keep them to the end.
   Train me to observe your law,
   to keep it with my heart.

Gospel Acclamation 1 Samuel 3:9; John 6:68

Alleluia.
Speak, Lord, your servant is listening;
you have the message of eternal life.
Alleluia.

Seventh Sunday in Ordinary Time YEAR A

Responsorial Psalm Psalm 102:1-4, 8, 10, 12-13. Response v.8

Geoff Nobes

The Lord is com - pas - sion, com - pas - sion and love.
S.L.

1. My soul, give thanks to the Lord,
   all my being, bless his holy name.
   My soul, give thanks to the Lord
   and never forget all his blessings.

2. It is he who forgives all your guilt,
   who heals every one of your ills,
   who redeems your life from the grave,
   who crowns you with love and compassion.

3. The Lord is compassion and love,
   slow to anger and rich in mercy.
   He does not treat us according to our sins
   nor repay us according to our faults.

4. As far as the east is from the west
   so far does he remove our sins.
   As a father has compassion on his sons,
   the Lord has pity on those who fear him.

Gospel Acclamation John 14:23

Alleluia.
If anyone loves me they will keep my word,
and my Father will love them and we shall come to them.
Alleluia.

or 1 John 2:5

Alleluia.
When anyone obeys what Christ has said,
God's love comes to perfection in him.
Alleluia.

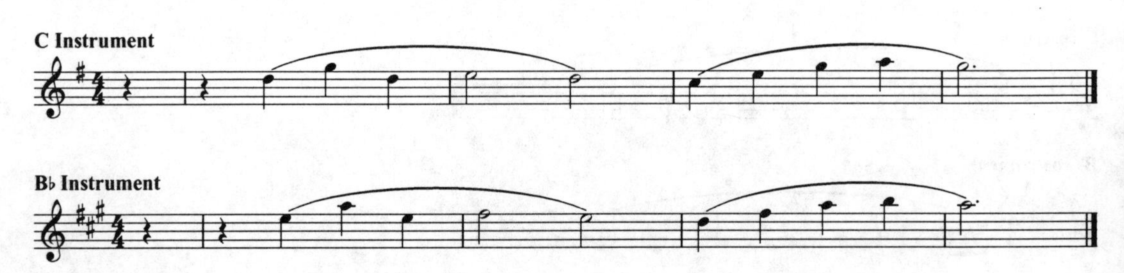

Eighth Sunday in Ordinary Time

YEAR A

Responsorial Psalm Psalm 61:2-3, 6-9. Response v.6

Andrew Moore

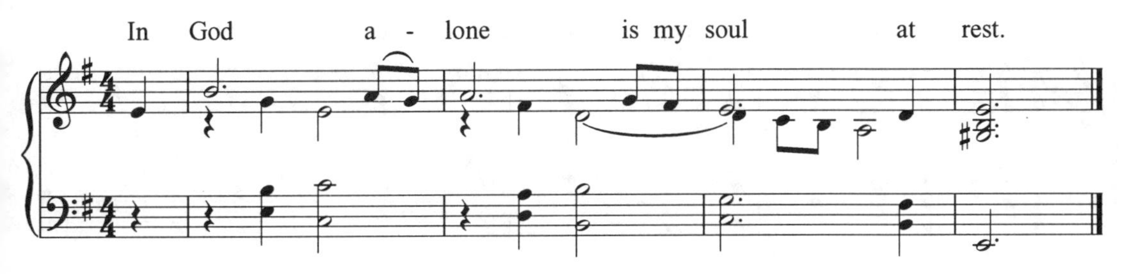

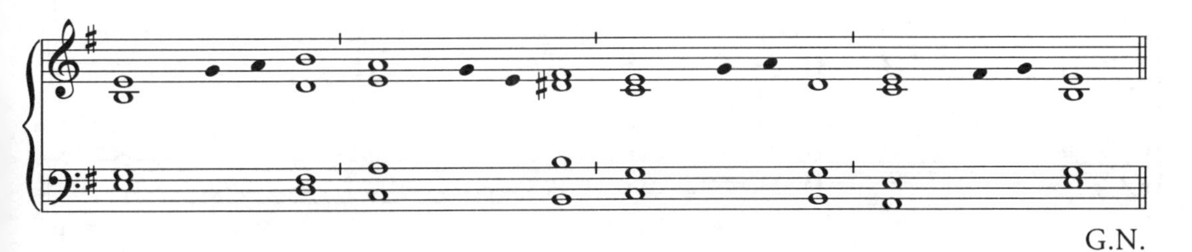

1. In God alone is my soul at rest;
   my help comes from him.
   He alone is my rock, my stronghold,
   my fortress: I stand firm.

2. In God alone be at rest, my soul;
   for my hope comes from him.
   He alone is my rock, my stronghold,
   my fortress: I stand firm.

3. In God is my safety and glory,
   the rock of my strength.
   Take refuge in God all you people.
   Trust him at all times.

Gospel Acclamation John 17:17

Alleluia.
Your word is truth, O Lord,
consecrate us in the truth.
Alleluia.

or Hebrews 4:12

Alleluia.
The word of God is something alive and active;
it can judge secret emotions and thoughts.
Alleluia.

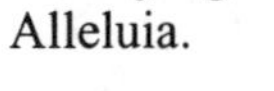

Ninth Sunday in Ordinary Time

YEAR A

Responsorial Psalm Psalm 30:2-4, 17, 25. Response v.3

Keith Duke

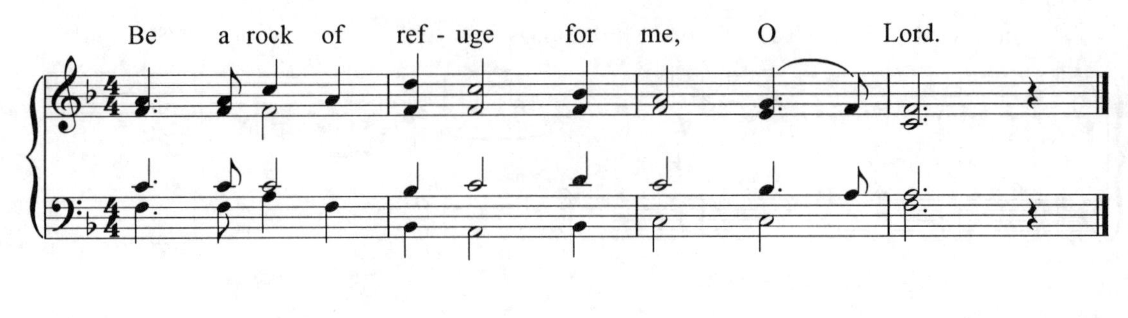

Be a rock of ref - uge for me, O Lord.

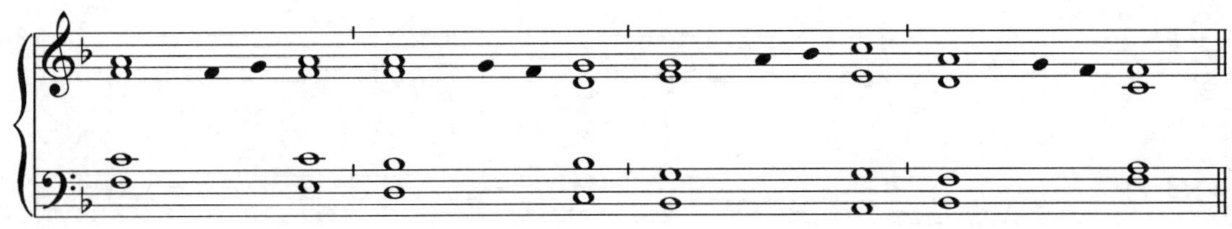

T.B.

1. In you, O Lord, I take refuge.
   Let me never be put to shame.
   In your justice, set me free,
   hear me and speedily rescue me.

2. Be a rock of refuge to me,
   a mighty stronghold to save me,
   for you are my rock, my stronghold.
   For your name's sake, lead me and guide me.

3. Let your face shine on your servant.
   Save me in your love.
   Be strong, let your heart take courage,
   all who hope in the Lord.

Gospel Acclamation John 14:23

Alleluia.
If anyone loves me they will keep my word,
and my Father will love them and we shall come to them.
Alleluia.

or John 15:5

Alleluia.
I am the vine, you are the branches, says the Lord.
Whoever remains in me, with me in him, bears fruit in plenty.
Alleluia.

C Instrument
B♭ Instrument

Tenth Sunday in Ordinary Time

YEAR A

Responsorial Psalm Psalm 49:1, 8, 12-15. Response v.23

John Bertalot

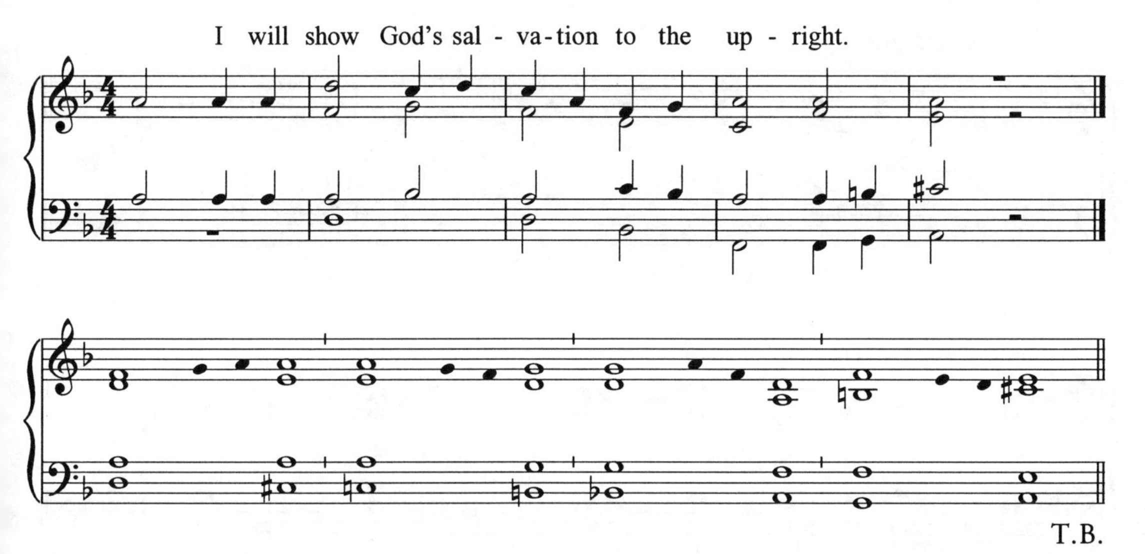
I will show God's sal - va-tion to the up - right.
T.B.

1. The God of gods, the Lord, has spoken
   and summoned the earth,
   from the rising of the sun to its setting.
   'I find no fault with your sacrifices,
   your offerings are always before me.'

2. 'Were I hungry, I would not tell you,
   for I own the world and all it holds.
   Do you think I eat the flesh of bulls,
   or drink the blood of goats?'

3. 'Pay your sacrifice of thanksgiving to God
   and render him your votive offerings.
   Call on me in the day of distress.
   I will free you and you shall honour me.'

Gospel Acclamation cf. Acts 16:14

Alleluia.
Open our heart, O Lord,
to accept the words of your Son.
Alleluia.

or Luke 4:18

Alleluia.
The Lord has sent me to bring the good news to the poor,
to proclaim liberty to captives.
Alleluia.

C Instrument
B♭ Instrument

Eleventh Sunday in Ordinary Time

YEAR A

Responsorial Psalm Psalm 99:2-3, 5. Response v.3

John McCann

1. Cry out with joy to the Lord, all the earth.
Serve the Lord with gladness.
Come before him, singing for joy.

2. Know that he, the Lord is God.
He made us, we belong to him,
we are his people, the sheep of his flock.

3. Indeed, how good is the Lord,
eternal his merciful love.
He is faithful from age to age.

Gospel Acclamation John 10:27

Alleluia.
The sheep that belong to me listen to my voice, says the Lord,
I know them and they follow me.
Alleluia.

or Mark 1:15

Alleluia.
The kingdom of God is close at hand.
Repent, and believe the Good News.
Alleluia.

Twelfth Sunday in Ordinary Time

YEAR A

Responsorial Psalm Psalm 68:8-10, 14, 17, 33-35. Response v.14

Andrew Moore

1. It is for you that I suffer taunts,
   that shame covers my face,
   that I have become a stranger to my brothers,
   an alien to my own mother's sons.
   I burn with zeal for your house
   and taunts against you fall on me.

2. This is my prayer to you,
   my prayer for your favour.
   In your great love, answer me, O God,
   with your help that never fails:
   Lord, answer, for your love is kind;
   in your compassion, turn towards me.

3. The poor when they see it will be glad
   and God-seeking hearts will revive;
   for the Lord listens to the needy
   and does not spurn his servants in their chains.
   Let the heavens and the earth give him praise,
   the sea and all its living creatures.

Gospel Acclamation John 1:14, 12

Alleluia.
The Word was made flesh and lived among us;
to all who did accept him
he gave power to become children of God.
Alleluia.

or John 15:26, 27

Alleluia.
The Spirit of truth will be my witness;
and you too will be my witnesses.
Alleluia.

Thirteenth Sunday in Ordinary Time YEAR A

Responsorial Psalm Psalm 88:2-3, 16-19. Response v.2

Gerry Fitzpatrick

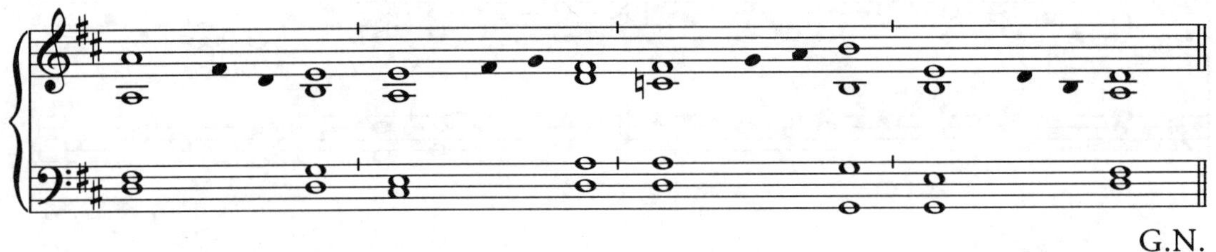

G.N.

1. I will sing for ever of your love, O Lord;
   through all ages my mouth
   will proclaim your truth.
   Of this I am sure, that your love lasts for ever,
   that your truth is firmly
   established as the heavens.

2. Happy the people who acclaim such a king,
   who walk, O Lord, in the light of your face,
   who find their joy every day in your name,
   who make your justice the
   source of their bliss.

3. For it is you, O Lord, who are the glory of their strength;
   it is by your favour that our might is exalted;
   for our ruler is in the keeping of the Lord;
   our king in the keeping of the Holy One of Israel.

Gospel Acclamation cf. Acts 16:14

Alleluia.
Open our heart, O Lord,
to accept the words of your Son.
Alleluia.

or 1 Peter 2:9

Alleluia.
You are a chosen race, a royal priesthood,
a people set apart to sing the praises of God
who called you out of darkness
into his wonderful light.
Alleluia.

C Instrument

B♭ Instrument

Fourteenth Sunday in Ordinary Time YEAR A

Responsorial Psalm Psalm 144:1-2, 8-11. 13-14. Response v.1

Simon Lesley

1. I will give you glory, O God my King,
   I will bless your name for ever.
   I will bless you day after day
   and praise your name for ever.

2. The Lord is kind and full of compassion,
   slow to anger, abounding in love.
   How good is the Lord to all,
   compassionate to all his creatures.

3. All your creatures shall thank you, O Lord,
   and your friends shall repeat their blessing.
   They shall speak of the glory of your reign
   and declare your might, O God.

4. The Lord is faithful in all his words
   and loving in all his deeds.
   The Lord supports all who fall
   and raises all who are bowed down.

Gospel Acclamation cf. Matthew 11:25

Alleluia.
Blessed are you, Father, Lord of heaven and earth,
for revealing the mysteries of the kingdom to mere children.
Alleluia.

C Instrument

8va

B♭ Instrument

Fifteenth Sunday in Ordinary Time YEAR A

Responsorial Psalm Psalm 64:10-14. Response Luke 8:8

Geoff Nobes

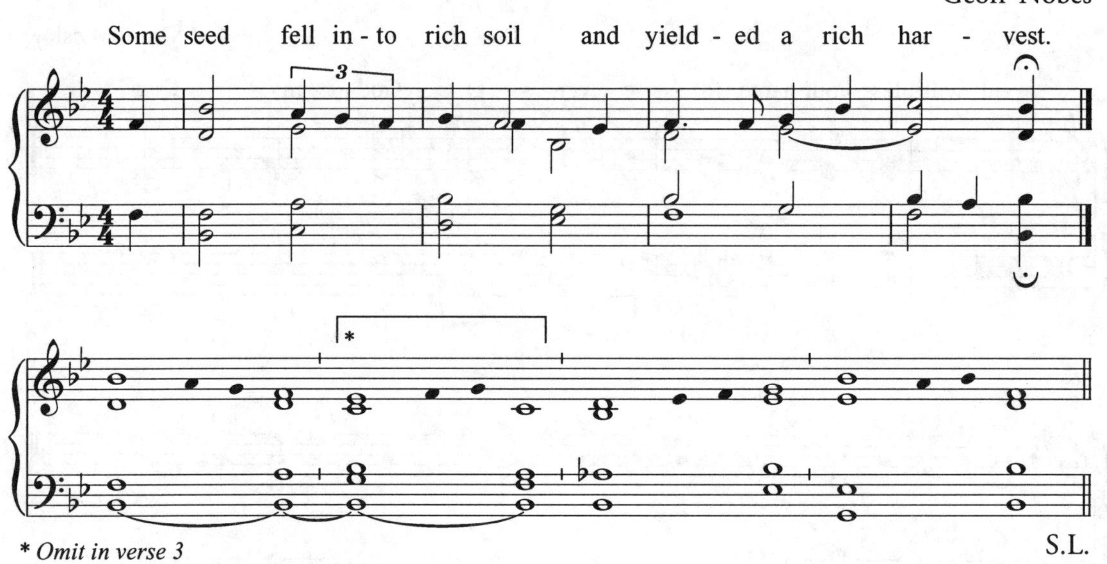

Some seed fell in - to rich soil and yield - ed a rich har - vest.
3
*

* *Omit in verse 3*

S.L.

1. You care for the earth, give it water,
   you fill it with riches.
   Your river in heaven brims over
   to provide its grain.

2. And thus you provide for the earth;
   you drench its furrows,
   you level it, soften it with showers,
   you bless its growth.

3. You crown the year with your goodness.
   Abundance flows in your steps,
   in the pastures of the wilderness it flows.

4. The hills are girded with joy,
   the meadows covered with flocks,
   the valleys are decked with wheat.
   They shout for joy, yes, they sing.

Gospel Acclamation 1 Samuel 3:9; John 6:68

Alleluia.
Speak, Lord, your servant is listening;
you have the message of eternal life.
Alleluia.

or

Alleluia.
The seed is the word of God, Christ the sower;
whoever finds this seed will remain for ever.
Alleluia.

Sixteenth Sunday in Ordinary Time YEAR A

Responsorial Psalm Psalm 85:5-6, 9-10, 15-16. Response v.5

Keith Duke

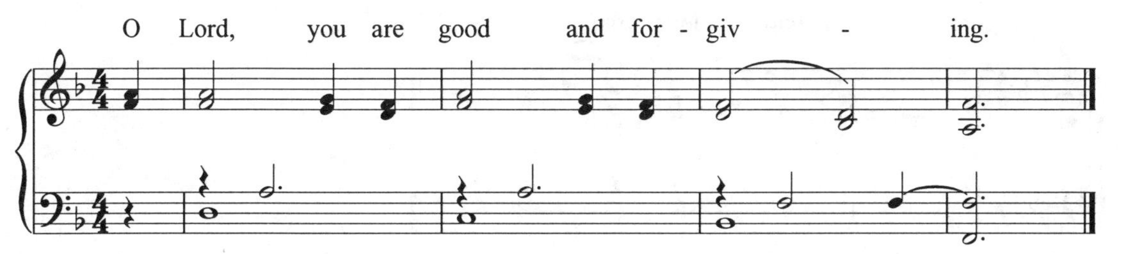

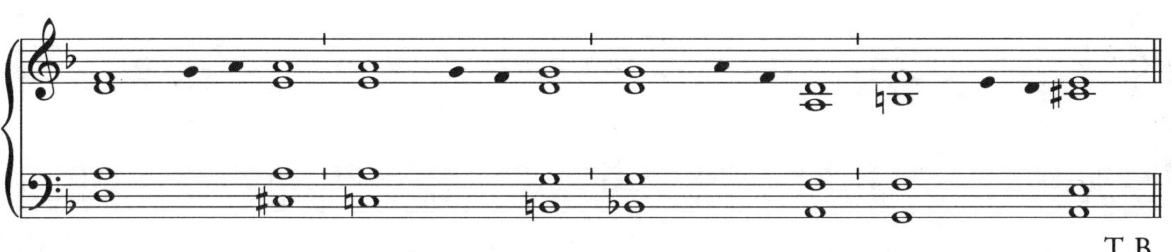

T.B.

1. O Lord, you are good and forgiving,
   full of love to all who call.
   Give heed, O Lord, to my prayer
   and attend to the sound of my voice.

2. All the nations shall come to adore you
   and glorify your name, O Lord:
   for you are great and do marvellous deeds,
   you who alone are God.

3. But you, God of mercy and compassion,
   slow to anger, O Lord,
   abounding in love and truth,
   turn and take pity on me.

Gospel Acclamation cf. Ephesians 1:17, 18

Alleluia.
May the Father of our Lord Jesus Christ enlighten the eyes of our mind,
so that we can see what hope his call holds for us.
Alleluia.

or cf. Matthew 11:25

Alleluia.
Blessed are you, Father, Lord of heaven and earth,
for revealing the mysteries of the kingdom to mere children.
Alleluia.

Seventeenth Sunday in Ordinary Time YEAR A

Responsorial Psalm Psalm 118:57, 72, 76-77, 127-130. Response v.97

Alan Rees

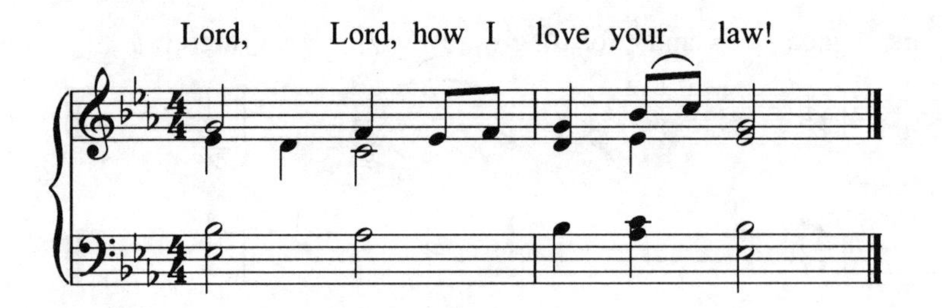
Lord, Lord, how I love your law!

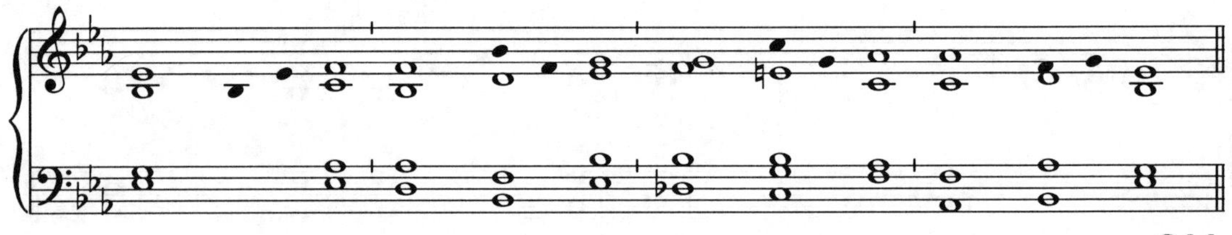

C.M.

1. My part, I have resolved, O Lord,
   is to obey your word.
   The law from your mouth means more to me
   than silver and gold.

2. Let your love be ready to console me
   by your promise to your servant.
   Let your love come to me and I shall live
   for your law is my delight.

3. That is why I love your commands
   more than finest gold.
   That is why I rule my life by your precepts;
   I hate false ways.

4. Your will is wonderful indeed;
   therefore I obey it.
   The unfolding of your word gives light
   and teaches the simple.

Gospel Acclamation John 15:15

Alleluia.
I call you friends, says the Lord,
because I have made known to you everything I have learnt from my Father.
Alleluia.

or cf. Matthew 11:25

Alleluia.
Blessed are you, Father, Lord of heaven and earth,
for revealing the mysteries of the kingdom to mere children.
Alleluia.

C Instrument

B♭ Instrument

Eighteenth Sunday in Ordinary Time YEAR A

Responsorial Psalm Psalm 144:8-9, 15-18. Response v.16

Colin Mawby

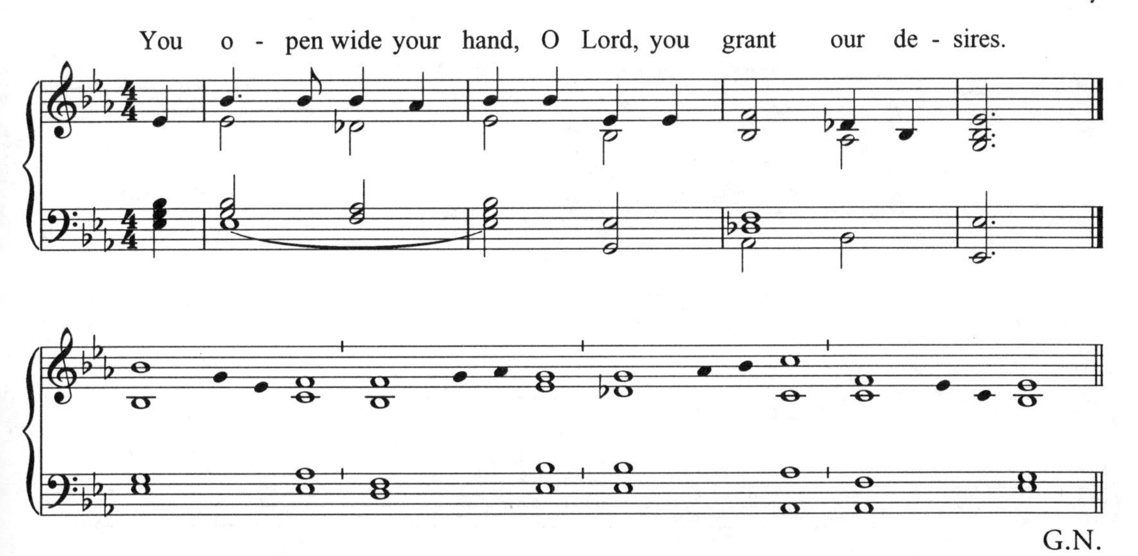
You o - pen wide your hand, O Lord, you grant our de - sires.
G.N.

1. The Lord is kind and full of compassion,
   slow to anger, abounding in love.
   How good is the Lord to all,
   compassionate to all his creatures.

2. The eyes of all creatures look to you
   and you give them their food in due time.
   You open wide your hand,
   grant the desires of all who live.

3. The Lord is just in all his ways
   and loving in all his deeds.
   He is close to all who call him,
   call on him from their hearts.

Gospel Acclamation Luke 19:38

Alleluia.
Blessings on the King who comes in the name of the Lord!
Peace in heaven and glory in the highest heavens!
Alleluia.

or Matthew 4:4

Alleluia.
Man does not live on bread alone,
but on every word that comes from the mouth of God.
Alleluia.

C Instrument
B♭ Instrument

Nineteenth Sunday in Ordinary Time YEAR A

Responsorial Psalm Psalm 84:9-14. Response v.8

John McCann

Let us see, O Lord, your mer - cy, and give us your sav - ing help.

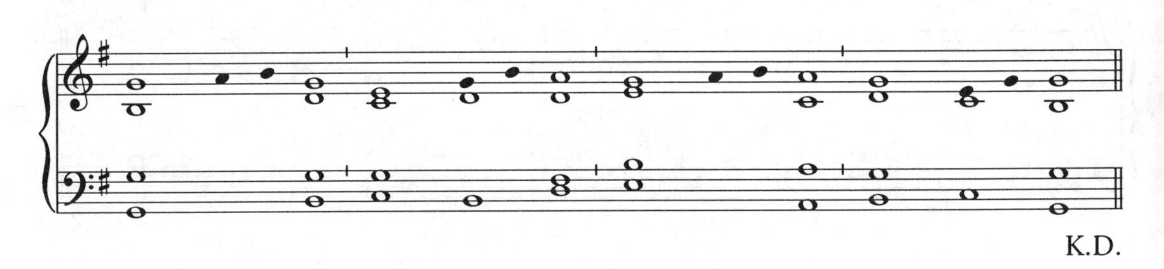
K.D.

1. I will hear what the Lord God has to say,
   a voice that speaks of peace.
   His help is near for those who fear him
   and his glory will dwell in our land.

2. Mercy and faithfulness have met;
   justice and peace have embraced.
   Faithfulness shall spring from the earth
   and justice look down from heaven.

3. The Lord will make us prosper
   and our earth shall yield its fruit.
   Justice shall march before him
   and peace shall follow his steps.

Gospel Acclamation Luke 19:38

Alleluia.
Blessings on the King who comes, in the name of the Lord!
Peace in heaven and glory in the highest heavens!
Alleluia.

or Psalm 129:5

Alleluia.
My soul is waiting for the Lord,
I count on his word.
Alleluia.

C Instrument
B♭ Instrument

Twentieth Sunday in Ordinary Time YEAR A

Responsorial Psalm Psalm 66:2-3, 5-6, 8. Response v.4

John Bertalot

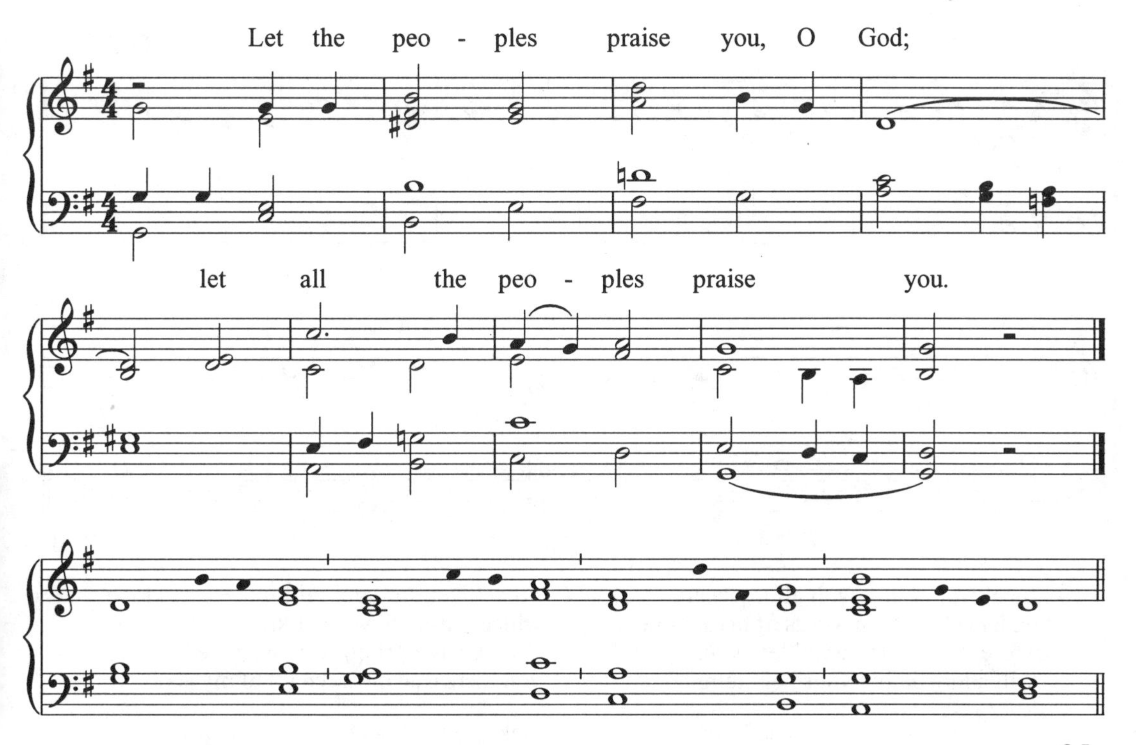

S.L.

1. O God, be gracious and bless us
   and let your face shed its light upon us.
   So will your ways be known upon earth
   and all nations learn your saving help.

2. Let the nations be glad and exult
   for you rule the world with justice.
   With fairness you rule the peoples,
   you guide the nations on earth.

3. Let the peoples praise you, O God;
   let all the peoples praise you.
   May God still give us his blessing
   till the ends of the earth revere him.

Gospel Acclamation John 10:27

Alleluia.
The sheep that belong to me listen
  to my voice, says the Lord,
I know them and they follow me.
Alleluia.

or cf. Matthew 4:23

Alleluia.
Jesus proclaimed the Good News of the kingdom,
and cured all kinds of sickness among the people.
Alleluia.

Twenty-First Sunday in Ordinary Time YEAR A

Responsorial Psalm Psalm 137:1-3, 6, 8. Response v.8

Richard Lloyd

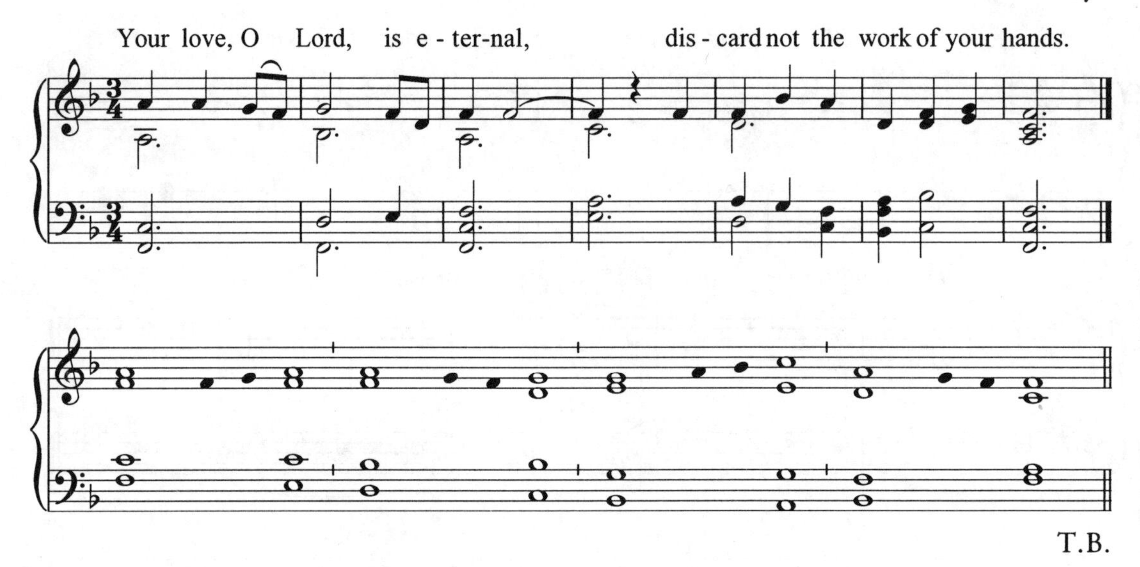

1. I thank you, Lord, with all my heart,
you have heard the words of my mouth.
Before the angels I will bless you.
I will adore before your holy temple.

2. I thank you for your faithfulness and love
which excel all we ever knew of you.
On the day I called, you answered;
you increased the strength of my soul.

3. The Lord is high yet he looks on the lowly
and the haughty he knows from afar.
Your love, O Lord, is eternal,
discard not the work of your hands.

Gospel Acclamation 2 Corinthians 5:19

Alleluia.
God in Christ was reconciling the world to himself,
and he has entrusted to us the news that they are reconciled.
Alleluia.

or Matthew 16:18

Alleluia.
You are Peter and on this rock I will build my Church.
And the gates of the underworld can never hold out against it.
Alleluia.

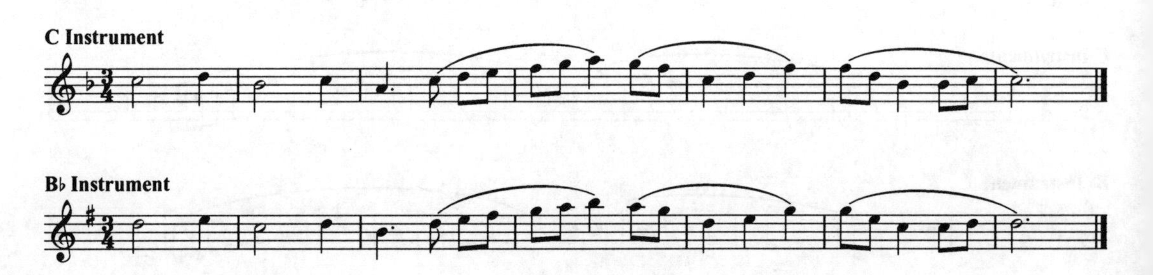

Twenty-Second Sunday in Ordinary Time

Responsorial Psalm Psalm 62:2-6, 8-9. Response v.2

YEAR A

Andrew Wright

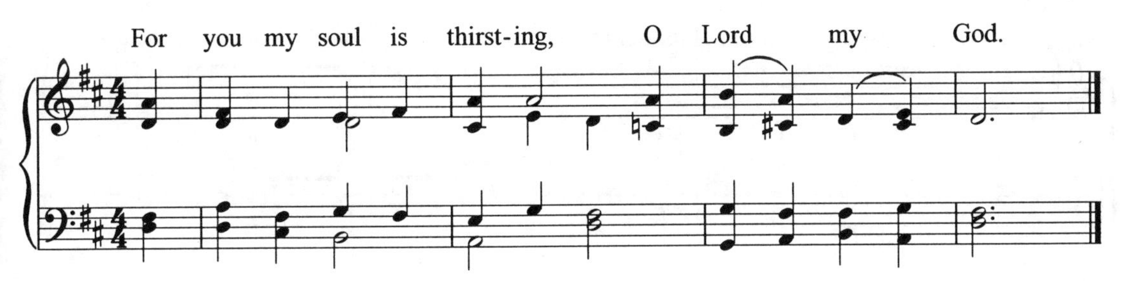
For you my soul is thirst-ing, O Lord my God.

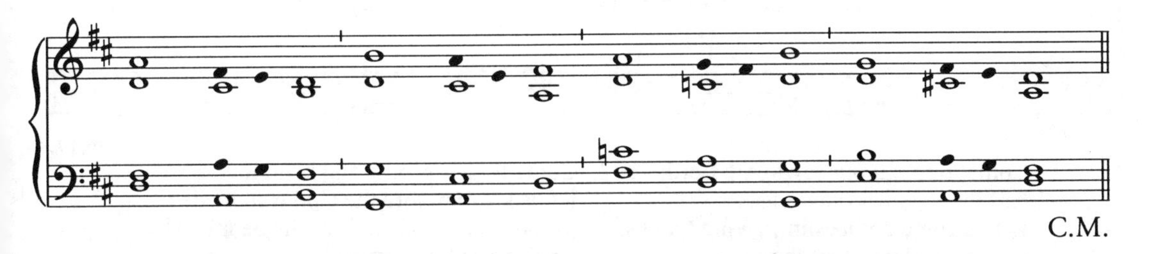
C.M.

1. O God, you are my God, for you I long:
   for you my soul is thirsting.
   My body pines for you
   like a dry, weary land without water.

2. So I gaze on you in the sanctuary
   to see your strength and your glory.
   For your love is better than life,
   my lips will speak your praise.

3. So I will bless you all my life,
   in your name I will lift up my hands.
   My soul shall be filled as with a banquet,
   my mouth shall praise you with joy.

4. For you have been my help;
   in the shadow of your wings I rejoice.
   My soul clings to you:
   your right hand holds me fast.

Gospel Acclamation cf. Ephesians 1:17,18

Alleluia.
May the Father of our Lord Jesus Christ enlighten the eyes of our mind,
so that we can see what hope his call holds for us.
Alleluia.

C Instrument
B♭ Instrument

Twenty-Third Sunday in Ordinary Time

Responsorial Psalm Psalm 94:1-2, 6-9. Response v.8

YEAR A

Gerry Fitzpatrick

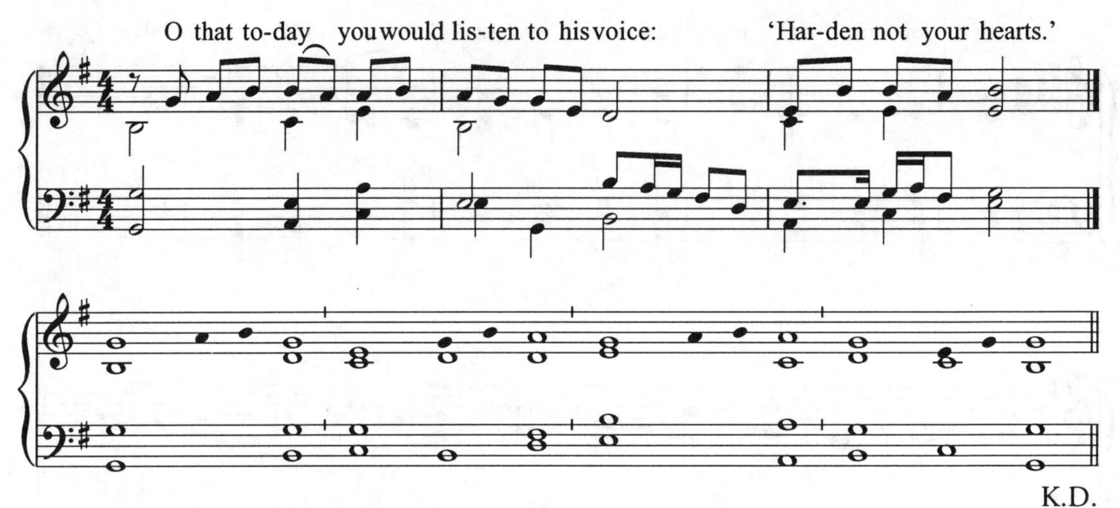

1. Come, ring out our joy to the Lord;
   hail the rock who saves us.
   Let us come before him, giving thanks,
   with songs let us hail the Lord.

2. Come in; let us bow and bend low;
   let us kneel before the God who made us
   for he is our God, and we the people who
   belong to his pasture,
   the flock that is led by his hand.

3. O that today you would listen to his voice!
   Harden not your hearts as at Meribah,
   as on that day at Massah in the desert, when your
   fathers put me to the test;
   when they tried me, though they saw my work.

Gospel Acclamation John 17:17

Alleluia.
Your word is truth, O Lord,
consecrate us in the truth.
Alleluia.

or 2 Corinthians 5:19

Alleluia.
God in Christ was reconciling the world to himself,
and he has entrusted to us the news that they are reconciled.
Alleluia.

Twenty-Fourth Sunday in Ordinary Time

Responsorial Psalm Psalm 102:1-4, 9-12. Response v.8 YEAR A

Keith Duke

The Lord is com - pas - sion and love.

S.L.

1. My soul, give thanks to the Lord,
   all my being, bless his holy name.
   My soul, give thanks to the Lord
   and never forget all his blessings.

2. It is he who forgives all your guilt,
   who heals every one of your ills,
   who redeems your life from the grave,
   who crowns you with love and compassion.

3. His wrath will come to an end;
   he will not be angry for ever.
   He does not treat us according to our sins
   nor repay us according to our faults.

4. For as the heavens are high above the earth
   so strong is his love for those who fear him.
   As far as the east is from the west
   so far does he remove our sins.

Gospel Acclamation 1 Samuel 3:9; John 6:68

Alleluia.
Speak, Lord, your servant is listening:
you have the message of eternal life.
Alleluia.

or John 13:34

Alleluia.
I give you a new commandment:
love one another, just as I have loved you, says the Lord.
Alleluia.

C Instrument

Twenty-Fifth Sunday in Ordinary Time YEAR A

Responsorial Psalm Psalm 144:2-3, 8-9, 17-18. Response v.18

Simon Lesley

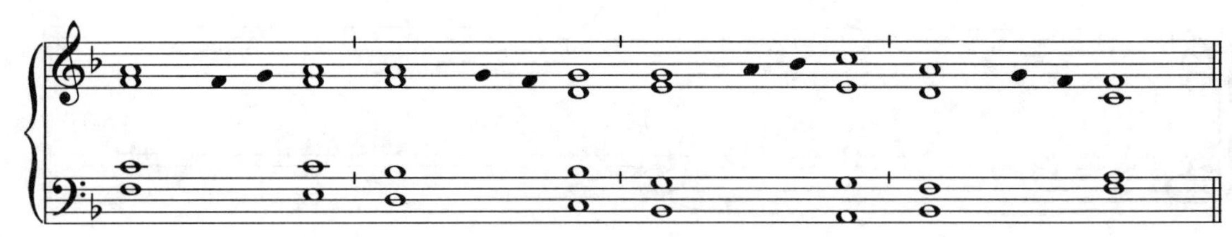

T.B.

1. I will bless you day after day
   and praise your name for ever.
   The Lord is great, highly to be praised,
   his greatness cannot be measured.

2. The Lord is kind and full of compassion,
   slow to anger, abounding in love.
   How good is the Lord to all,
   compassionate to all his creatures.

3. The Lord is just in all his ways
   and loving in all his deeds.
   He is close to all who call him,
   who call on him from their hearts.

Gospel Acclamation Luke 19:38

Alleluia.
Blessings on the King who comes, in the name of the Lord!
Peace in heaven and glory in the highest heavens!
Alleluia.

or cf. Acts 16:14

Alleluia.
Open our heart, O Lord,
to accept the words of your Son.
Alleluia.

C Instrument

B♭ Instrument

Twenty-Sixth Sunday in Ordinary Time YEAR A

Responsorial Psalm Psalm 24:4-9. Response v.6

Andrew Moore

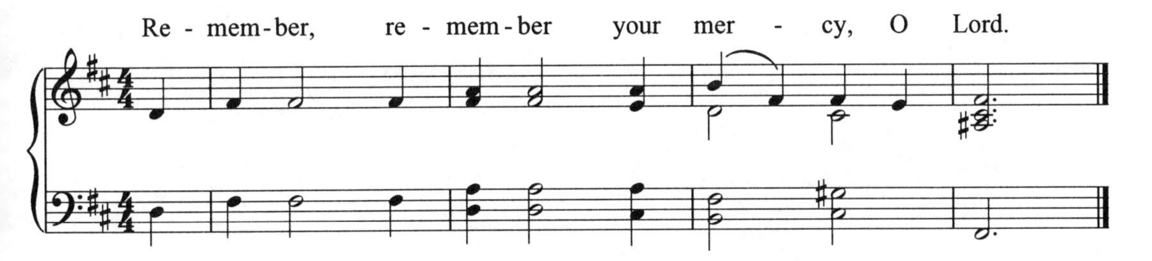

1. Lord, make me know your ways.
   Lord, teach me your paths.
   Make me walk in your truth, and teach me;
   for you are God my saviour.

2. Remember your mercy, Lord,
   and the love you have shown from of old.
   Do not remember the sins of my youth.
   In your love remember me.

3. The Lord is good and upright.
   He shows the path to those who stray,
   he guides the humble in the right path;
   he teaches his way to the poor.

Gospel Acclamation John 14:23

Alleluia.
If anyone loves me they will keep my word.
and my Father will love them and we shall come to them.
Alleluia.

or John 10:27

Alleluia.
The sheep that belong to me listen to my voice says the Lord,
I know them and they follow me.
Alleluia.

Responsorial Psalms

Twenty-Seventh Sunday in Ordinary Time

Responsorial Psalm Psalm 79:9, 12-16, 19-20. Response Isaiah 5:7

YEAR A

Gerry Fitzpatrick

The vine-yard of the Lord is the house of Is - ra - el.

C.M.

1. You brought a vine out of Egypt;
   to plant it you drove out the nations.
   It stretched out its branches to the sea,
   to the Great River it stretched out its shoots.

2. Then why have you broken down its walls?
   It is plucked by all who pass by.
   It is ravaged by the boar of the forest,
   devoured by the beasts of the field.

3. God of hosts, turn again, we implore,
   look down from heaven and see.
   Visit this vine and protect it,
   the vine your right hand has planted.

4. And we shall never forsake you again:
   give us life that we may call upon your name.
   God of hosts, bring us back;
   let your face shine on us and we shall be saved.

Gospel Acclamation John 15:15

Alleluia.
I call you friends, says the Lord,
because I have made known to you everything I have learnt from my Father.
Alleluia.

or cf. John 15:16

Alleluia.
I chose you from the world to go out and bear fruit,
fruit that will last, says the Lord.
Alleluia.

C Instrument
B♭ Instrument

Twenty-Eighth Sunday in Ordinary Time

Responsorial Psalm Psalm 22. Response v.1

YEAR A

Geoff Nobes

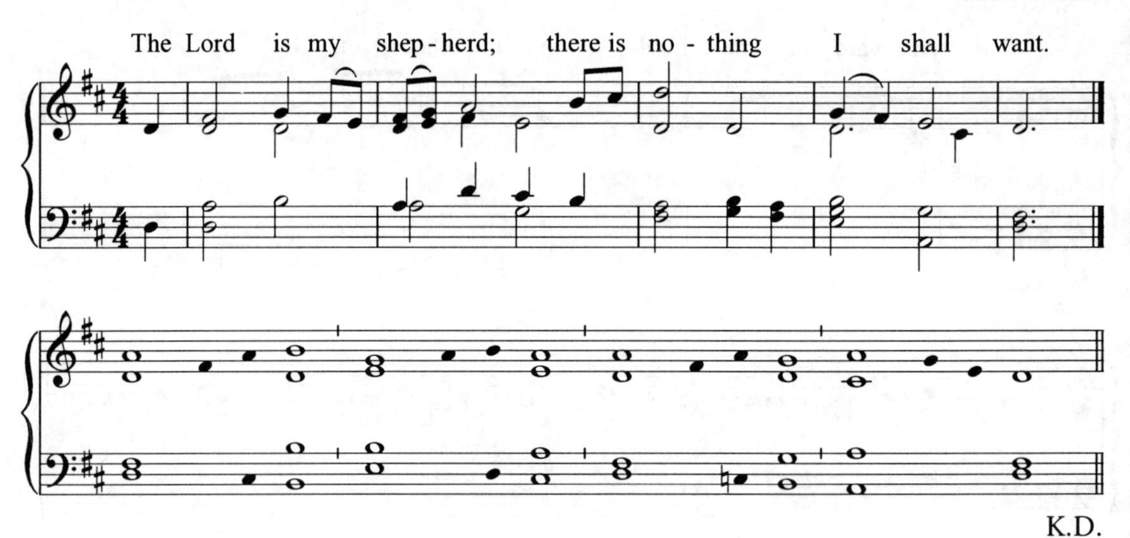

K.D.

1. The Lord is my shepherd;
there is nothing I shall want.
Fresh and green are the pastures
where he gives me repose.

2. Near restful waters he leads me,
to revive my drooping spirit.
He guides me along the right path;
he is true to his name.

3. If I should walk in the valley of darkness
no evil would I fear.
You are there with your crook and your staff;
with these you give me comfort.

4. You have prepared a banquet for me
in the sight of my foes.
My head you have anointed with oil;
my cup is overflowing.

5. Surely goodness and kindness shall follow me
all the days of my life.
In the Lord's own house shall I dwell
for ever and ever.

Note: Verse 3 may be omitted.

Gospel Acclamation John 1:12,14

Alleluia.
The Word was made flesh and lived among us;
to all who did accept him he gave power to become children of God.
Alleluia.

or cf. Ephesians 1:17, 18

Alleluia.
May the Father of our Lord Jesus Christ enlighten the eyes of our mind,
so that we can see what hope his call holds for us.
Alleluia.

Twenty-Ninth Sunday in Ordinary Time

Responsorial Psalm Psalm 95:1, 3-5, 7-10. Response v.7

YEAR A

Alan Rees

S.L.

1. O sing a new song to the Lord,
   sing to the Lord all the earth.
   Tell among the nations his glory
   and his wonders among all the peoples.

2. The Lord is great and worthy of praise,
   to be feared above all gods;
   the gods of the heathens are naught.
   It was the Lord who made the heavens.

3. Give the Lord, you families of peoples,
   give the Lord glory and power,
   give the Lord the glory of his name.
   Bring an offering and enter his courts.

4. Worship the Lord in his temple.
   O earth, tremble before him.
   Proclaim to the nations: 'God is king.'
   He will judge the peoples in fairness.

Gospel Acclamation John 17:17

Alleluia.
Your word is truth, O Lord,
consecrate us in the truth.
Alleluia.

or Philippians 2:15-16

Alleluia.
You will shine in the world like bright stars
because you are offering it the word of life.
Alleluia.

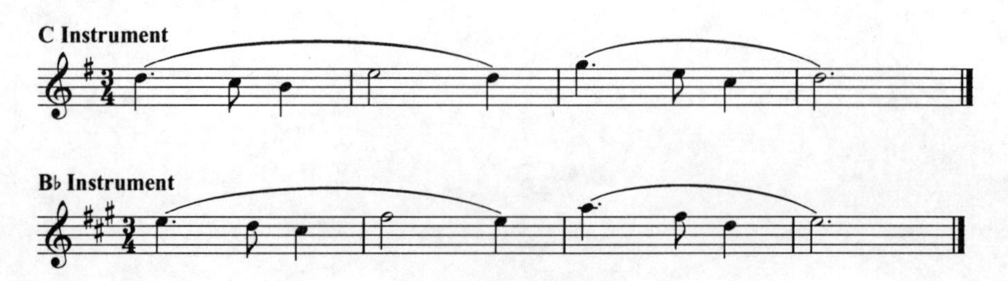

Thirtieth Sunday in Ordinary Time

YEAR A

Responsorial Psalm Psalm 17:2-4, 47, 51. Response cf. v.2

Richard Lloyd

I love you, Lord, O God, my strength.

T.B.

1. My God is the rock where I take refuge;
   my shield, my mighty help, my stronghold.
   The Lord is worthy of all praise.
   When I call I am saved from my foes.

2. Long life to the Lord, my rock!
   Praised be the God who saves me.
   He has given great victories to his king
   and shown his love for his anointed.

Gospel Acclamation cf. Acts 16:14

Alleluia.
Open our heart, O Lord,
to accept the words of your Son.
Alleluia.

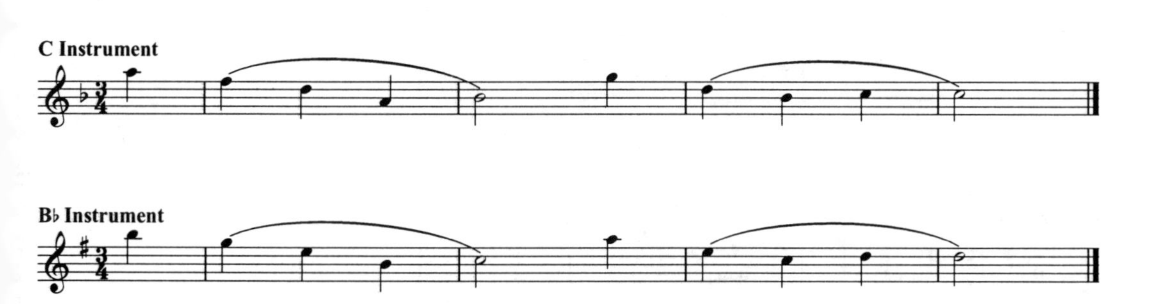
C Instrument
B♭ Instrument

Thirty-First Sunday in Ordinary Time YEAR A

Responsorial Psalm Psalm 130. Response cf. v.2

Gerry Fitzpatrick

Keep my soul in peace be - fore you, O Lord.

C.M.

1. O Lord, my heart is not proud
   nor haughty my eyes.
   I have not gone after things too great
   nor marvels beyond me.

2. Truly I have set my soul in silence and peace.
   A weaned child on its mother's breast, even so is my soul.
   O Israel, hope in the Lord
   both now and for ever.

Gospel Acclamation 1 Samuel 3:9. John 6:68

Alleluia.
Speak, Lord, your servant is listening;
you have the message of eternal life.
Alleluia.

Thirty-Second Sunday in Ordinary Time

Responsorial Psalm Psalm 62:2-8. Response v.2 YEAR A

John Bertalot

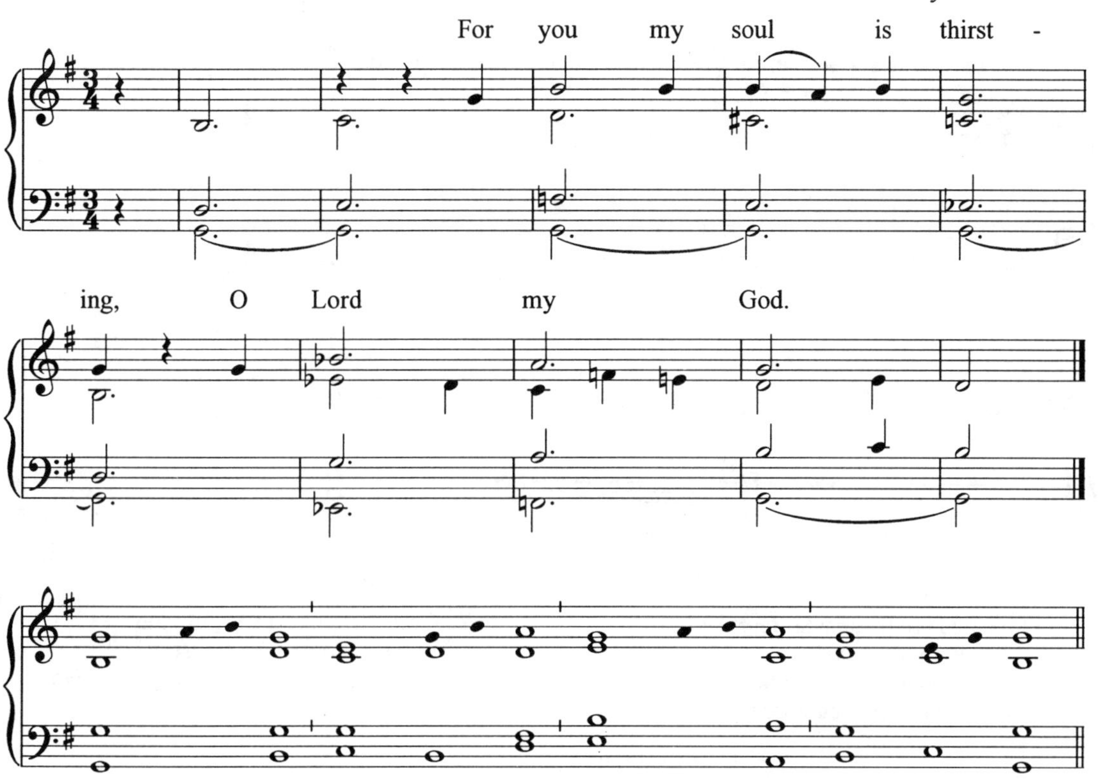
For you my soul is thirst - ing, O Lord my God.

K.D.

1. O God, you are my God, for you I long;
   for you my soul is thirsting.
   My body pines for you
   like a dry, weary land without water.

2. So I gaze on you in the sanctuary
   to see your strength and your glory.
   For your love is better than life,
   my lips will speak your praise.

3. So I will bless you all my life,
   in your name I will lift up my hands.
   My soul shall be filled as with a banquet,
   my mouth shall praise you with joy.

4. On my bed I remember you.
   On you I muse through the night
   for you have been my help;
   in the shadow of your wings I rejoice.

Gospel Acclamation Matthew 24:42, 44

Alleluia.
Stay awake and stand ready,
because you do not know the hour when the Son of Man is coming.
Alleluia.

C Instrument
B♭ Instrument

Thirty-Third Sunday in Ordinary Time YEAR A

Responsorial Psalm Psalm 127:1-5. Response v.1

John McCann

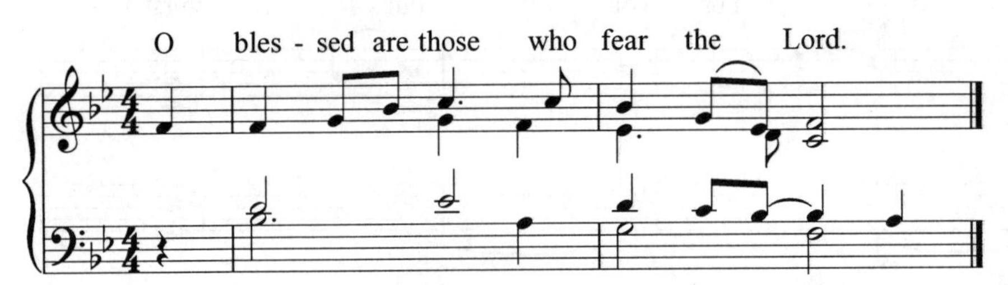

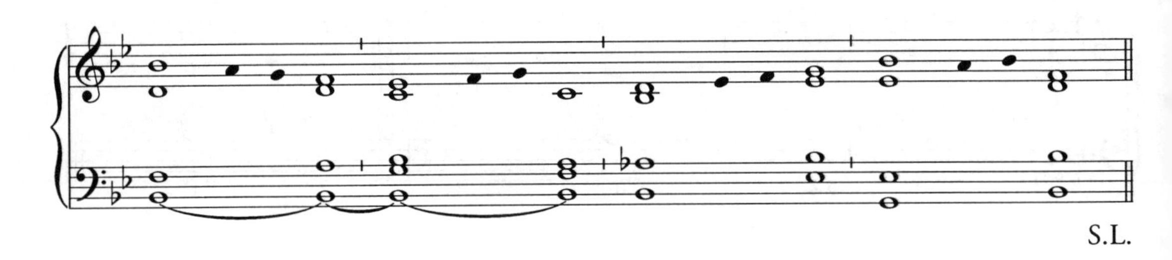

S.L.

1. O blessed are those who fear the Lord
   and walk in his ways!
   By the labour of your hands you shall eat.
   You will be happy and prosper.

2. Your wife like a fruitful vine
   in the heart of your house;
   your children like shoots of the olive,
   around your table.

3. Indeed thus shall be blessed
   those who fear the Lord.
   May the Lord bless you from Zion
   in a happy Jerusalem.

Gospel Acclamation Revelation 2:10

Alleluia
Even if you have to die, says the Lord,
keep faithful, and I will give you the crown of life.
Alleluia.

or John 15:4,5

Alleluia.
Make your home in me, as I make mine in you, says the Lord.
Whoever remains in me bears fruit in plenty.
Alleluia.

Last Sunday in Ordinary Time YEAR A

Our Lord Jesus Christ, Universal King

Responsorial Psalm Psalm 22. Response v.1 Colin Mawby

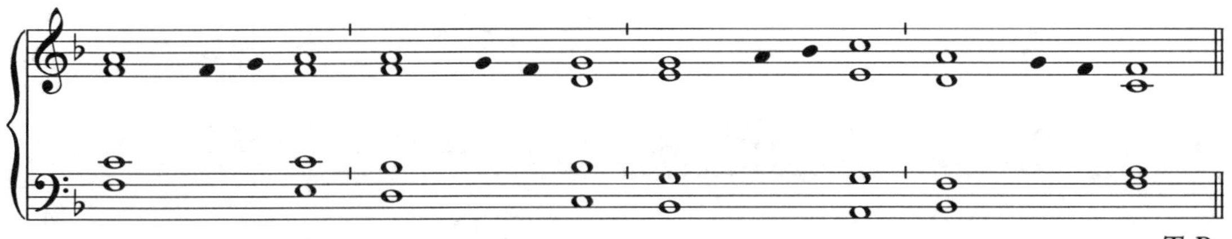

1. The Lord is my shepherd;
   there is nothing I shall want.
   Fresh and green are the pastures
   where he gives me repose.

2. Near restful waters he leads me,
   to revive my drooping spirit.
   He guides me along the right path;
   he is true to his name.

3. If I should walk in the valley of darkness
   no evil would I fear.
   You are there with your crook and your staff,
   with these you give me comfort.

4. You have prepared a banquet for me
   in the sight of my foes.
   My head you have anointed with oil;
   my cup is overflowing.

5. Surely goodness and kindness shall follow me
   all the days of my life.
   In the Lord's own house shall I dwell
   for ever and ever.

Note: Verse 3 may be omitted.

Gospel Acclamation Mark 11:10

Alleluia.
Blessings on him who comes in the name of the Lord!
Blessings on the coming kingdom of our father David!
Alleluia.

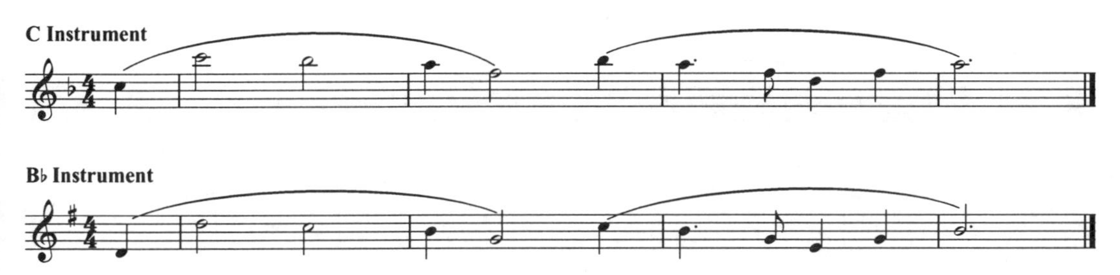

Second Sunday in Ordinary Time

YEAR B

Responsorial Psalm Psalm 39:2, 4, 7-10. Response vv.8, 9

Geoff Nobes

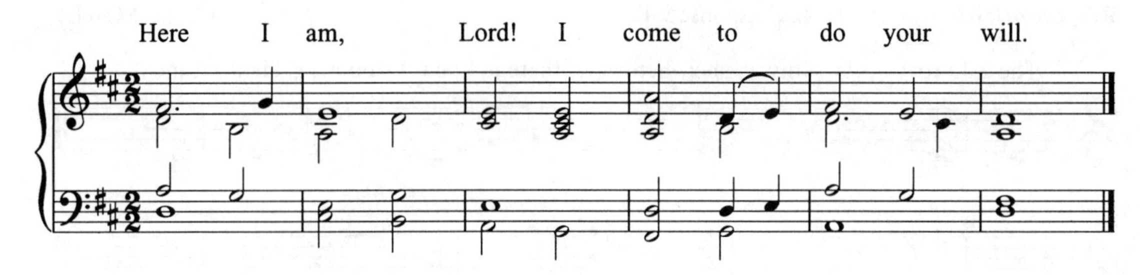
Here I am, Lord! I come to do your will.

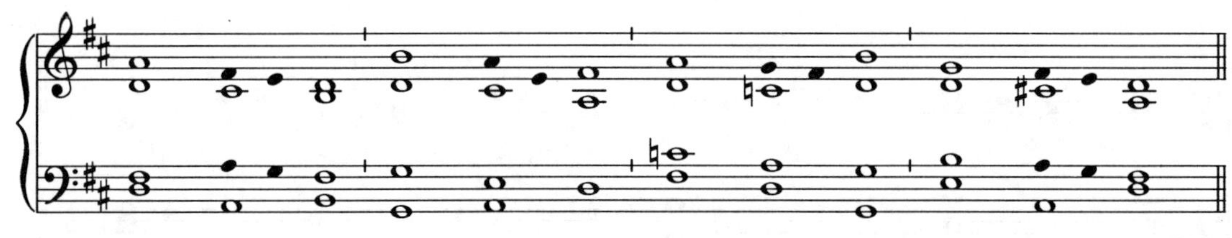

C.M.

1. I waited, I waited for the Lord and he
   stooped down to me;
   he heard my cry.
   He put a new song into my mouth,
   praise of our God.

2. You do not ask for sacrifice and offerings,
   but an open ear.
   You do not ask for holocaust and victim.
   Instead, here am I.

3. In the scroll of the book it stands written
   that I should do your will.
   My God, I delight in your law
   in the depth of my heart.

4. Your justice I have proclaimed
   in the great assembly.
   My lips I have not sealed;
   you know it, O Lord.

Gospel Acclamation 1 Samuel 3:9

Alleluia.
Speak, Lord, your servant is listening:
you have the message of eternal life.
Alleluia.

or John 6:68

Alleluia.
We have found the Messiah – which means the Christ –
grace and truth have come through him.
Alleluia.

C Instrument

B♭ Instrument

Third Sunday in Ordinary Time

YEAR B

Responsorial Psalm Psalm 24:4-9. Response v.4

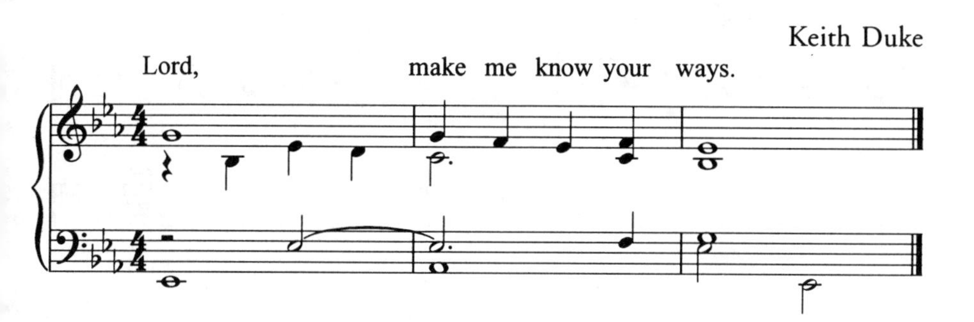

G.N.

1. Lord, make me know your ways.
   Lord, teach me your paths.
   Make me walk in your truth, and teach me:
   for you are God my saviour.

2. Remember your mercy Lord,
   and the love you have shown from of old.
   In your love remember me,
   because of your goodness, O Lord.

3. The Lord is good and upright.
   He shows the path to those who stray,
   he guides the humble in the right path;
   he teaches his way to the poor.

Gospel Acclamation Mark 1:15

Alleluia.
The kingdom of God is close at hand;
believe the Good News.
Alleluia.

C Instrument

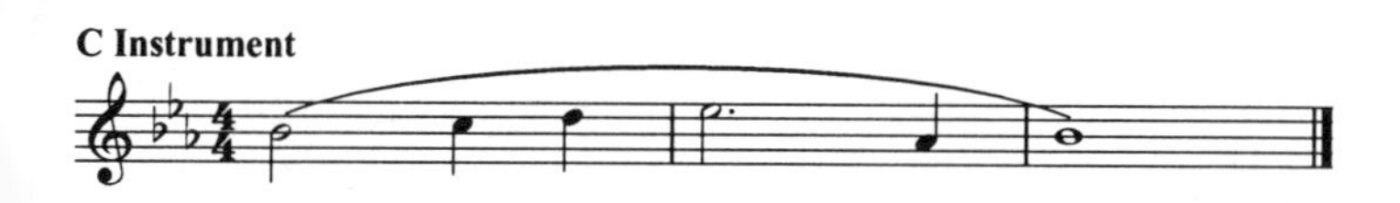

B♭ Instrument

Fourth Sunday in Ordinary Time YEAR B

Responsorial Psalm Psalm 94:1-2, 6-9. Response v.9

Gerry Fitzpatrick

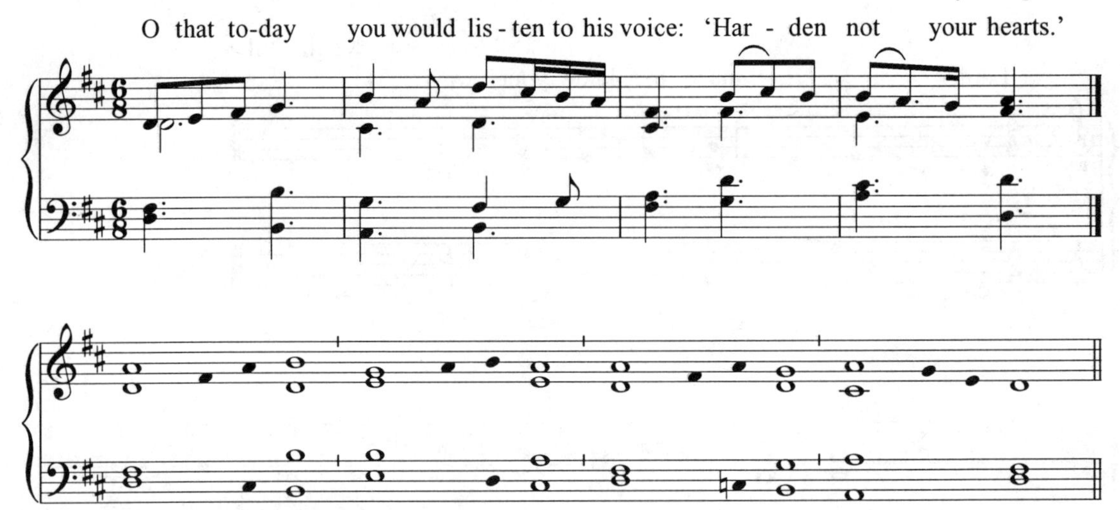

K.D.

1. Come, ring out our joy to the Lord;
 hail the rock who saves us.
 Let us come before him, giving thanks,
 with songs let us hail the Lord.

2. Come in; let us kneel and bend low;
 let us kneel before the God who made us
 for he is our God, and we the people who
 belong to his pasture,
 the flock that is led by his hand.

3. O that today you would listen to his voice!
 'Harden not your hearts as at Meribah,
 as on that day at Massah in the desert, when
 your fathers put me to the test;
 when they tried me, though they saw my work.'

Gospel Acclamation cf. Matthew 11:25

Alleluia.
Blessed are you, Father, Lord of heaven and earth,
for revealing the mysteries of the kingdom to mere children.
Alleluia.

or Matthew 4.16

Alleluia.
The people that lived in darkness have seen a great light;
on those who dwell in the land and shadow of death a light has dawned.
Alleluia.

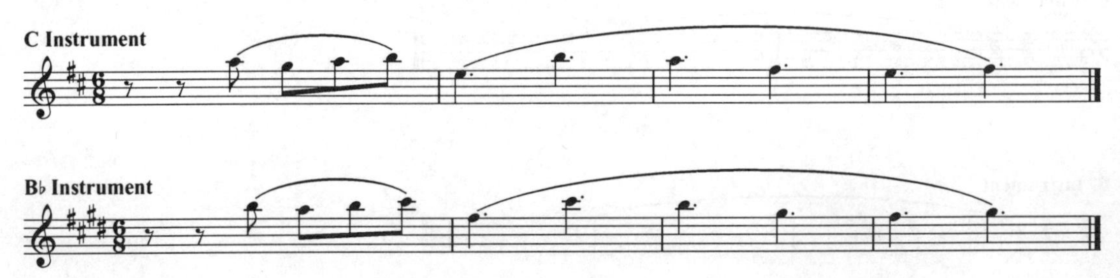

Fifth Sunday in Ordinary Time

YEAR B

Responsorial Psalm Psalm 146:1-6. Response v.3

Richard Lloyd

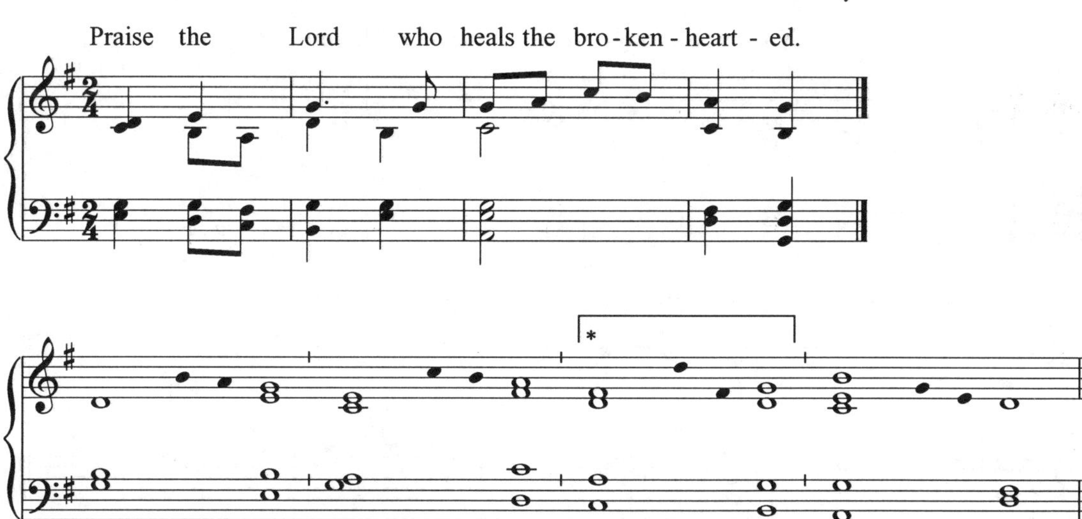

** Omit in verse 1*

S.L.

1. Praise the Lord for he is good;
   sing to our God for he is loving:
   to him our praise is due.

2. The Lord builds up Jerusalem
   and brings back Israel's exiles,
   he heals the broken-hearted,
   he binds up all their wounds.

3. Our Lord is great and almighty;
   his wisdom can never be measured.
   The Lord raises the lowly;
   he humbles the wicked to the dust.

Gospel Acclamation John 8:12

Alleluia.
I am the light of the world, says the Lord,
anyone who follows me will have the light of life.
Alleluia.

or Matthew 8:17

Alleluia.
He took our sicknesses away,
and carried our diseases for us.
Alleluia.

C Instrument

B♭ Instrument

Sixth Sunday in Ordinary Time

YEAR B

Responsorial Psalm Psalm 31:1-2, 5, 11. Response v.7

John Bertalot

T.B.

1. Happy are those whose offence is forgiven,
   whose sin is remitted.
   O happy are those to whom the Lord
   imputes no guilt.

2. But now I have acknowledged my sins;
   my guilt I did not hide,
   and you, Lord, have forgiven
   the guilt of my sin.

3. Rejoice, rejoice in the Lord,
   exult, you just!
   O come, ring out your joy,
   all you upright of heart.

Gospel Acclamation cf. Ephesians 1:17, 18

Alleluia.
May the Father of our Lord Jesus Christ enlighten the eyes of our mind,
so that we can see what hope his call holds for us.
Alleluia.

or Luke 7:16

Alleluia.
A great prophet has appeared among us;
God has visited his people.
Alleluia.

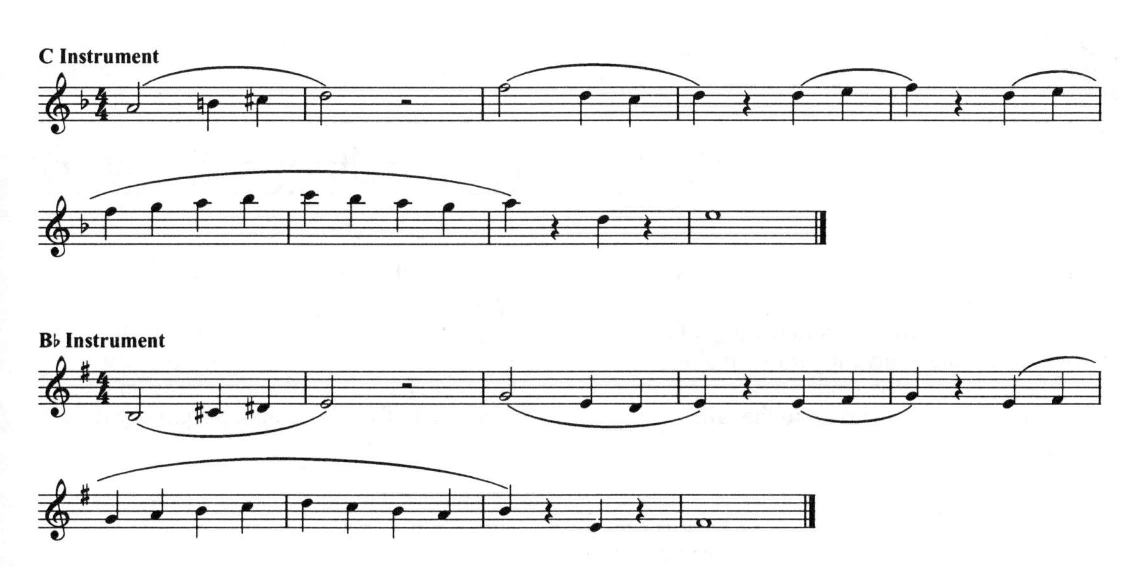

Seventh Sunday in Ordinary Time

YEAR B

Responsorial Psalm Psalm 40:2-5, 13-14. Response v.5

Alan Rees

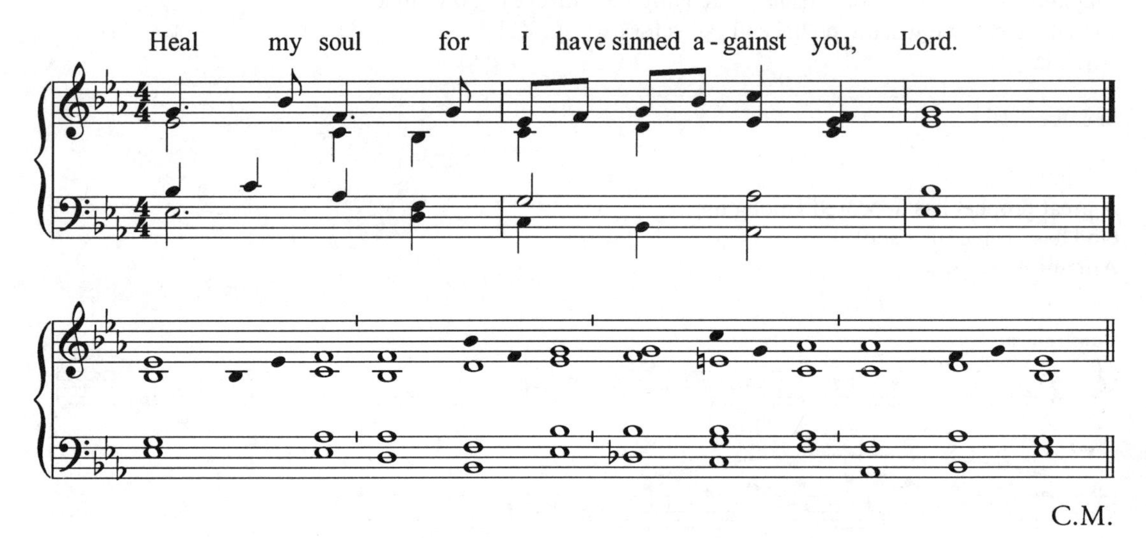

1. Happy are those who consider the poor
   and the weak.
   The Lord will save them in the day of evil,
   will guard them, give them life, make
   them happy in the land
   and will not give them up to the will
   of their foes.

2. The Lord will give them strength
   in their pain,
   he will bring them back from sickness to
   health.
   As for me, I said: 'Lord, have mercy on me,
   heal my soul for I have sinned against you.'

3. If you uphold me I shall be unharmed
   and set in your presence for evermore.
   Blessed be the Lord, the God of Israel
   from age to age. Amen. Amen.

Gospel Acclamation John 1:12, 14

Alleluia.
The Word was made flesh and lived among us;
to all who did accept him he gave power to become children of God.
Alleluia.

or Luke 4:18

Alleluia.
The Lord has sent me to bring the good news to the poor,
to proclaim liberty to captives.
Alleluia.

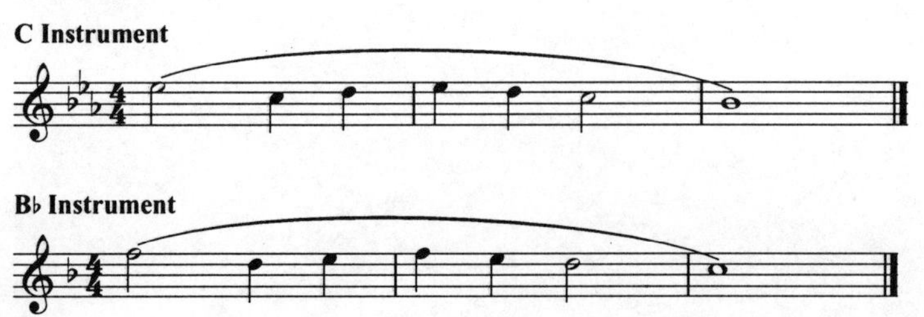

Eighth Sunday in Ordinary Time

YEAR B

Responsorial Psalm Psalm 102:1-4, 8, 10, 12-13. Response v.8

Simon Lesley

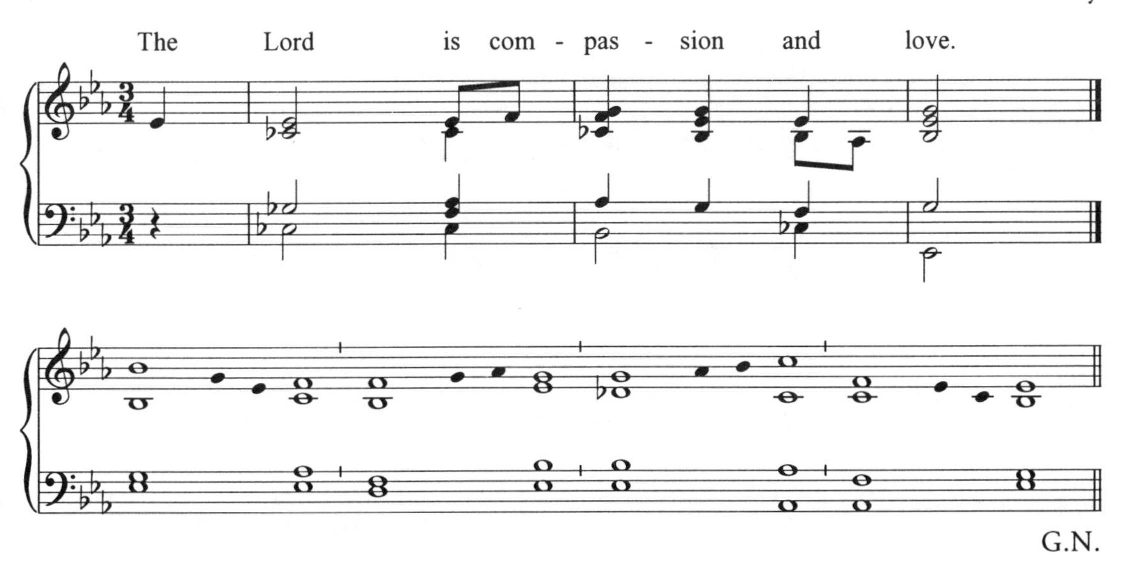

1. My soul, give thanks to the Lord,
all my being, bless his holy name.
My soul, give thanks to the Lord
and never forget all his blessings.

2. It is he who forgives all your guilt,
who heals every one of your ills,
who redeems your life from the grave,
who crowns you with love and compassion.

3. The Lord is compassion and love,
slow to anger and rich in mercy.
He does not treat us according to our sins
nor repay us according to our faults.

4. So far as the east is from the west
so far does he remove our sins.
As a father has compassion on his sons,
the Lord has pity on those who fear him.

Gospel Acclamation John 10:27

Alleluia.
The sheep that belong to me listen to my voice, says the Lord,
I know them and they follow me.
Alleluia.

or James 1:18

Alleluia.
By his own choice the Father made us his children by the message of the truth,
so that we should be a sort of first-fruits of all that he created.
Alleluia.

Ninth Sunday in Ordinary Time

YEAR B

Responsorial Psalm Psalm 80:3-8, 10-11. Response v.2

John McCann

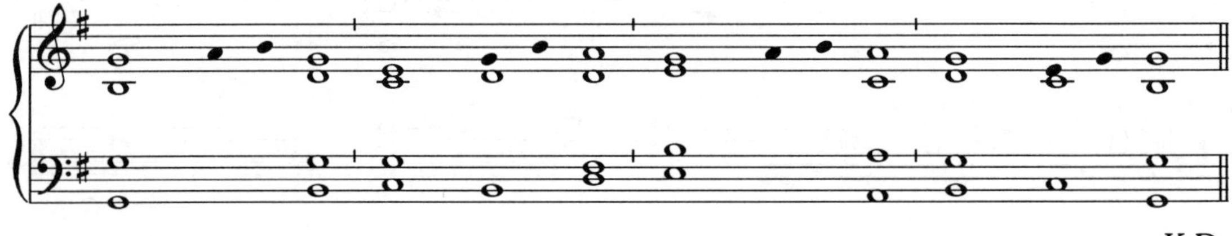

K.D.

1. Raise a song and sound the timbrel,
   the sweet-sounding harp and the lute,
   blow the trumpet at the new moon,
   when the moon is full, on our feast.

2. For this is Israel's law,
   a command of the God of Jacob.
   He imposed it as a rule on Joseph,
   when he went out against the land of Egypt.

3. A voice I did not know said to me:
   'I freed your shoulder from the burden;
   your hands were freed from the load.
   You called in distress and I saved you.

4. 'Let there be no foreign god among you,
   no worship of an alien god.
   I am the Lord your God,
   who brought you from the land of Egypt.'

Gospel Acclamation cf. John 6:63, 68

Alleluia.
Your words are spirit, Lord, and they are life:
you have the message of eternal life.
Alleluia.

or cf. John 17:17

Alleluia.
Your word is truth, O Lord,
consecrate us in the truth.
Alleluia.

C Instrument

B♭ Instrument

Tenth Sunday in Ordinary Time

YEAR B

Responsorial Psalm Psalm 129. Response v.7

Keith Duke

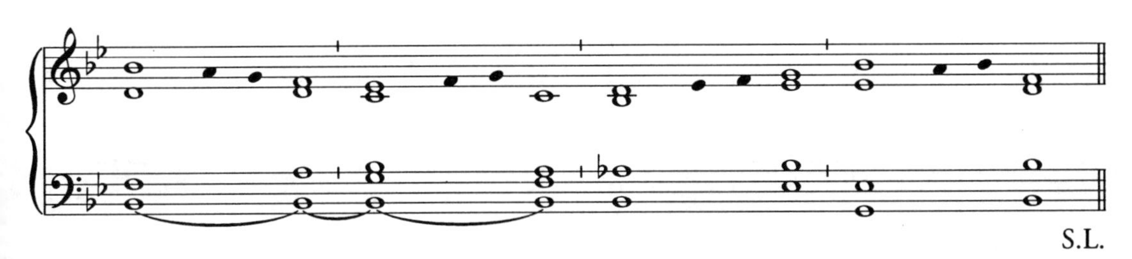

1. Out of the depths I cry to you, O Lord,
   Lord, hear my voice!
   O let your ears be attentive
   to the voice of my pleading.

2. If you, O Lord, should mark our guilt,
   Lord, who would survive?
   But with you is found forgiveness:
   for this we revere you.

3. My soul is waiting for the Lord,
   I count on his word.
   My soul is longing for the Lord
   more than watchman for daybreak.

4. Because with the Lord there is mercy
   and fullness of redemption,
   Israel indeed he will redeem
   from all its iniquity.

Gospel Acclamation John 14:23

Alleluia.
If anyone loves me they will keep my word,
and my Father will love them and we shall come to them.
Alleluia.

or John 12:31, 32

Alleluia.
Now the prince of this world is to be overthrown, says the Lord.
And when I am lifted up from the earth, I shall draw all men to myself.
Alleluia.

Eleventh Sunday in Ordinary Time YEAR B

Responsorial Psalm Psalm 91:2-3, 13-16. Response cf. v.2

Andrew Moore

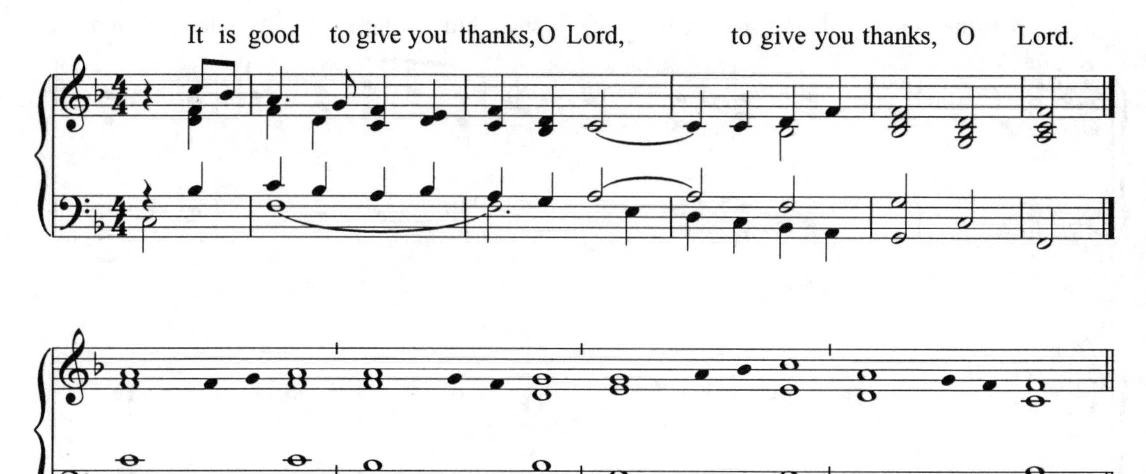
It is good to give you thanks, O Lord, to give you thanks, O Lord.

T.B.

1. It is good to give thanks to the Lord
to make music to your name, O Most High,
to proclaim your love in the morning
and your truth in the watches of the night.

2. The just will flourish like the palm-tree
and grow like a Lebanon cedar.
Planted in the house of the Lord
they will flourish in the courts of our God.

3. Still bearing fruit when they are old,
still full of sap, still green,
they will proclaim that the Lord is just.
In him, my rock, there is no wrong.

Gospel Acclamation John 15:15

Alleluia.
I call you friends, says the Lord,
because I have made known to you everything I have learnt from my Father.
Alleluia.

or

Alleluia.
The seed is the word of God, Christ the sower;
whoever finds the seed will remain for ever.
Alleluia.

C Instrument
B♭ Instrument

Twelfth Sunday in Ordinary Time

YEAR B

Responsorial Psalm Psalm 106:23-26, 28-31. Response v.1

Colin Mawby

O give thanks to the Lord, for his love en-dures for e - ver.

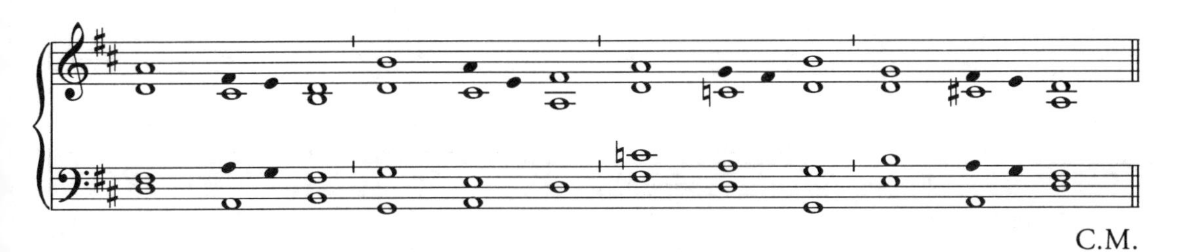

C.M.

1. Some sailed to the sea in ships
   to trade on the mighty waters.
   These have seen the Lord's deeds,
   the wonders he does in the deep.

2. For he spoke; he summoned the gale,
   tossing the waves of the sea
   up to heaven and back into the deep;
   their soul melted away in their distress.

3. Then they cried to the Lord in their need
   and he rescued them from their distress.
   He stilled the storm to a whisper:
   all the waves of the sea were hushed.

4. They rejoiced because of the calm
   and he led them to the haven they desired.
   Let them thank the Lord for his love,
   the wonders he does for his people.

Gospel Acclamation cf. Ephesians 1:17, 18

Alleluia.
May the Father of our Lord Jesus Christ enlighten the eyes of our mind,
so that we can see what hope his call holds for us.
Alleluia.

or Luke 7:16

Alleluia.
A great prophet has appeared among us;
God has visited his people.
Alleluia.

C Instrument
B♭ Instrument

Thirteenth Sunday in Ordinary Time YEAR B

Responsorial Psalm Psalm 29:2, 4-6, 11-13. Response v.2

Andrew Wright

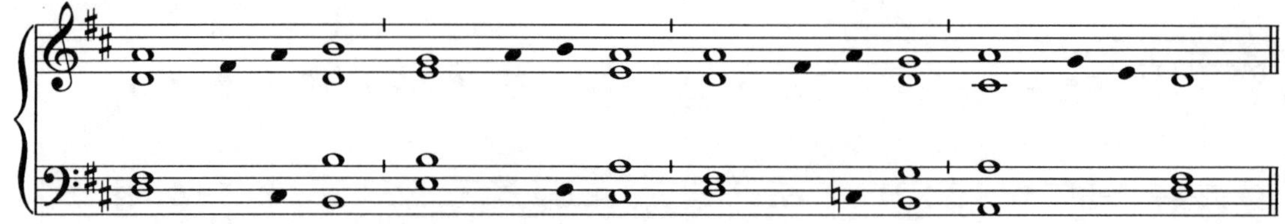

K.D.

1. I will praise you, Lord, you have rescued me
   and have not let my enemies rejoice over me.
   O Lord, you have raised my soul from the dead,
   restored me to life from those who sink into the grave.

2. Sing psalms to the Lord, you who love him,
   give thanks to his holy name.
   His anger lasts but a moment; his favour through life.
   At night there are tears, but joy comes with dawn.

3. The Lord listened and had pity.
   The Lord came to my help.
   For me you have changed my mourning into dancing,
   O Lord my God, I will thank you for ever.

Gospel Acclamation cf. John 6:63, 68

Alleluia.
Your words are spirit, Lord, and they are life:
you have the message of eternal life.
Alleluia.

Fourteenth Sunday in Ordinary Time YEAR B

Responsorial Psalm Psalm 122. Response v.2

John Bertalot

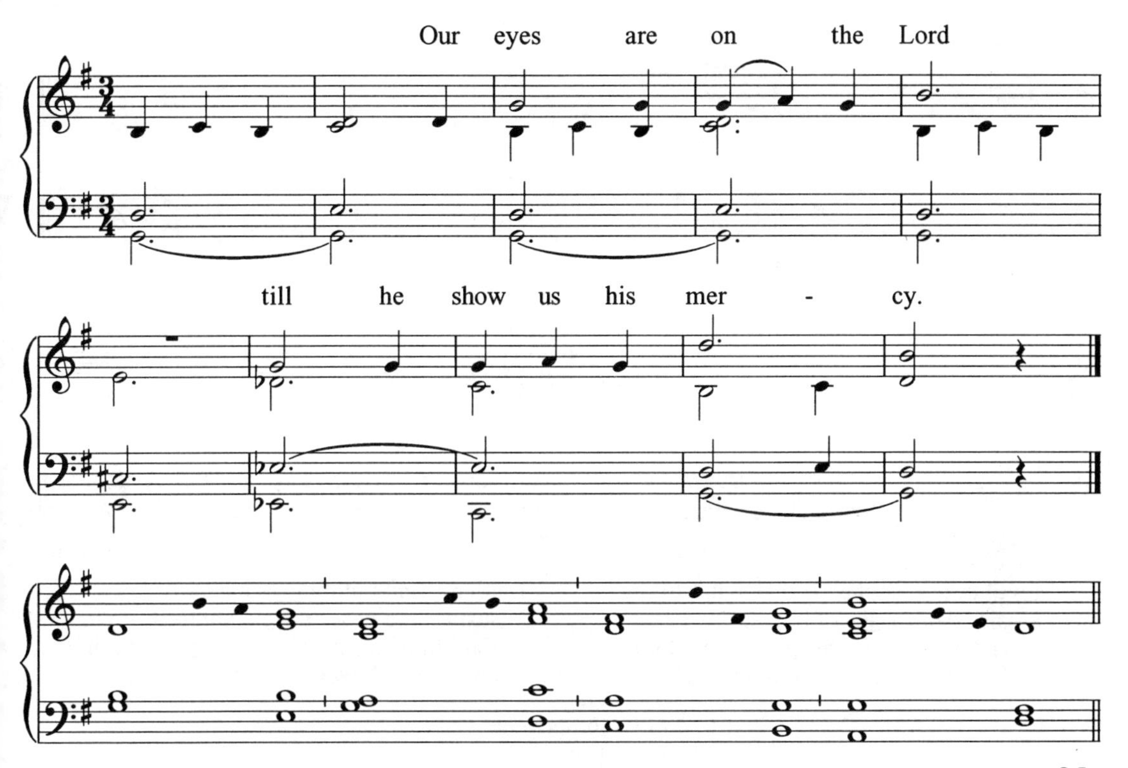

S.L.

1. To you have I lifted up my eyes,
   you who dwell in the heavens:
   my eyes, like the eyes of slaves
   on the hand of their lords.

2. Like the eyes of a servant
   on the hand of his mistress,
   so our eyes are on the Lord our God
   till he show us his mercy.

3. Have mercy on us, Lord, have mercy.
   We are filled with contempt.
   Indeed all too full is our soul
   with the scorn of the rich.

Gospel Acclamation John 1:12, 14

Alleluia.
The Word was made flesh and lived among us;
to all who did accept him he gave power
to become children of God.
Alleluia.

or Luke 4:18

Alleluia.
The Lord has sent me to bring the good news to the poor,
to proclaim liberty to captives.
Alleluia.

Fifteenth Sunday in Ordinary Time

YEAR B

Responsorial Psalm Psalm 84:9-14. Response v.8

Richard Lloyd

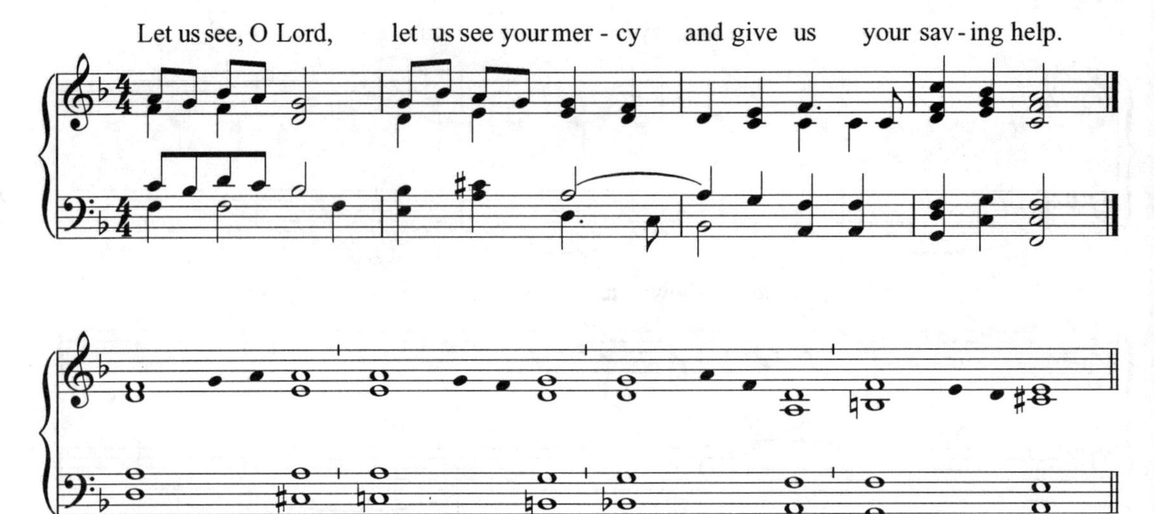

Let us see, O Lord, let us see your mer - cy and give us your sav - ing help.

T.B.

1. I will hear what the Lord God has to say,
   a voice that speaks of peace.
   His help is near for those who fear him
   and his glory will dwell in our land.

2. Mercy and faithfulness have met;
   justice and peace have embraced.
   Faithfulness shall spring from the earth
   and justice look down from heaven.

3. The Lord will make us prosper
   and our earth shall yield its fruit.
   Justice shall march before him
   and peace shall follow his steps.

Gospel Acclamation cf. John 6:63, 68

Alleluia.
Your words are spirit, Lord, and they are life:
you have the message of eternal life.
Alleluia.

or cf. Ephesians 1:17, 18

Alleluia.
May the Father of our Lord Jesus Christ enlighten the eyes of our mind,
so that we can see what hope his call holds for us.
Alleluia.

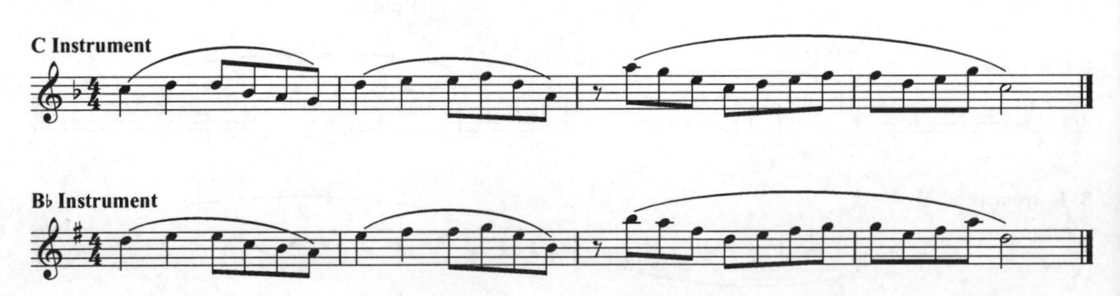

Sixteenth Sunday in Ordinary Time

YEAR B

Responsorial Psalm Psalm 22. Response v.2

Alan Rees

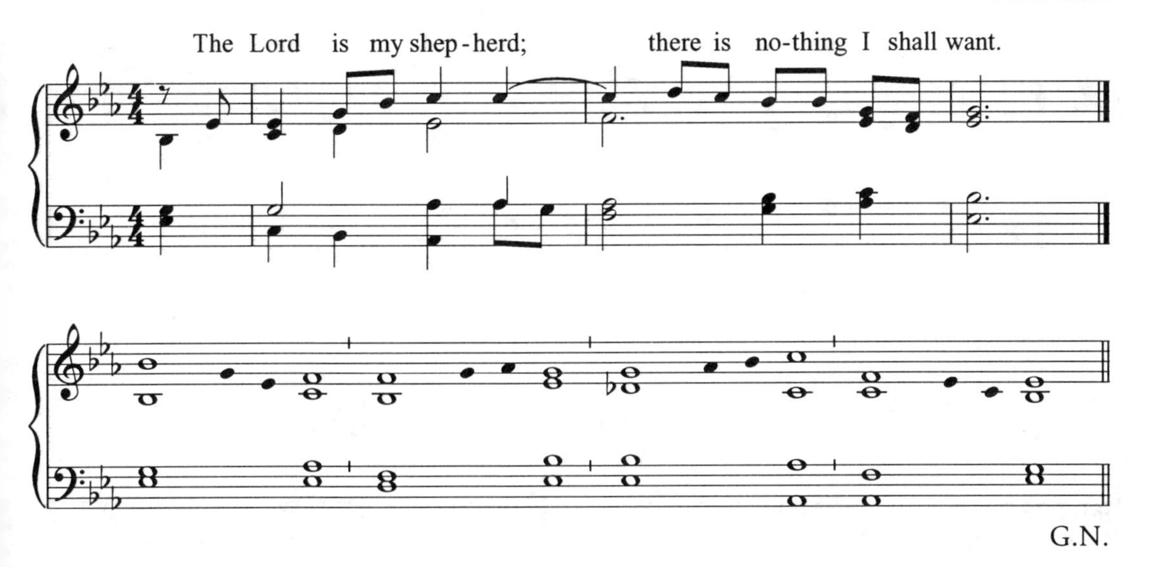

1. The Lord is my shepherd;
   there is nothing I shall want.
   Fresh and green are the pastures
   where he gives me repose.

2. Near restful waters he leads me,
   to revive my drooping spirit.
   He guides me along the right path;
   he is true to his name.

3. If I should walk in the valley of darkness
   no evil would I fear.
   You are there with your crook and your staff;
   with these you give me comfort.

4. You have prepared a banquet for me
   in the sight of my foes.
   My head you have anointed with oil;
   my cup is overflowing.

5. Surely goodness and kindness shall follow me
   all the days of my life.
   In the Lord's own house shall I dwell
   for ever and ever.

Note: Verse 3 may be omitted.

Gospel Acclamation John 10:27

Alleluia.
The sheep that belong to me listen to my voice, says the Lord,
I know them and they follow me.
Alleluia.

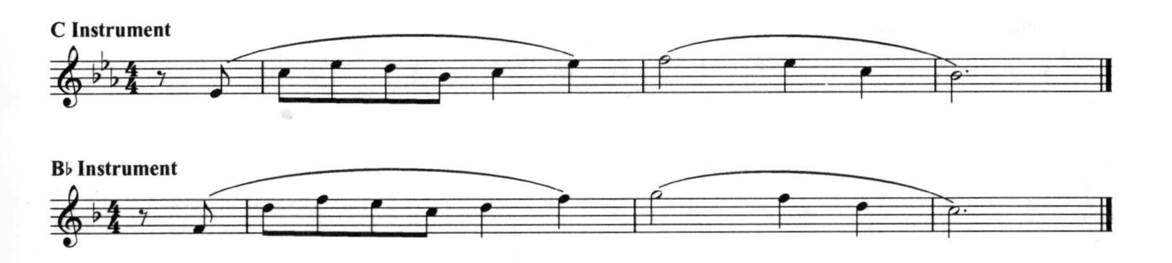

Seventeenth Sunday in Ordinary Time YEAR B

Responsorial Psalm Psalm 144:10-11, 15-18. Response v.16

Andrew Moore

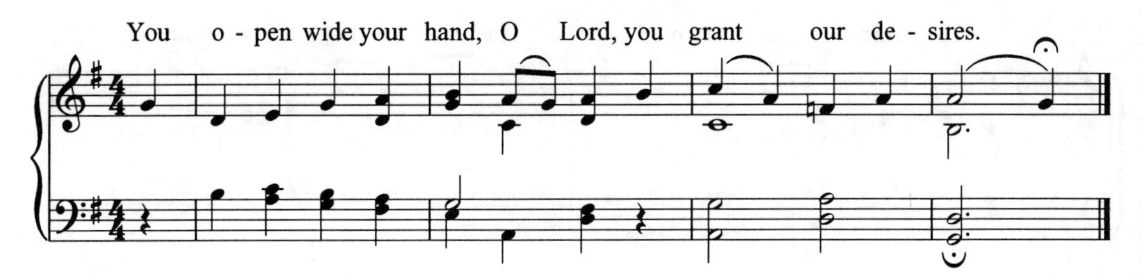

You o - pen wide your hand, O Lord, you grant our de - sires.

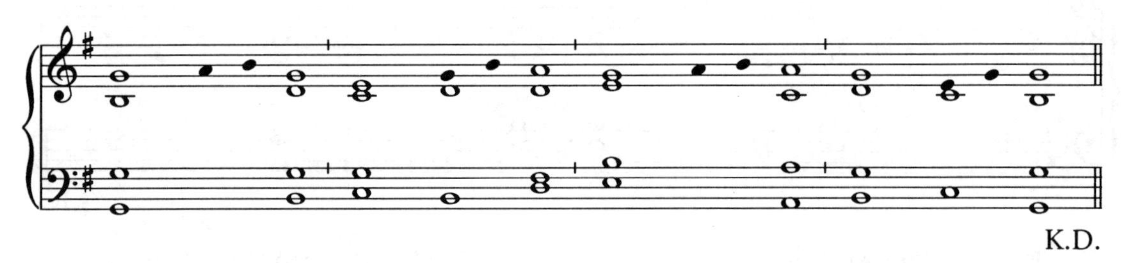

K.D.

1. All your creatures shall thank you, O Lord,
   and your friends shall repeat their blessing.
   They shall speak of the glory of your reign
   and declare your might, O God.

2. The eyes of all creatures look to you
   and you give them their food in due time.
   You open wide your hand,
   grant the desires of all who live.

3. The Lord is just in all his ways
   and loving in all his deeds.
   He is close to all who call him,
   who call on him from their hearts.

Gospel Acclamation cf. John 6:63, 68

Alleluia.
Your words are spirit, Lord, and they are life:
you have the message of eternal life.
Alleluia.

or Luke 7:16

Alleluia.
A great prophet has appeared among us;
God has visited his people.
Alleluia.

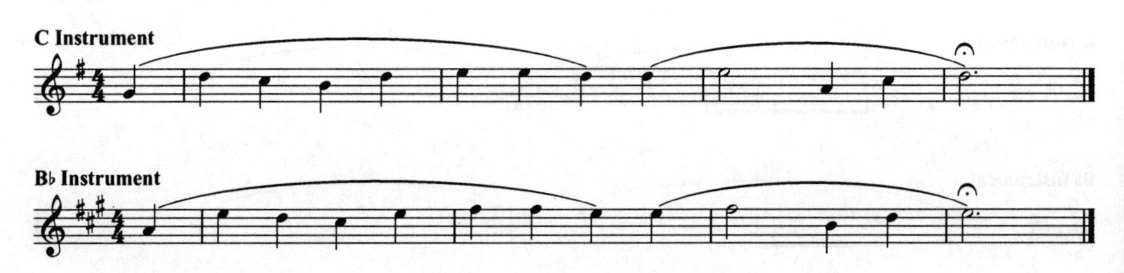

Eighteenth Sunday in Ordinary Time YEAR B

Responsorial Psalm Psalm 77:3-4, 23-25, 54. Response v.24

Gerry Fitzpatrick

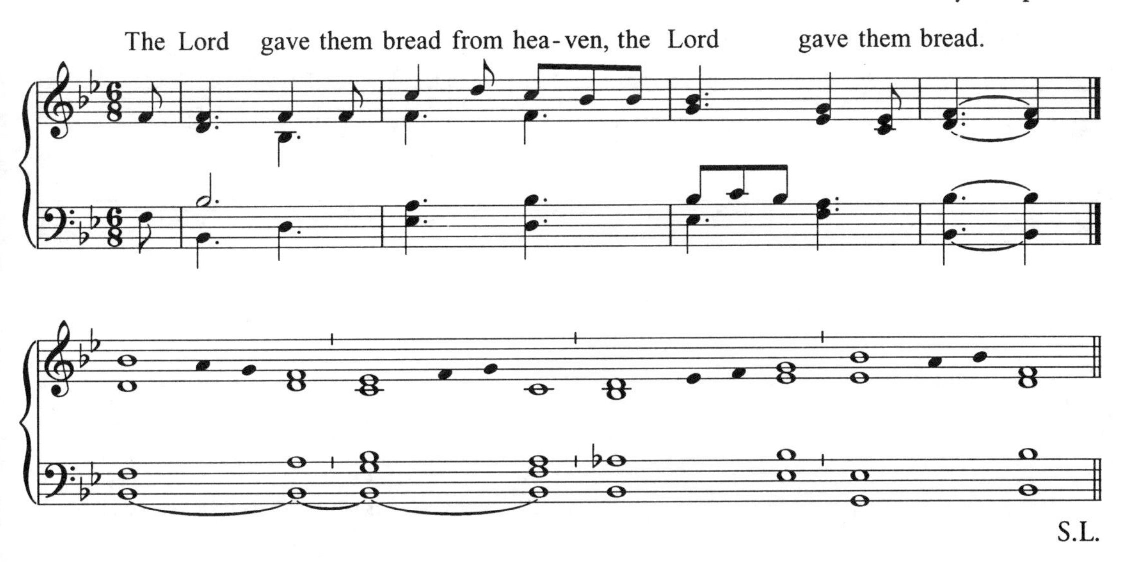
The Lord gave them bread from hea-ven, the Lord gave them bread.
S.L.

1. The things we have heard and understood,
   the things our forebears have told us,
   we will tell to the next generation:
   the glories of the Lord and his might.

2. He commanded the clouds above
   and opened the gate of heaven.
   He rained down manna for their food,
   and gave them bread from heaven.

3. Mere mortals ate the bread of angels.
   He sent them abundance of food.
   He brought them to his holy land,
   to the mountain which his right hand had won.

Gospel Acclamation John 14:5

Alleluia.
I am the Way, the Truth and the Life, says the Lord;
no one can come to the Father except through me.
Alleluia.

or Matthew 4:4

Alleluia.
Man does not live on bread alone,
but on every word that comes from the mouth of God.
Alleluia.

C Instrument
B♭ Instrument

Nineteenth Sunday in Ordinary Time YEAR B

Responsorial Psalm Psalm 33:2-9. Response v.9

Colin Mawby

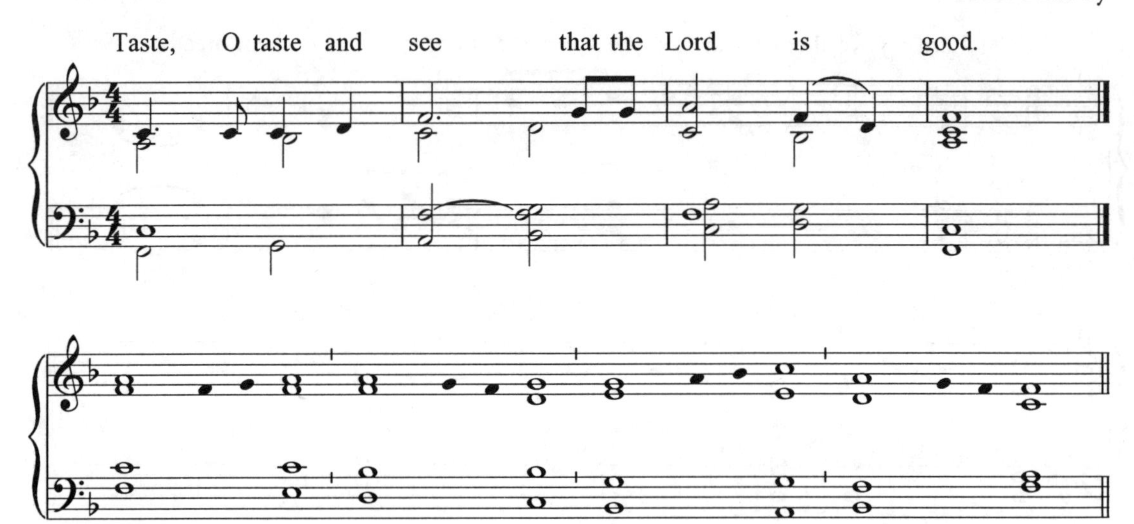
Taste, O taste and see that the Lord is good.
T.B.

1. I will bless the Lord at all times,
   his praise always on my lips;
   in the Lord my soul shall make its boast.
   The humble shall hear and be glad.

2. Glorify the Lord with me.
   Together let us praise his name.
   I sought the Lord and he answered me;
   from all my terrors he set me free.

3. Look towards him and be radiant;
   let your faces not be abashed.
   When the poor cry out the Lord hears them
   and rescues them from all their distress.

4. The angel of the Lord is encamped
   around those who revere him, to rescue them.
   Taste and see that the Lord is good.
   They are happy who seek refuge in him.

Gospel Acclamation John 14:23

Alleluia.
If anyone loves me they will keep my word,
and my Father will love them, and we shall come to them.
Alleluia.

or John 6:51

Alleluia.
I am the living bread which has come down from heaven, says the Lord.
Anyone who eats this bread will live for ever.
Alleluia.

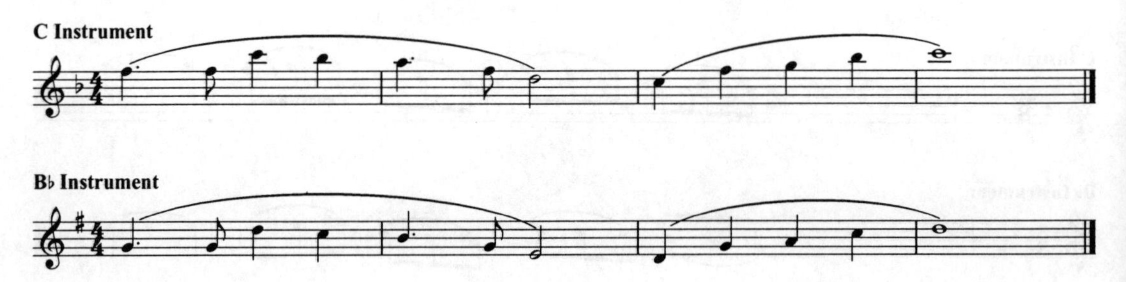
C Instrument
B♭ Instrument

Twentieth Sunday in Ordinary Time YEAR B

Responsorial Psalm Psalm 33:2-3, 10-15. Response v.9

Gerry Fitzpatrick

Taste, O taste and see that the Lord is good.

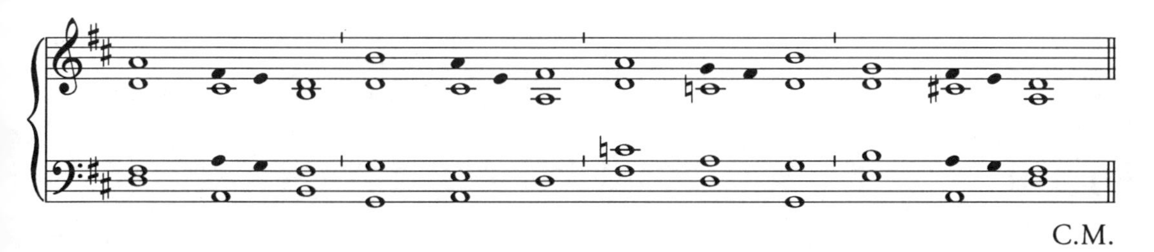

C.M.

1. I will bless the Lord at all times,
   his praise always on my lips;
   in the Lord my soul shall make its boast.
   The humble shall hear and be glad.

2. Revere the Lord, you his saints.
   They lack nothing, those who revere him.
   Strong lions suffer want and go hungry
   but those who seek the Lord lack no blessing.

3. Come, children, and hear me
   that I may teach you the fear of the Lord.
   Who are they who long for life
   and many days, to enjoy their prosperity?

4. Then keep your tongue from evil
   and your lips from speaking deceit.
   Turn aside from evil and do good;
   seek and strive after peace.

Gospel Acclamation John 1:12, 14

Alleluia.
The Word was made flesh and lived among us;
to all who did accept him he gave power to become children of God.
Alleluia.

or John 6:56

Alleluia.
They who eat my flesh and drink my blood
live in me, and I live in them, says the Lord.
Alleluia.

C Instrument

B♭ Instrument

Twenty-First Sunday in Ordinary Time YEAR B

Responsorial Psalm Psalm 33:2-3, 16-23. Response v.9

Andrew Wright

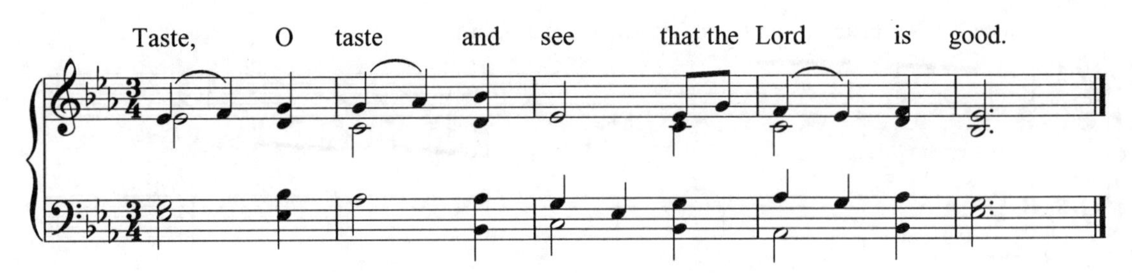
Taste, O taste and see that the Lord is good.

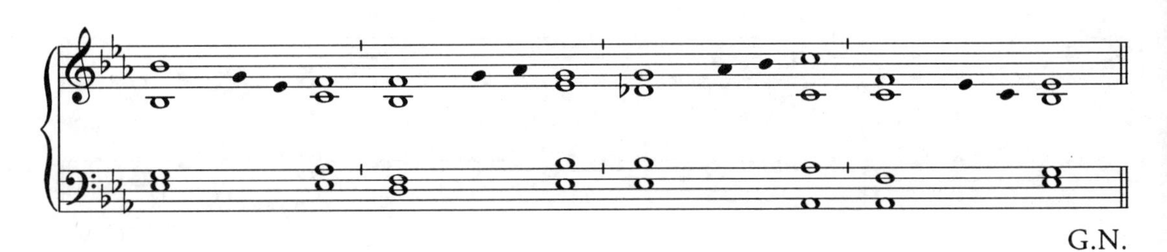
G.N.

1. I will bless the Lord at all times,
   his praise always on my lips;
   in the Lord my soul shall make its boast.
   The humble shall hear and be glad.

2. The Lord turns his face against the wicked
   to destroy their remembrance from the earth.
   The Lord turns his eyes to the just
   and his ears to their appeal.

3. They call and the Lord hears
   and rescues them in all their distress.
   The Lord is close to the broken-hearted;
   those whose spirit is crushed he will save.

4. Evil brings death to the wicked;
   those who hate the good are doomed.
   The Lord ransoms the souls of his servants.
   Those who hide in him shall not be condemned.

Gospel Acclamation cf. John 6:63, 68

Alleluia.
Your words are spirit, Lord, and they are life:
you have the message of eternal life.
Alleluia.

C Instrument
B♭ Instrument

Twenty-Second Sunday in Ordinary Time

Responsorial Psalm Psalm 14:2-5. Response v.1 YEAR B

John Bertalot

The just will live in the pre - sence of the Lord.

K.D.

1. Lord, who shall dwell on your holy mountain?
   Those who walk without fault;
   those who act with justice
   and speak the truth from their hearts.

2. Those who do no wrong to their kindred,
   who cast no slur on their neighbours,
   who hold the godless in disdain,
   but honour those who fear the Lord.

3. Those who keep their pledge, come what may;
   who take no interest on a loan
   and accept no bribes against the innocent.
   Such people will stand firm for ever.

Gospel Acclamation cf. John 6:63, 68

Alleluia.
Your words are spirit, Lord, and they are life:
you have the message of eternal life.
Alleluia.

or James 1:18

Alleluia.
By his own choice the Father made us his children by the message of the truth,
so that we should be a sort of first-fruits of all that he created.
Alleluia.

Twenty-Third Sunday in Ordinary Time

Responsorial Psalm Psalm 145:7-10. Response v.1 YEAR B

Andrew Moore

My soul, give praise, give praise to the Lord.

S.L.

1. It is the Lord who keeps faith for ever,
   who is just to those who are oppressed.
   It is he who gives bread to the hungry,
   the Lord, who sets prisoners free.

2. It is the Lord who gives sight to the blind,
   who raises up those who are bowed down,
   the Lord who loves the just,
   the Lord, who protects the stranger.

3. The Lord upholds the widow and orphan,
   but thwarts the path of the wicked.
   The Lord will reign for ever,
   Zion's God, from age to age.

Gospel Acclamation 1 Samuel 3:9; John 6:68

Alleluia.
Speak, Lord, your servant is listening:
you have the message of eternal life.
Alleluia.

or cf. Matthew 4:23

Alleluia.
Jesus proclaimed the Good News of the kingdom,
and cured all kinds of sickness among the people.
Alleluia.

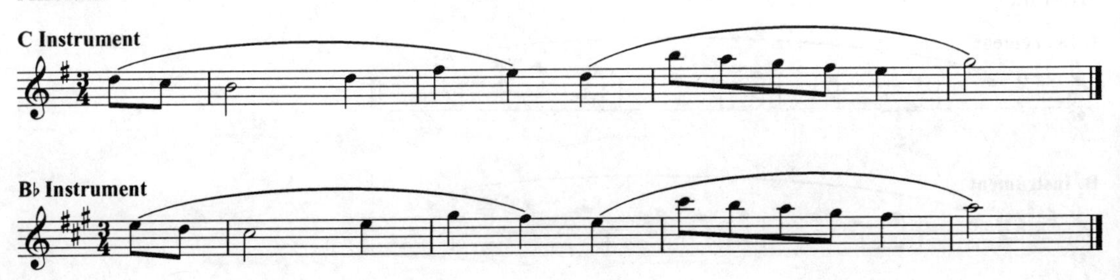
C Instrument
B♭ Instrument

Twenty-Fourth Sunday in Ordinary Time

Responsorial Psalm Psalm 114:1-6, 8-9. Response v.9 YEAR B

Richard Lloyd

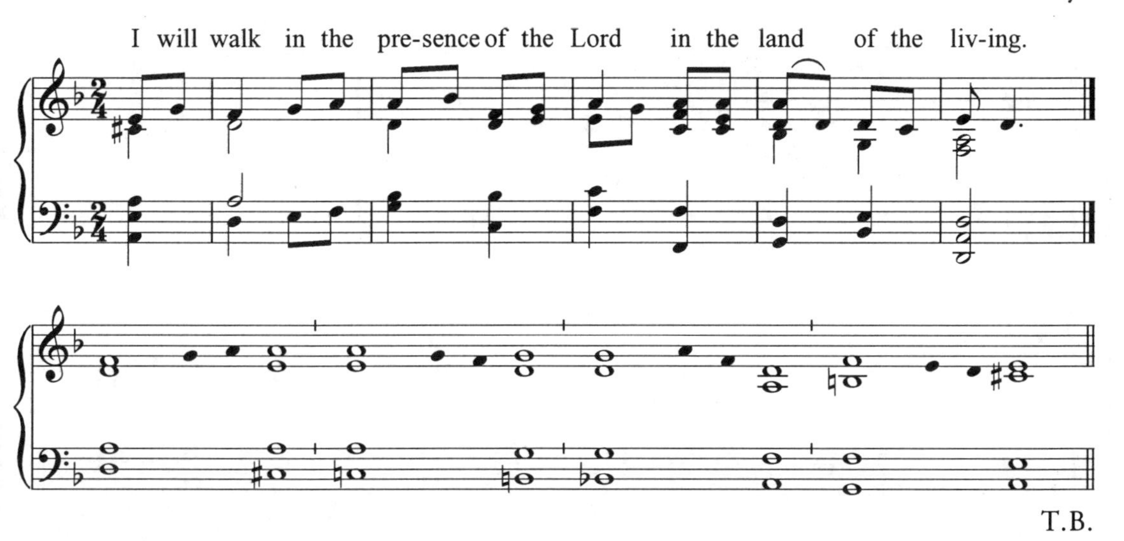

1. I love the Lord for he has heard
the cry of my appeal;
for he turned his ear to me
in the day when I called him.

2. They surrounded me, the snares of death,
with the anguish of the tomb;
they caught me, sorrow and distress.
O Lord my God, deliver me!

3. How gracious is the Lord, and just;
our God has compassion.
The Lord protects the simple hearts;
I was helpless so he saved me.

4. He has kept my soul from death, my eyes
from tears
and my feet from stumbling.
I will walk in the presence of the Lord
in the land of the living.

Gospel Acclamation John 14:5

Alleluia.
I am the Way, the Truth and the Life, says the Lord;
no one can come to the Father except through me.
Alleluia.

or Galatians 6:14

Alleluia.
The only thing I can boast about is the cross of our Lord,
through whom the world is crucified to me, and I to the world.
Alleluia.

Twenty-Fifth Sunday in Ordinary Time YEAR B

Responsorial Psalm Psalm 53:3-6, 8. Response v.6

Andrew Wright

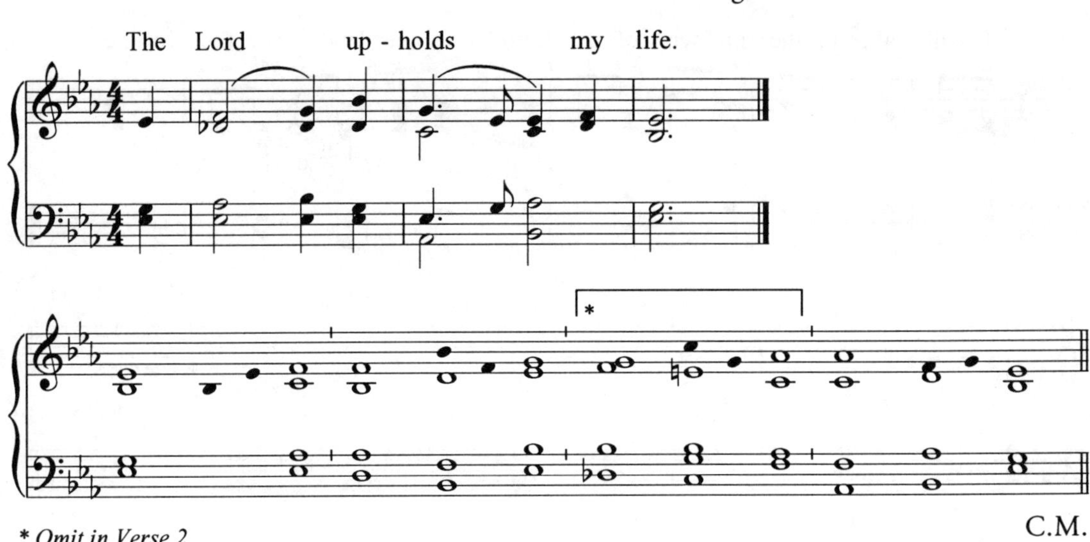

* *Omit in Verse 2*

C.M.

1. O God, save me by your name;
by your power, uphold my cause.
O God, hear my prayer;
listen to the words of my mouth.

2. For the proud have risen against me,
ruthless foes seek my life.
They have no regard for God.

3. But I have God for my help.
The Lord upholds my life.
I will sacrifice to you with willing heart
and praise your name for it is good.

Gospel Acclamation John 8:12

Alleluia.
I am the light of the world, says the Lord,
anyone who follows me will have the light of life.
Alleluia.

or cf. 2 Thessalonians 2:14

Alleluia.
Through the Good News God has called us
to share the glory of our Lord Jesus Christ.
Alleluia!

C Instrument

B♭ Instrument

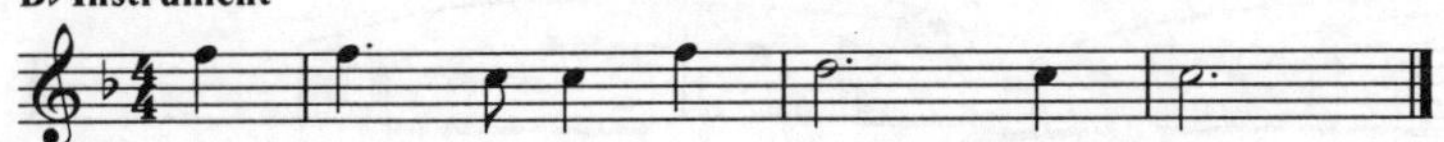

Twenty-Sixth Sunday in Ordinary Time YEAR B

Responsorial Psalm Psalm 18:8, 10, 12-14. Response v.9

Gerry Fitzpatrick

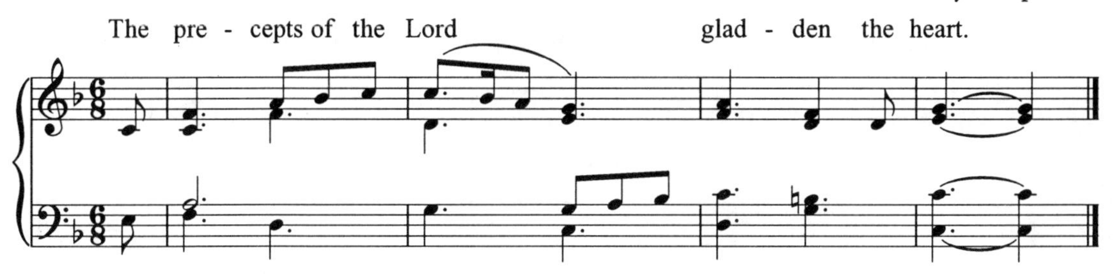

The pre - cepts of the Lord glad - den the heart.

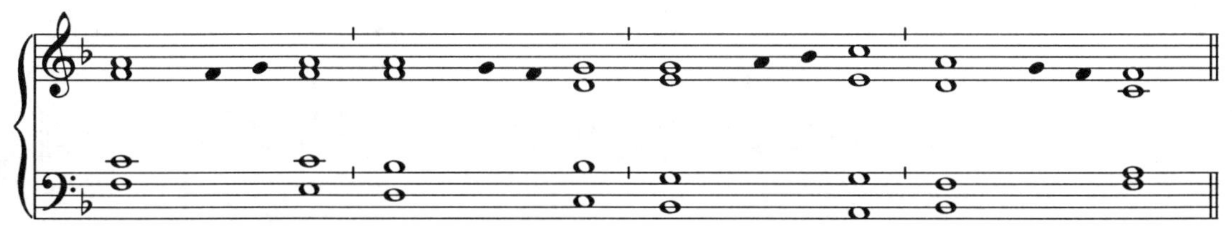

T.B.

1. The law of the Lord is perfect,
   it revives the soul.
   The rule of the Lord is to be trusted,
   it gives wisdom to the simple.

2. The fear of the Lord is holy,
   abiding for ever.
   The decrees of the Lord are truth
   and all of them just.

3. So in them your servant finds instruction;
   great reward is in their keeping.
   But who can detect all their errors?
   From hidden faults acquit me.

4. From presumption restrain your servant
   and let it not rule me.
   Then shall I be blameless,
   clean from grave sin.

Gospel Acclamation cf. John 17:17

Alleluia.
Your word is truth, O Lord
consecrate us in the truth.
Alleluia.

C Instrument

B♭ Instrument

Twenty-Seventh Sunday in Ordinary Time

Responsorial Psalm Psalm 127. Response v.5 YEAR B

Colin Mawby

1. O blessed are those who fear the Lord
 and walk in his ways!
 By the labour of your hands you shall eat.
 You will be happy and prosper.

2. Your wife will be like a fruitful vine
 in the heart of your house;
 your children like shoots of the olive,
 around your table.

3. Indeed thus shall be blessed
 those who fear the Lord.
 May the Lord bless you from Zion
 in a happy Jerusalem.

Gospel Acclamation cf. John 17:17

Alleluia.
Your word is truth, O Lord,
consecrate us in the truth.
Alleluia.

or 1 John 4:12

Alleluia.
As long as we love one another
God will live in us and his love will be complete in us.
Alleluia.

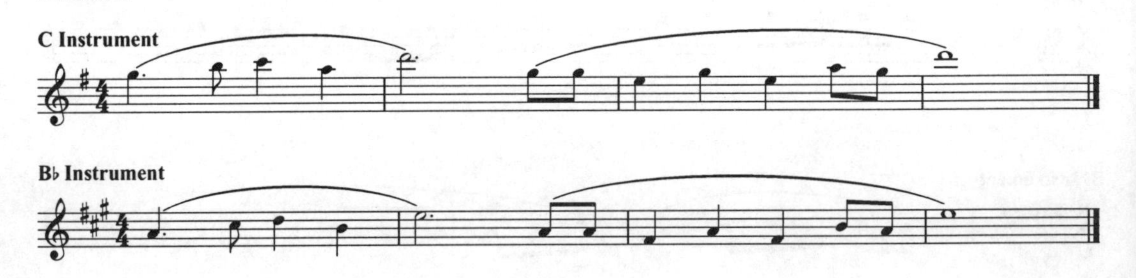

Twenty-Eighth Sunday in Ordinary Time

Responsorial Psalm Psalm 89:12-17. Response v.14 YEAR B

Alan Rees

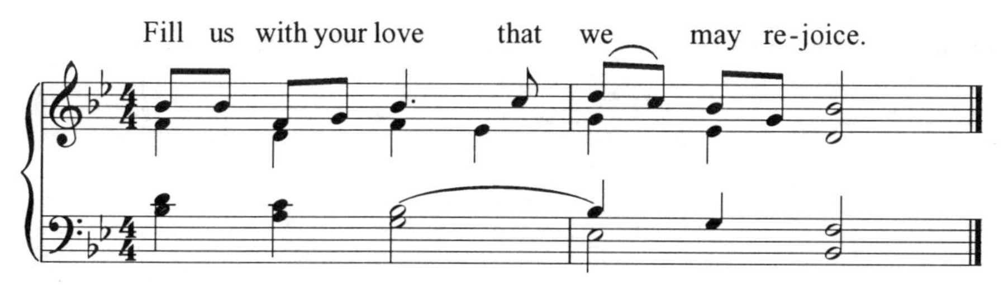

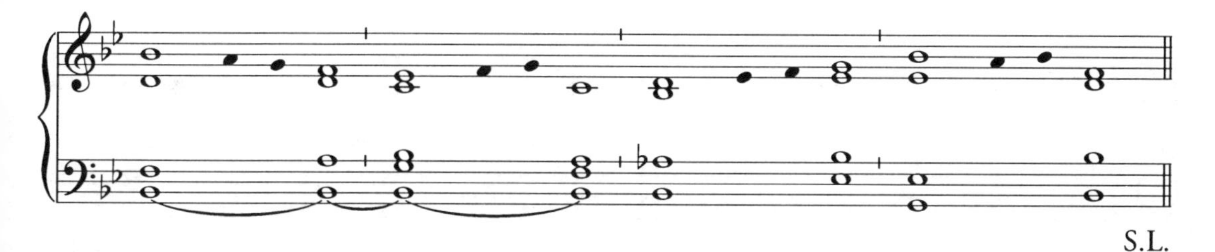

S.L.

1. Make us know the shortness <u>of</u> our life
   that we may gain wis<u>dom</u> of heart.
   Lord, relent! Is your an<u>ger</u> for ever?
   Show pity <u>to</u> your servants.

2. In the morning, fill us <u>with</u> your love;
   we shall exult and rejoice <u>all</u> our days.
   Give us joy to balance <u>our</u> affliction
   for the years when we <u>knew</u> misfortune.

3. Show forth your work <u>to</u> your servants;
   let your glory shine <u>on</u> their children.
   Let the favour of the Lord <u>be</u> upon us:
   give success to the work <u>of</u> our hands.

Gospel Acclamation cf. Matthew 11:25

Alleluia.
Blessed are you, Father, Lord of hea<u>ven</u> and earth,
for revealing the mysteries of the kingdom <u>to</u> mere children.
Alleluia.

or Matthew 5:3

Alleluia.
How happy are the <u>poor</u> in spirit;
theirs is the king<u>dom</u> of heaven.
Alleluia.

C Instrument

B♭ Instrument

Twenty-Ninth Sunday in Ordinary Time

Responsorial Psalm Psalm 32:4-5, 18-20, 22. Response v.22 YEAR B

John Bertalot

1. The word of the Lord is faithful
   and all his works to be trusted.
   The Lord loves justice and right
   and fills the earth with his love.

2. The Lord looks on those who revere him,
   on those who hope in his love,
   to rescue their souls from death,
   to keep them alive in famine.

3. Our soul is waiting for the Lord.
   The Lord is our help and our shield.
   May your love be upon us, O Lord,
   as we place all our hope in you.

Gospel Acclamation John 14:15

Alleluia.
I am the Way, the Truth and the Life, says the Lord;
no one can come to the Father except through me.
Alleluia.

or Mark 10:45

Alleluia.
The Son of Man came to serve,
and to give his life as a ransom for many.
Alleluia.

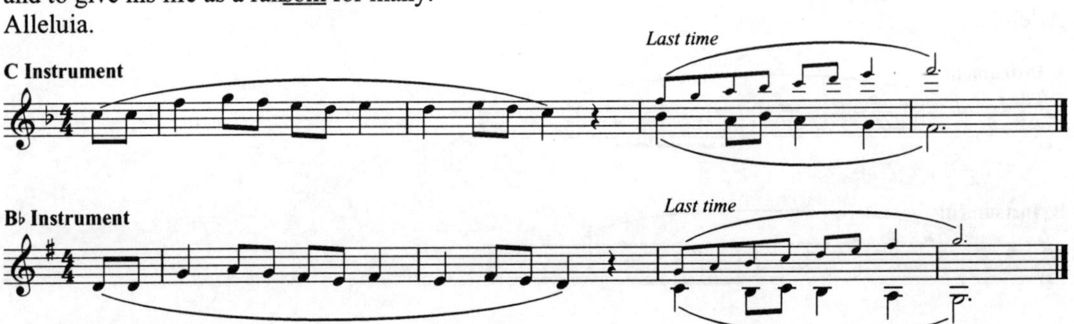

Thirtieth Sunday in Ordinary Time YEAR B

Responsorial Psalm Psalm 125. Response v.3

Simon Lesley

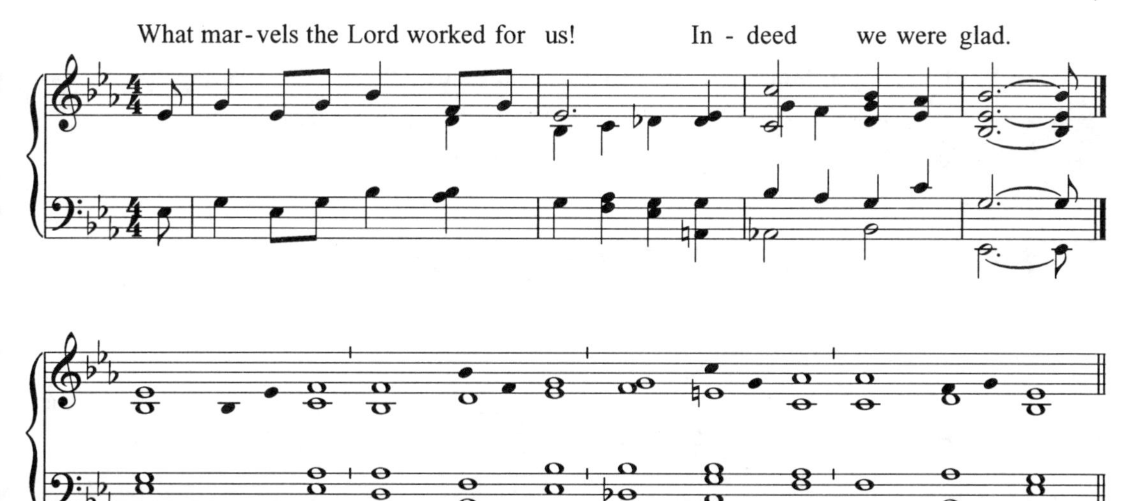

C.M.

1. When the Lord delivered Zion from bondage,
   it seemed like a dream.
   Then was our mouth filled with laughter,
   on our lips there were songs.

2. The heathens themselves said: 'What marvels
   the Lord worked for them!'
   What marvels the Lord worked for us!
   Indeed we were glad.

3. Deliver us, O Lord, from our bondage
   as streams in dry land.
   Those who are sowing in tears
   will sing when they reap.

4. They go out, they go out, full of tears,
   carrying seed for the sowing:
   they come back, they come back, full of song,
   carrying their sheaves.

Gospel Acclamation John 8:12

Alleluia.
I am the light of the world, says the Lord,
anyone who follows me will have the light of life.
Alleluia.

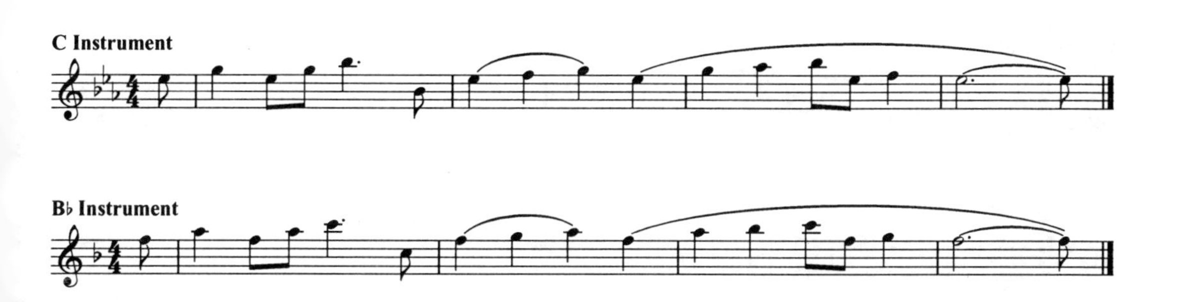

Thirty-First Sunday in Ordinary Time YEAR B

Responsorial Psalm Psalm 17:2-4, 47, 51. Response v.2

John McCann

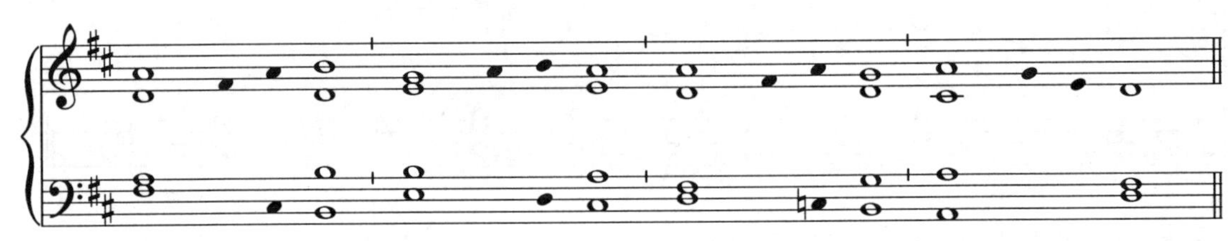

K.D.

1. I love you, Lord, my strength,
   my rock, my fortress, my saviour.
   My God is the rock where I take refuge;
   my shield, my mighty help, my stronghold.

2. The Lord is worthy of all praise:
   when I call I am saved from my foes.
   Long life to the Lord, my rock!
   Praised be the God who saves me.

Gospel Acclamation cf. John 6:63, 68

Alleluia.
Your words are spirit, Lord, and they are life:
you have the message of eternal life.
Alleluia.

or John 14:23

Alleluia.
If anyone loves me they will keep my word,
and my Father will love them and we shall come to them.
Alleluia.

C Instrument

B♭ Instrument

Thirty-Second Sunday in Ordinary Time

Responsorial Psalm Psalm 145:7-10. Response v.2

YEAR B

Andrew Moore

My soul, give praise, give praise to the Lord.

S.L.

1. It is the Lord who keeps faith for ever,
   who is just to those who are oppressed.
   It is he who gives bread to the hungry,
   the Lord, who sets prisoners free.

2. It is the Lord who gives sight to the blind,
   who raises up those who are bowed down.
   It is the Lord who loves the just,
   the Lord, who protects the stranger.

3. The Lord upholds the widow and orphan
   but thwarts the path of the wicked.
   The Lord will reign for ever,
   Zion's God, from age to age.

Gospel Acclamation Revelation 2:10

Alleluia.
Even if you have to die, says the Lord,
keep faithful, and I will give you the crown of life.
Alleluia.

or Matthew 5:3

Alleluia.
How happy are the poor in spirit;
theirs is the kingdom of heaven.
Alleluia.

C Instrument
B♭ Instrument

Thirty-Third Sunday in Ordinary Time

Responsorial Psalm Psalm 15:5, 8-11. Response v.1

YEAR B

Andrew Wright

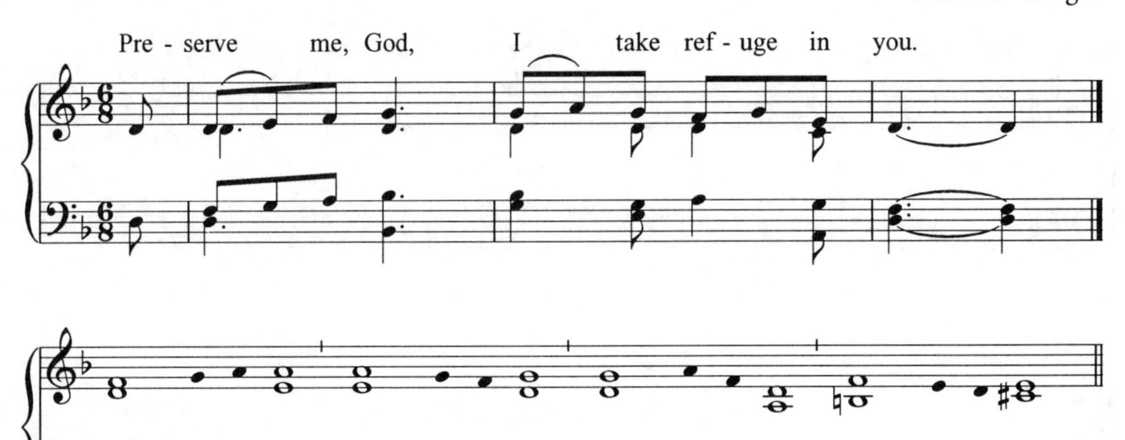
Pre - serve me, God, I take ref - uge in you.

T.B.

1. O Lord, it is you who are my portion and cup;
   it is you yourself who are my prize.
   I keep the Lord ever in my sight:
   since he is at my right hand, I shall stand firm.

2. And so my heart rejoices, my soul is glad;
   even my body shall rest in safety.
   For you will not leave my soul among the dead,
   nor let your beloved know decay.

3. O Lord, you will show me
   the path of life,
   the fullness of joy in your presence,
   at your right hand happiness for ever.

Gospel Acclamation Matthew 24:42, 44

Alleluia.
Stay awake and stand ready,
because you do not know the hour when the Son of Man is coming.
Alleluia.

or Luke 21:36

Alleluia.
Stay awake, praying at all times
for the strength to stand with confidence before the Son of Man.
Alleluia.

C Instrument
B♭ Instrument

Last Sunday in Ordinary Time YEAR B

Our Lord Jesus Christ, Universal King

Responsorial Psalm Psalm 92:1-2, 5. Response v.1 Richard Lloyd

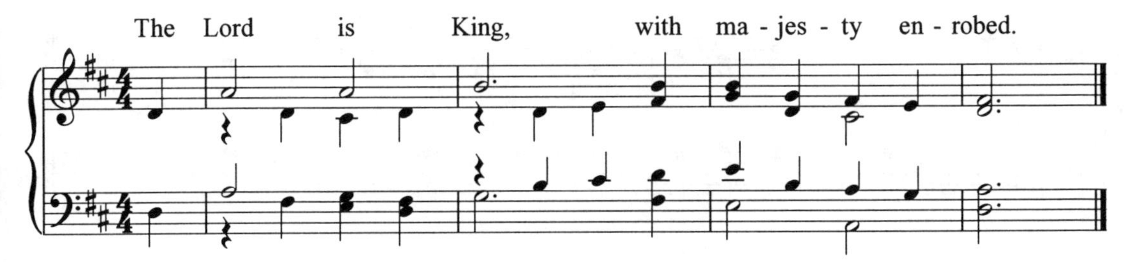

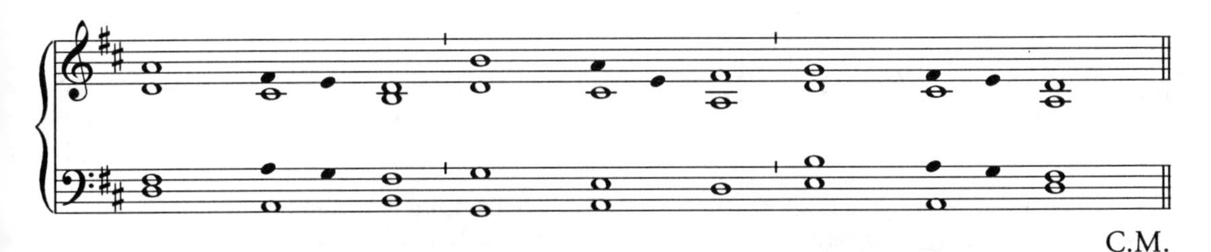

1. The Lord is King, with majesty enrobed;
 the Lord has robed himself with might,
 he has girded himself with power.

2. The world you made firm, not to be moved;
 your throne has stood firm from of old.
 From all eternity, O Lord, you are.

3. Truly your decrees are to be trusted.
 Holiness is fitting to your house,
 O Lord, until the end of time.

Gospel Acclamation Mark 11:9, 10

Alleluia.
Blessings on him who comes in the name of the Lord!
Blessings on the coming kingdom of our father David!
Alleluia.

Second Sunday in Ordinary Time

YEAR C

Responsorial Psalm Psalm 95:1-3, 7-10. Response v.3

Andrew Wright

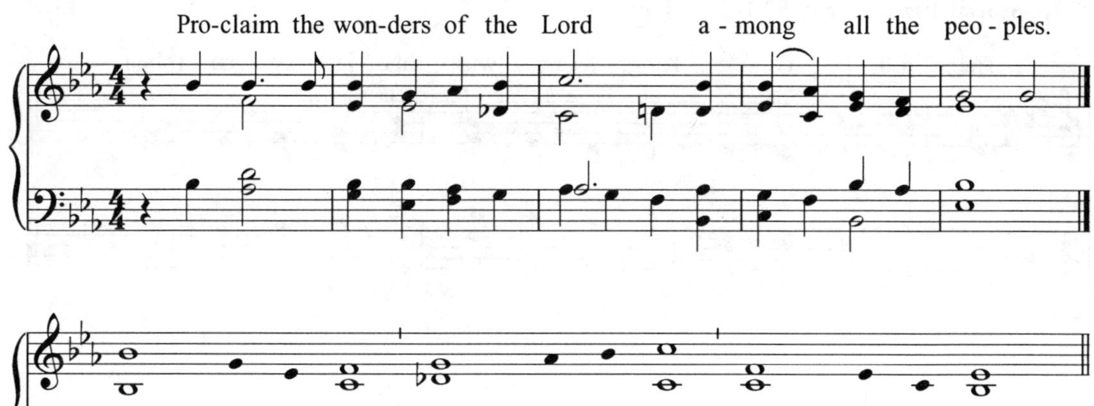

Pro-claim the won-ders of the Lord a - mong all the peo - ples.

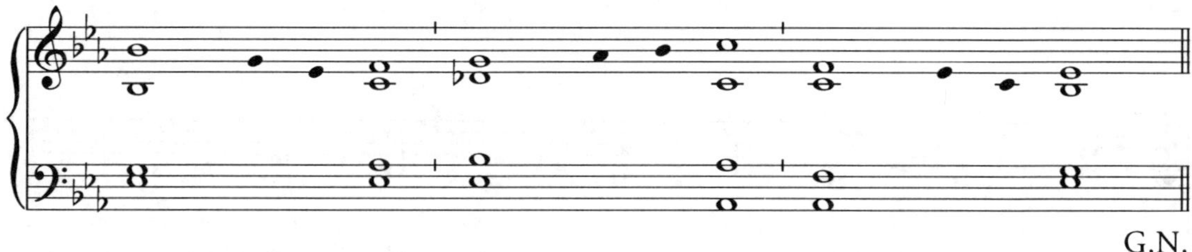

G.N.

1. O sing a new song to the Lord,
sing to the Lord all the earth.
O sing to the Lord, bless his name.

2. Proclaim his help day by day,
tell among the nations his glory
and his wonders among all the peoples.

3. Give the Lord, you families of peoples,
give the Lord glory and power,
give the Lord the glory of his name.

4. Worship the Lord in his temple.
O earth, tremble before him.
Proclaim to the nations: God is king.'

Gospel Acclamation cf. John 6:63, 68

Alleluia.
Your words are spirit, Lord, and they are life:
you have the message of eternal life.
Alleluia.

or cf. 2 Thessalonians 2:14

Alleluia.
Through the Good News God has called us
to share the glory of our Lord Jesus Christ.
Alleluia.

Third Sunday in Ordinary Time

YEAR C

Responsorial Psalm Psalm 18:8-10, 15. Response John 6:63

John Bertalot

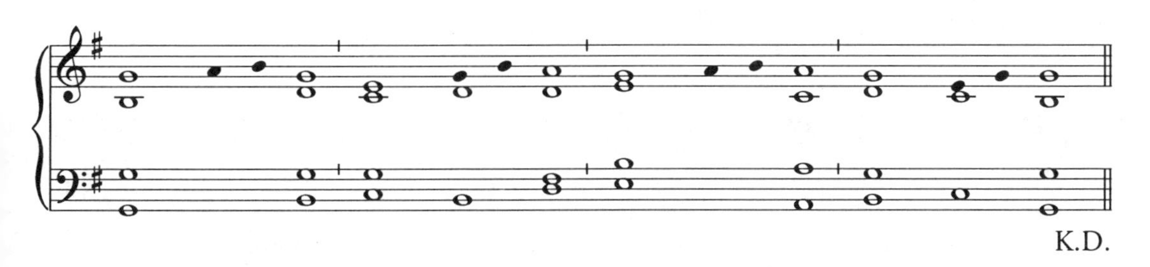

1. The law of the Lord is perfect,
   it revives the soul.
   The rule of the Lord is to be trusted,
   it gives wisdom to the simple.

2. The precepts of the Lord are right,
   they gladden the heart.
   The command of the Lord is clear,
   it gives light to the eyes.

3. The fear of the Lord is holy,
   abiding for ever.
   The decrees of the Lord are truth
   and all of them just.

4. May the spoken words of my mouth,
   the thoughts of my heart,
   win favour in your sight, O Lord,
   my rescuer, my rock!

Gospel Acclamation Luke 4:18

Alleluia.
The Lord has sent me to bring the good news to the poor,
to proclaim liberty to captives.
Alleluia.

Fourth Sunday in Ordinary Time

YEAR C

Responsorial Psalm Psalm 70:1-6, 15, 17. Response v.15

Alan Rees

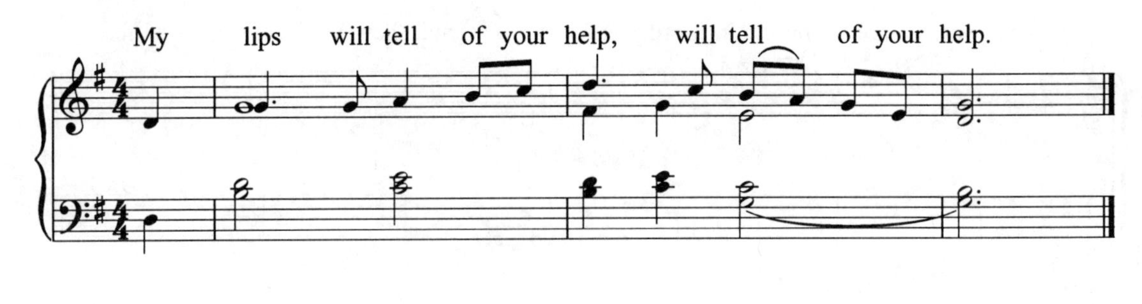

S.L.

1. In you, O Lord, I take refuge;
   let me never be put to shame.
   In your justice rescue me, free me:
   pay heed to me and save me.

2. Be a rock where I can take refuge,
   a mighty stronghold to save me;
   for you are my rock, my stronghold.
   Free me from the hand of the wicked.

3. It is you, O Lord, who are my hope,
   my trust, O Lord, since my youth.
   On you I have leaned from my birth,
   from my mother's womb you have been my help.

4. My lips will tell of your justice
   and day by day of your help.
   O God, you have taught me from my youth
   and I proclaim your wonders still.

Gospel Acclamation John 14:5

Alleluia.
I am the Way, the Truth and the Life, says the Lord;
no one can come to the Father except through me.
Alleluia.

or Luke 4:18

Alleluia.
The Lord has sent me to bring the good news to the poor,
to proclaim liberty to captives.
Alleluia.

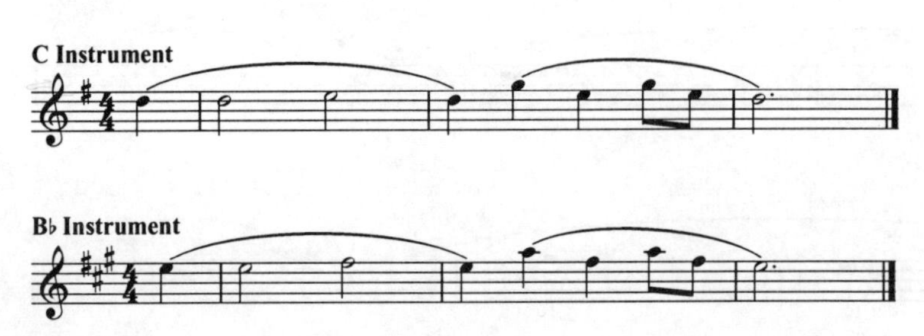

Fifth Sunday in Ordinary Time

YEAR C

Responsorial Psalm Psalm 137:1-5, 7-8. Response v.1

Gerry Fitzpatrick

T.B.

1. I thank you, Lord, with all my heart,
   you have heard the words of my mouth.
   Before the angels I will bless you.
   I will adore before your holy temple.

2. I thank you for your faithfulness and love
   which excel all we ever knew of you.
   On the day I called, you answered;
   you increased the strength of my soul.

3. All earth's kings shall thank you
   when they hear the words of your mouth.
   They shall sing of the Lord's ways:
   'How great is the glory of the Lord!'

4. You stretch out your hand and save me,
   your hand will do all things for me.
   Your love, O Lord, is eternal,
   discard not the work of your hand.

Gospel Acclamation John 15:15

Alleluia.
I call you friends, says the Lord,
because I have made known to you everything I have learnt from my Father.
Alleluia.

or Matthew 4:19

Alleluia.
Follow me, says the Lord,
and I will make you fishers of men.
Alleluia.

Sixth Sunday in Ordinary Time

YEAR C

Responsorial Psalm Psalm 1:1-4, 6. Response Psalm 39:5

Andrew Wright

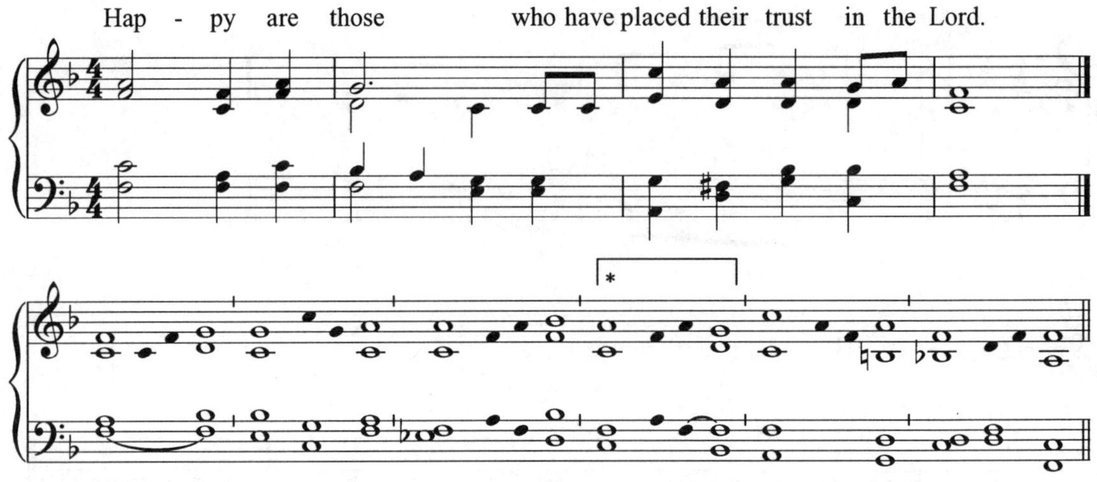

Hap - py are those who have placed their trust in the Lord.
*

* *Omit in Verses 2 and 3.*

C.M.

1. Happy indeed are those
   who follow not the counsel of the wicked;
   nor linger in the way of sinners
   nor sit in the company of scorners,
   but whose delight is the law of the Lord
   and who ponder his law day and night.

2. They are like a tree that is planted
   beside the flowing waters,
   that yields its fruit in due season
   and whose leaves shall never fade;
   and all that they do shall prosper.

3. Not so are the wicked, not so!
   For they like winnowed chaff
   shall be driven away by the wind.
   For the Lord guards the way of the just
   but the way of the wicked leads to doom.

Gospel Acclamation cf. Matthew 11:25

Alleluia.
Blessed are you, Father, Lord of heaven and earth,
for revealing the mysteries of the kingdom to mere children.
Alleluia.

or Luke 6:23

Alleluia.
Rejoice and be glad:
your reward will be great in heaven.
Alleluia.

Seventh Sunday in Ordinary Time

YEAR C

Responsorial Psalm Psalm 102:1-4, 8, 10, 12-13. Response v.8

Alan Rees

The Lord is com - pas - sion, com-pas - sion and love.

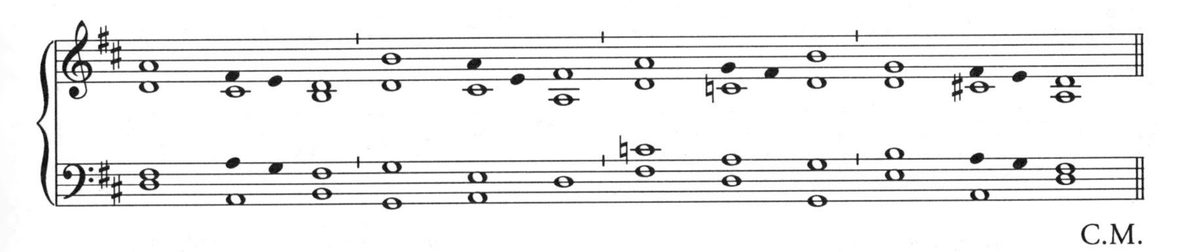
C.M.

1. My soul, give thanks to the Lord,
   all my being, bless his holy name.
   My soul, give thanks to the Lord
   and never forget all his blessings.

2. It is he who forgives all your guilt,
   who heals every one of your ills,
   who redeems your life from the grave,
   who crowns you with love and compassion.

3. The Lord is compassion and love,
   slow to anger and rich in mercy.
   He does not treat us according to our sins
   nor repay us according to our faults.

4. As far as the east is from the west
   so far does he remove our sins.
   As a father has compassion on his sons,
   the Lord has pity on those who fear him.

Gospel Acclamation cf. Acts 16:14

Alleluia.
Open our heart, O Lord,
to accept the words of your Son.
Alleluia.

or John 13:34

Alleluia.
I give you a new commandment: love one another,
just as I have loved you, says the Lord.
Alleluia.

C Instrument
B♭ Instrument

Eighth Sunday in Ordinary Time

YEAR C

Responsorial Psalm Psalm 9 1:2-3, 13-16. Response cf. v.2

Richard Lloyd

It is good to give you thanks, give you thanks, O Lord.
K.D.

1. It is good to give thanks to the Lord
   to make music to your name, O Most High,
   to proclaim your love in the morning
   and your truth in the watches of the night.

2. The just will flourish like the palm-tree
   and grow like a Lebanon cedar.
   Planted in the house of the Lord
   they will flourish in the courts of our God.

3. Still bearing fruit when they are old,
   still full of sap, still green,
   they will proclaim that the Lord is just.
   In him, my rock, there is no wrong.

Gospel Acclamation cf. Acts 16:14

Alleluia.
Open our hearts, O Lord,
to accept the words of your Son.
Alleluia.

or Philippians 2:15-16

Alleluia.
You will shine in the world like bright stars
because you are offering it the word of life.
Alleluia.

C Instrument
B♭ Instrument

Ninth Sunday in Ordinary Time

YEAR C

Responsorial Psalm Psalm 116:1-2. Response Mark 16:15

Colin Mawby

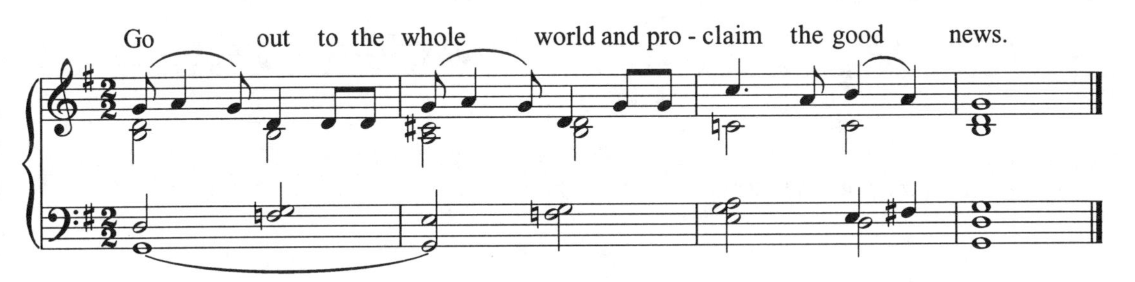
Go out to the whole world and pro - claim the good news.

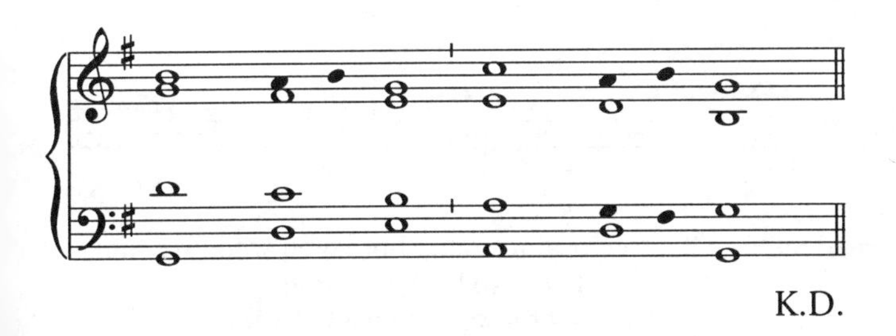

K.D.

1. O praise the Lord, all you nations,
   acclaim him all you peoples!

2. Strong is his love for us;
   he is faithful for ever.

Gospel Acclamation John 1:14, 12

Alleluia.
The Word was made flesh and lived among us;
to all who did accept him he gave power to become children of God.
Alleluia.

or John 3:16

Alleluia.
God loved the world so much that he gave his only Son
so that everyone who believes in him may have eternal life.
Alleluia.

C Instrument
B♭ Instrument

Tenth Sunday in Ordinary Time

YEAR C

Responsorial Psalm Psalm 29:2, 4-6, 11-13. Response v.2

Andrew Wright

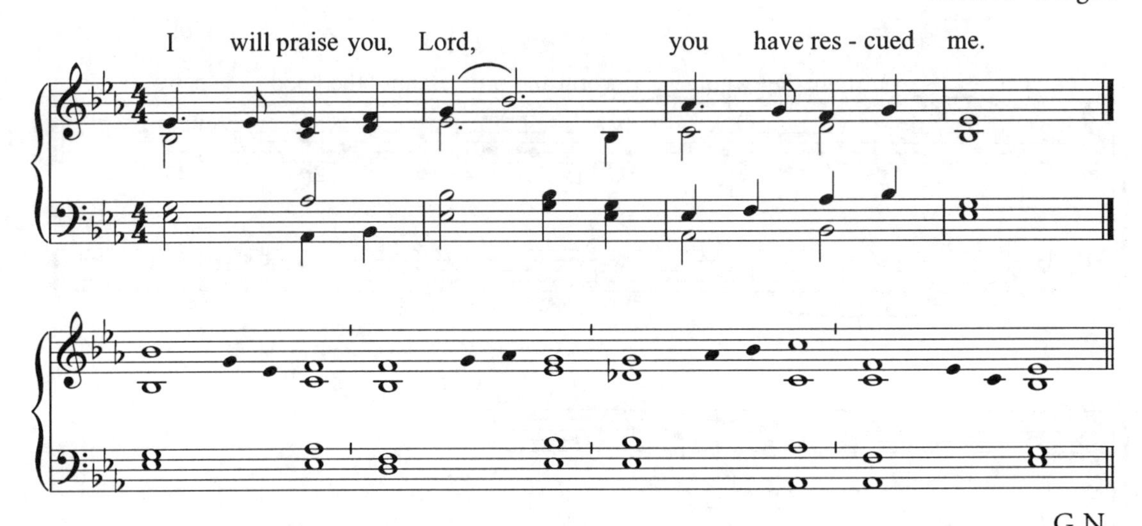

1. I will praise you, Lord, you have rescued me
   and have not let my enemies rejoice over me.
   O Lord, you have raised my soul from the dead,
   restored me to life from those who sink into the grave.

2. Sing psalms to the Lord, you who love him,
   give thanks to his holy name.
   His anger lasts a moment; his favour through life.
   At night there are tears, but joy comes with dawn.

3. The Lord listened and had pity.
   The Lord came to my help.
   For me you have changed my mourning into dancing;
   O Lord my God, I will thank you for ever.

Gospel Acclamation cf. Ephesians 1:17, 18

Alleluia.
May the Father of our Lord Jesus Christ enlighten the eyes of our mind,
so that we can see what hope his call holds for us.
Alleluia.

or Luke 7:16

Alleluia.
A great prophet has appeared among us;
God has visited his people.
Alleluia.

Eleventh Sunday in Ordinary Time YEAR C

Responsorial Psalm Psalm 31:1-2, 5, 7, 11. Response cf. v.5

Simon Lesley

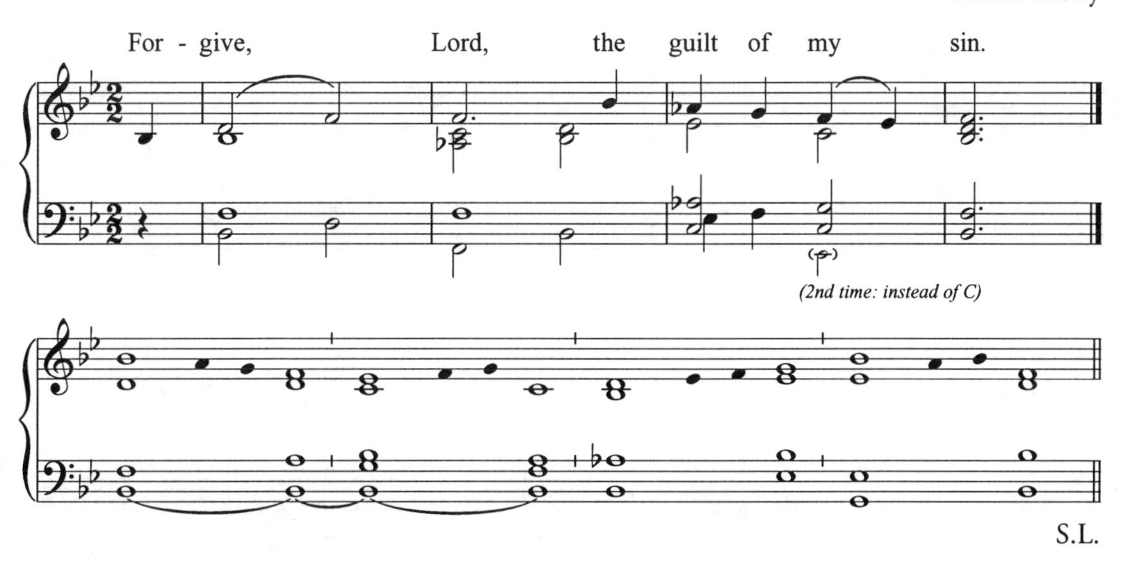

1. Happy are those whose offence is forgiven
   whose sin is remitted.
   O happy are those to whom the Lord
   imputes no guilt.

2. But now I have acknowledged my sins:
   my guilt I did not hide.
   And you, Lord, have forgiven
   the guilt of my sin.

3. Rejoice, rejoice in the Lord,
   exult, you just!
   O come, ring out your joy,
   all you upright of heart.

Gospel Acclamation John 14:5

Alleluia.
I am the Way, the Truth and the Life, says the Lord;
no one can come to the Father except through me.
Alleluia.

or 1 John 4:10

Alleluia.
God so loved us when he sent his Son
to be the sacrifice that takes our sins away.
Alleluia.

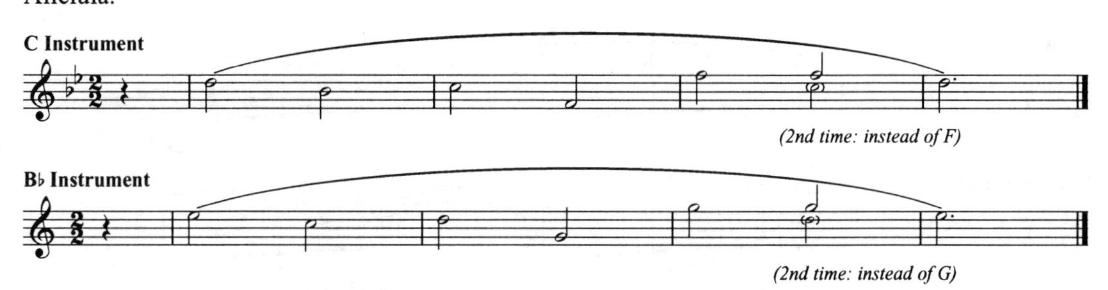

Twelfth Sunday in Ordinary Time YEAR C

Responsorial Psalm Psalm 62:2-6, 8-9. Response v.2

John McCann

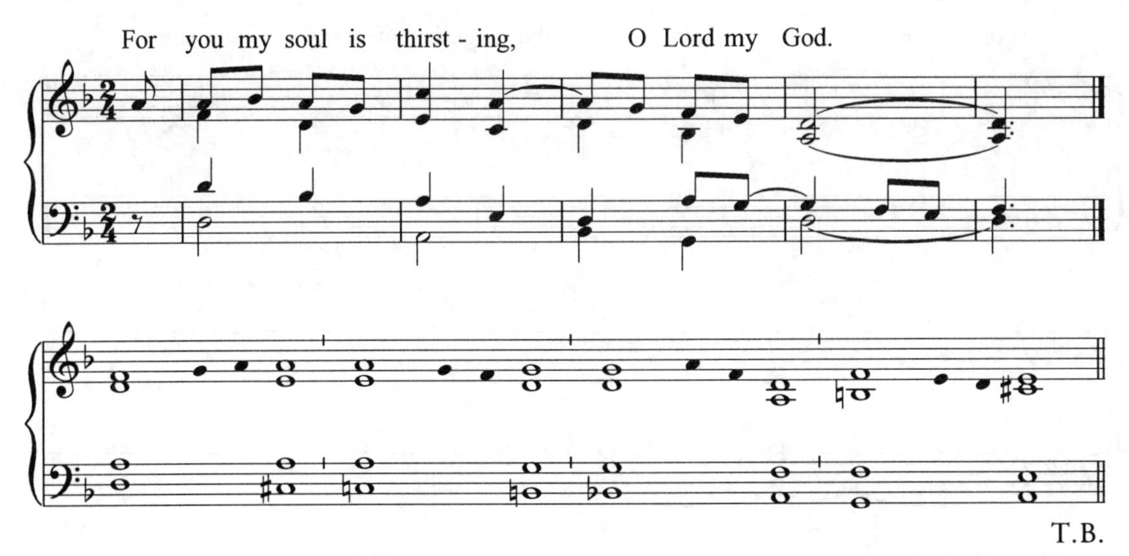
For you my soul is thirst - ing, O Lord my God.
T.B.

1. O God, you are my God, for you I long;
for you my soul is thirsting.
My body pines for you
like a dry, weary land without water.

2. So I gaze on you in the sanctuary
to see your strength and your glory.
For your love is better than life,
my lips will speak your praise.

3. So I will bless you all my life,
in your name I will lift up my hands.
My soul shall be filled as with a banquet,
my mouth shall praise you with joy.

4. For you have been my help;
in the shadow of your wings I rejoice.
My soul clings to you;
your right hand holds me fast.

Gospel Acclamation John 8:12

Alleluia.
I am the light of the world, says the Lord,
anyone who follows me will have the light of life.
Alleluia.

or John 10:27

Alleluia.
The sheep that belong to me listen to my voice, says the Lord,
I know them and they follow me.
Alleluia.

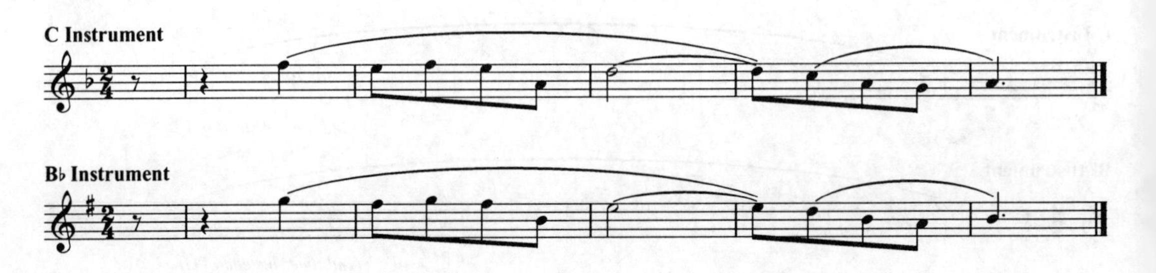
C Instrument
B♭ Instrument

Thirteenth Sunday in Ordinary Time YEAR C

Responsorial Psalm Psalm 15:1-2, 5, 7-11. Response v.1

Simon Lesley

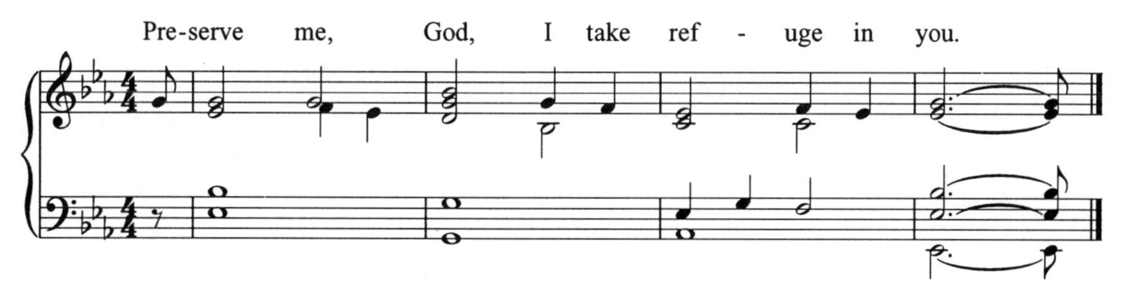

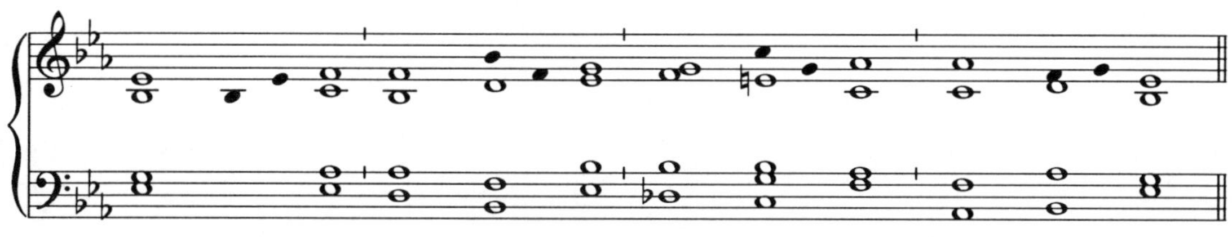

C.M.

1. Preserve me, God, I take refuge in you.
I say to the Lord: 'You are my God.'
O Lord, it is you who are my portion and cup;
it is you yourself who are my prize.

2. I will bless the Lord who gives me counsel,
who even at night directs my heart.
I keep the Lord ever in my sight:
since he is at my right hand, I shall stand firm.

3. And so my heart rejoices, my soul is glad;
even my body shall rest in safety.
For you will not leave my soul among the dead,
nor let your beloved know decay.

4. O Lord, you will show me
the path of life,
the fullness of joy in your presence,
at your right hand happiness for ever.

Gospel Acclamation 1 Samuel 3:9; John 6:68

Alleluia.
Speak, Lord, your servant is listening:
you have the message of eternal life.
Alleluia.

Responsorial Psalms

Fourteenth Sunday in Ordinary Time YEAR C

Responsorial Psalm Psalm 65:1-7, 16, 20. Response v.1

Keith Duke

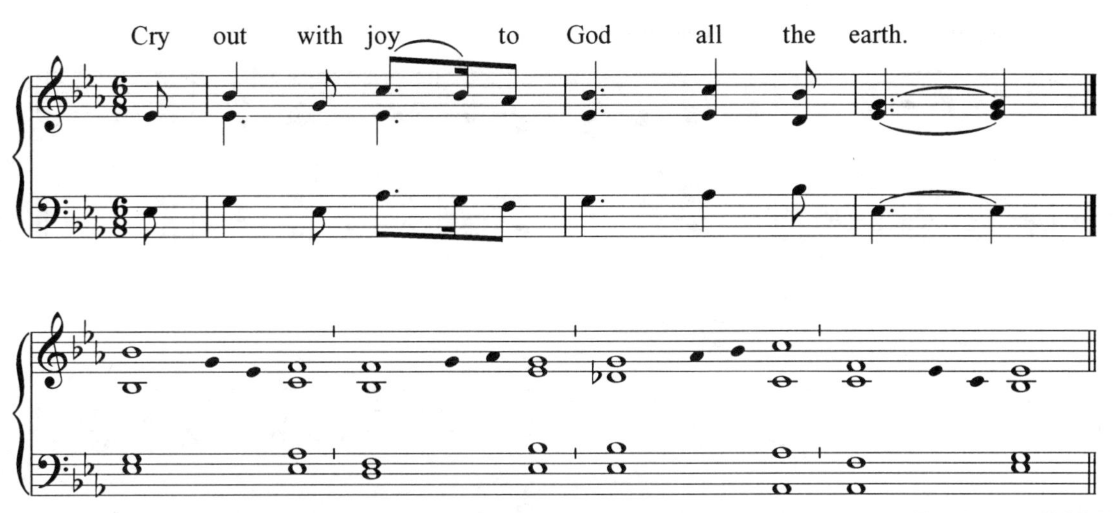

G.N.

1. Cry out with joy to God all the earth,
   O sing to the glory of his name.
   O render him glorious praise.
   Say to God: 'How tremendous your deeds!'

2. 'Before you all the earth shall bow;
   shall sing to you, sing to your name!'
   Come and see the works of God,
   tremendous his deeds among men.

3. He turned the sea into dry land,
   they passed through the river dry-shod.
   Let our joy then be in him;
   he rules for ever by his might.

4. Come and hear, all who fear God.
   I will tell what he did for my soul.
   Blessed be God who did not reject my prayer
   nor withhold his love from me.

Gospel Acclamation John 15:15

Alleluia.
I call you friends, says the Lord,
because I have made known to you everything I have learnt from my Father.
Alleluia.

or Colossians 3:15, 16

Alleluia.
May the peace of Christ reign in your hearts,
because it is for this that you were called together as parts of one body.
Alleluia.

Fifteenth Sunday in Ordinary Time

YEAR C

Responsorial Psalm Psalm 68:14, 17, 30-31, 33-34, 36-37. Response cf. v.33

Andrew Moore

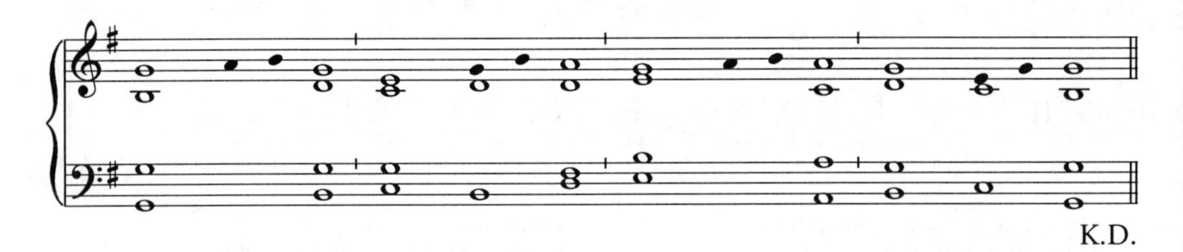

1. This is my prayer to you, my prayer <u>for</u> your favour.
   In your great love, answer <u>me</u>, O God,
   with your help that <u>ne</u>ver fails:
   Lord, answer, for your <u>love</u> is kind.

2. As for me in my pover<u>ty</u> and pain
   let your help, O God, <u>lift</u> me up.
   I will praise God's name <u>with</u> a song;
   I will glorify him <u>with</u> thanksgiving.

3. The poor when they see it <u>will</u> be glad
   and God-seeking hearts <u>will</u> revive;
   for the Lord listens <u>to</u> the needy
   and does not spurn his servants <u>in</u> their chains.

4. For God will bring <u>help</u> to Zion
   and rebuild the cit<u>ies</u> of Judah.
   The sons of his servants <u>shall</u> inherit it;
   those who love his <u>name</u> shall dwell there.

The Gospel Acclamation will be found on the next page.

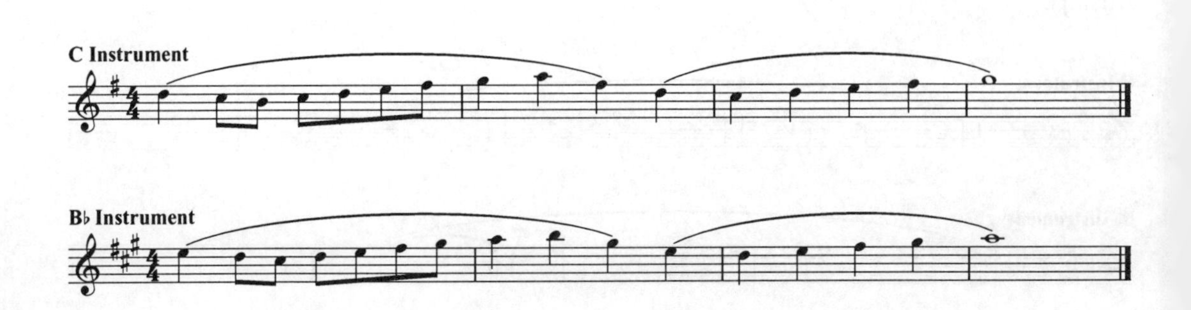

Alternative Responsorial Psalm Psalm 18:8-11. Response v.9

Andrew Wright

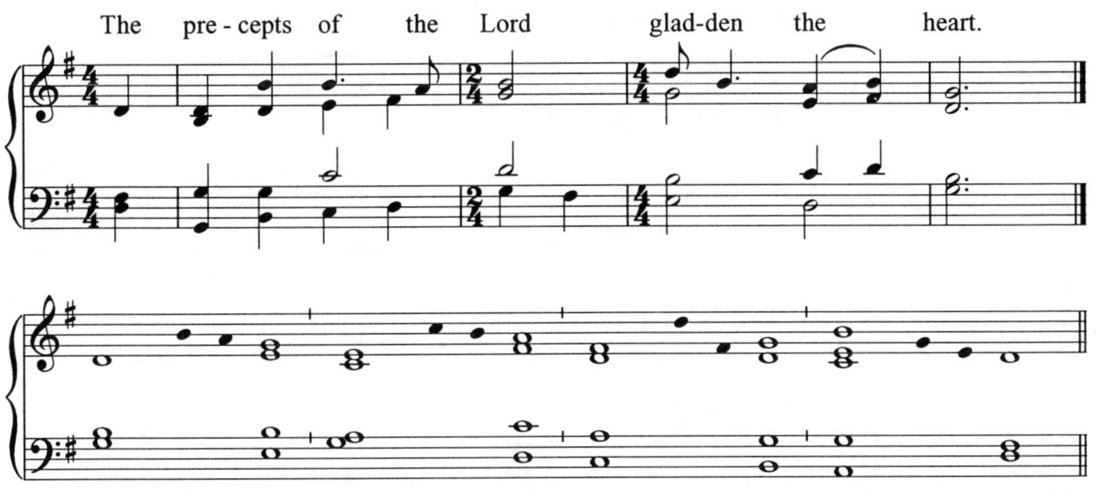

S.L.

1. The law of the Lord is perfect,
   it revives the soul.
   The rule of the Lord is to be trusted,
   it gives wisdom to the simple.

2. The precepts of the Lord are right,
   they gladden the heart.
   The command of the Lord is clear,
   it gives light to the eyes.

3. The fear of the Lord is holy,
   abiding for ever.
   The decrees of the Lord are truth
   and all of them just.

4. They are more to be desired than gold,
   than the purest of gold
   and sweeter are they than honey,
   than honey from the comb.

Gospel Acclamation John 10:27

Alleluia.
The sheep that belong to me listen to my voice, says the Lord,
I know them and they follow me.
Alleluia.

or cf. John 6:63, 68

Alleluia.
Your words are spirit, Lord, and they are life:
you have the message of eternal life.
Alleluia.

C Instrument

B♭ Instrument

Sixteenth Sunday in Ordinary Time

Responsorial Psalm Psalm 14:2-5. Response v.1

John Bertalot

The just will live in the pre-sence of the Lord.

T.B.

1. Lord, who shall dwell on your holy mountain?
   Those who walk without fault;
   Those who act with justice
   and speak the truth from their hearts.

2. They who do no wrong to their kindred
   who cast no slur on their neighbour,
   who hold the godless in disdain,
   but honour those who fear the Lord.

3. Those who keep their pledge, come what may;
   who take no interest on a loan
   and accept no bribes against the innocent.
   Such people will stand firm for ever.

Gospel Acclamation Acts 16:14

Alleluia.
Open our heart, O Lord,
to accept the words of your Son.
Alleluia.

or cf. Luke 8:15

Alleluia.
Blessed are those who, with a noble and generous heart,
take the word of God to themselves and yield a harvest through their perseverance.
Alleluia.

Seventeenth Sunday in Ordinary Time YEAR C

Responsorial Psalm Psalm 137:1-3, 6-8. Response v.3

Keith Duke

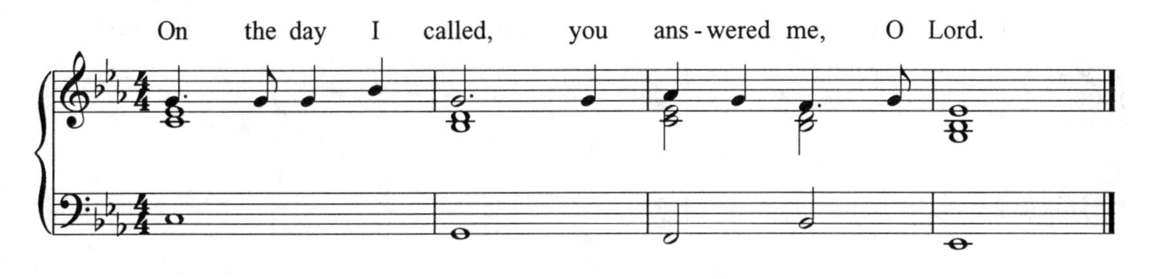

C.M.

1. I thank you, Lord, with all my heart,
   you have heard the words of my mouth.
   Before the angels I will bless you.
   I will adore before your holy temple.

2. I thank you for your faithfulness and love
   which excel all we ever knew of you.
   On the day I called, you answered;
   you increased the strength of my soul.

3. The Lord is high yet he looks on the lowly
   and the haughty he knows from afar.
   Though I walk in the midst of affliction
   you give me life and frustrate my foes.

4. You stretch out your hand and save me,
   your hand will do all things for me.
   Your love, O Lord, is eternal,
   discard not the work of your hands.

Gospel Acclamation John 1:12,14

Alleluia.
The Word was made flesh and lived among us;
to all who did accept him he gave power to become children of God.
Alleluia.

or Romans 8:15

Alleluia.
The spirit you received is the spirit of children,
and it makes us cry out, 'Abba, Father!'
Alleluia.

Eighteenth Sunday in Ordinary Time YEAR C

Responsorial Psalm Psalm 89:3-6, 12-14, 17. Response v.1

Geoff Nobes

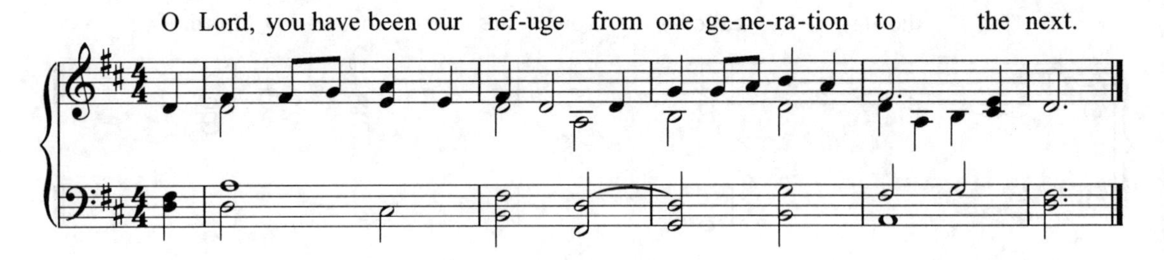

O Lord, you have been our ref-uge from one ge-ne-ra-tion to the next.

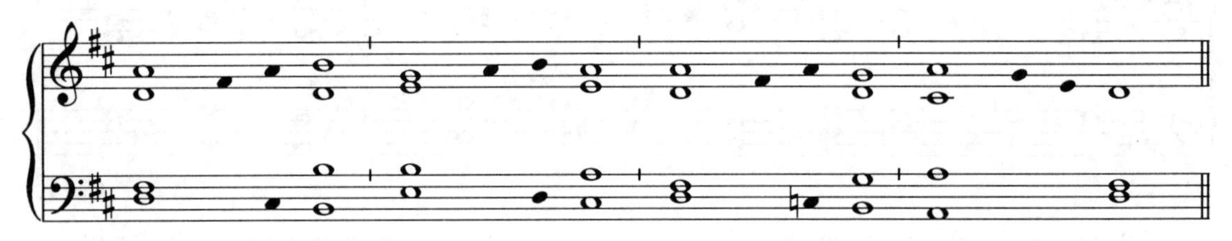

K.D.

1. You turn us back into dust
   and say: 'Go back children of the earth.'
   To your eyes a thousand years are like
   yesterday, come and gone,
   no more than a watch in the night.

2. You sweep us away like a dream,
   like grass which springs up in the morning.
   In the morning it springs up and flowers:
   by evening it withers and fades.

3. Make us know the shortness of our life
   that we may gain wisdom of heart.
   Lord, relent! Is your anger for ever?
   Show pity to your servants.

4. In the morning, fill us with your love;
   we shall exult and rejoice all our days.
   Let the favour of the Lord be upon us:
   give success to the work of our hands.

The Gospel Acclamation will be found on the next page.

Alternative Responsorial Psalm Psalm 94:1-2, 6-9. Response vv.7-8

Andrew Moore

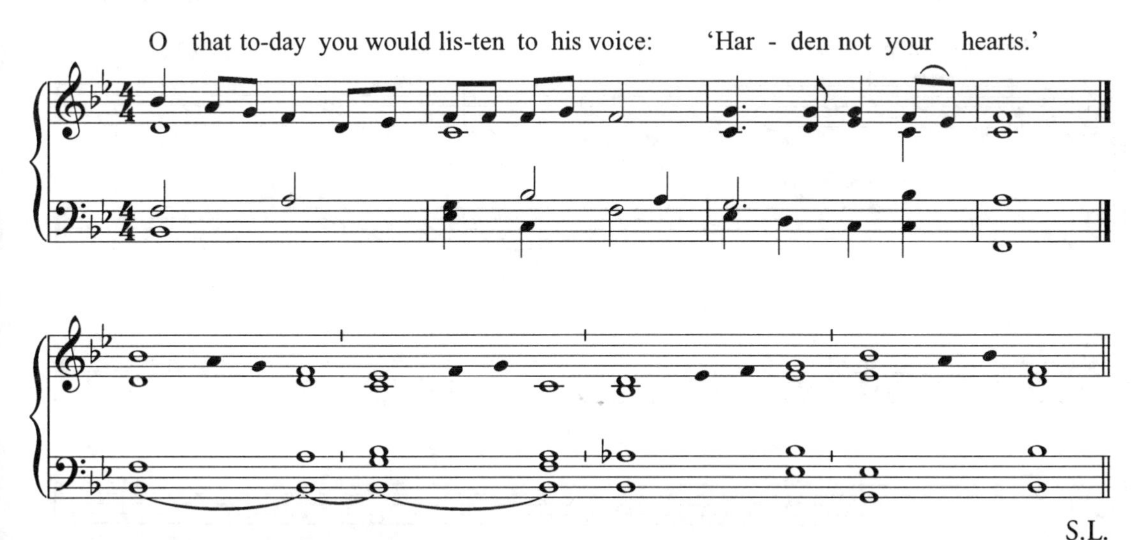

1. Come, ring out our joy to the Lord;
   hail the rock who saves us.
   Let us come before him, giving thanks,
   with songs let us hail the Lord.

2. Come in; let us bow and bend low;
   let us kneel before the God who made us
   for he is our God, and we the people who
   belong to his pasture,
   the flock that is led by his hand.

3. O that today you would listen to his voice!
   'Harden not your hearts as at Meribah,
   as on that day at Massah in the desert, when
   your fathers put me to the test;
   when they tried me, though they saw my work.'

Gospel Acclamation cf. John 17:17

Alleluia.
Your word is truth, O Lord,
consecrate us in the truth.
Alleluia.

or Matthew 5:3

Alleluia.
How happy are the poor in spirit;
theirs is the kingdom of heaven.
Alleluia.

Nineteenth Sunday in Ordinary Time YEAR C

Responsorial Psalm Psalm 32:1, 12, 18-20, 22. Response v.12

Simon Lesley

Hap - py the peo-ple the Lord has cho-sen as his own.

T.B.

1. Ring out your joy to the Lord, O you just;
   for praise is fitting for loyal hearts.
   They are happy, whose God is the Lord,
   the people he has chosen as his own.

2. The Lord looks on those who revere him,
   on those who hope in his love,
   to rescue their souls from death,
   to keep them alive in famine.

3. Our soul is waiting for the Lord.
   The Lord is our help and our shield.
   May your love be upon us, O Lord,
   as we place all our hope in you.

Gospel Acclamation cf. Matthew 11:25

Alleluia.
Blessed are you, Father, Lord of heaven and earth,
for revealing the mysteries of the kingdom to mere children.
Alleluia.

or Matthew 24:42, 44

Alleluia.
Stay awake and stand ready,
because you do not know the hour when the Son of Man is coming.
Alleluia.

C Instrument

B♭ Instrument

Twentieth Sunday in Ordinary Time YEAR C

Responsorial Psalm Psalm 39:2-4, 18. Response v.14

Colin Mawby

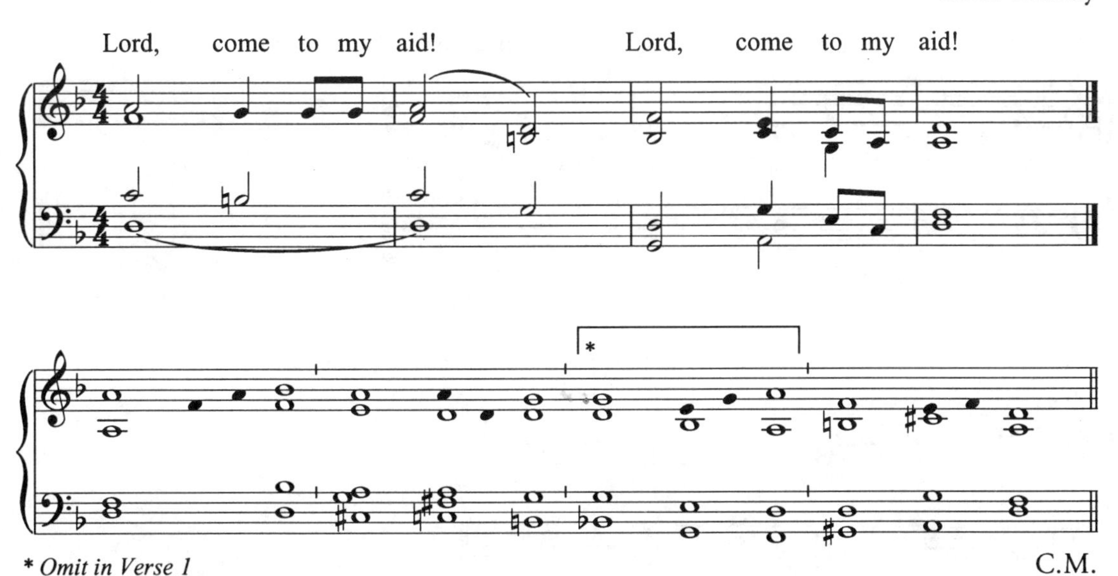

* *Omit in Verse 1*

C.M.

1. I waited, I waited for the Lord
   and he stooped down to me;
   he heard my cry.

2. He drew me from the deadly pit,
   from the miry clay.
   He set my feet upon a rock
   and made my footsteps firm.

3. He put a new song into my mouth,
   praise of our God.
   Many shall see and fear
   and shall trust in the Lord.

4. As for me, wretched and poor,
   the Lord thinks of me.
   You are my rescuer, my help,
   O God, do not delay.

Gospel Acclamation cf Acts 16:14

Alleluia.
Open our heart, O Lord,
to accept the words of your Son.
Alleluia.

or John 10:27

Alleluia.
The sheep that belong to me listen to my voice, says the Lord,
I know them and they follow me.
Alleluia.

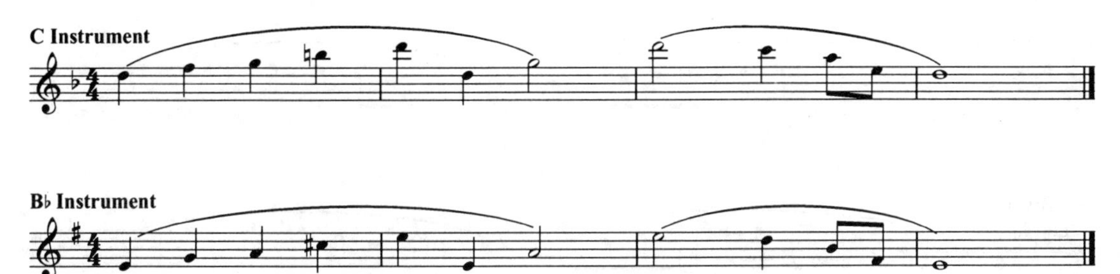

Twenty-First Sunday in Ordinary Time YEAR C

Responsorial Psalm Psalm 116. Response Mark 16:15

Richard Lloyd

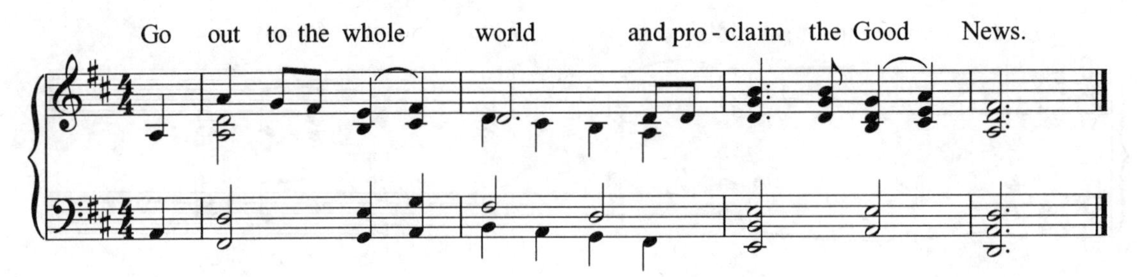
Go out to the whole world and pro - claim the Good News.

C.M.

1. O praise the Lord, all you nations,
   acclaim him all you peoples!

2. Strong is his love for us;
   he is faithful for ever.

Gospel Acclamation John 14:23

Alleluia.
If anyone loves me they will keep my word,
and my Father will love them and we shall come to them.
Alleluia.

or John 14:6

Alleluia.
I am the Way, the Truth and the Life, says the Lord;
no one can come to the Father except through me.
Alleluia.

C Instrument
B♭ Instrument

Twenty-Second Sunday in Ordinary Time

Responsorial Psalm Psalm 67:4-7, 10-11. Response cf. v.11 YEAR C

Andrew Moore

In your good-ness, O God, you pre-pared a home for the poor.
G.N.

1. The just shall rejoice at the presence of God,
   they shall exult and dance for joy.
   O sing to the Lord, make music to his name;
   rejoice in the Lord, exult at his presence.

2. Father of the orphan, defender of the widow,
   such is God in his holy place.
   God gives the lonely a home to live in;
   he leads the prisoners forth into freedom.

3. You poured down, O God, a generous rain:
   when your people were starved you gave them new life.
   It was there that your people found a home,
   prepared in your goodness, O God, for the poor.

Gospel Acclamation John 14:23

Alleluia.
If anyone loves me they will keep my word,
and my Father will love them and we shall come to them.
Alleluia.

or Matthew 11:29

Alleluia.
Shoulder my yoke and learn from me,
for I am gentle and humble in heart.
Alleluia.

Twenty-Third Sunday in Ordinary Time

Responsorial Psalm Psalm 89:3-6, 12-14, 17. Response v.1 YEAR C

John Bertalot

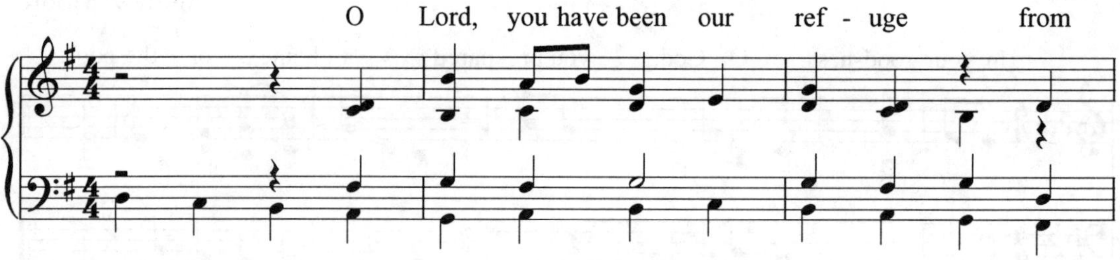

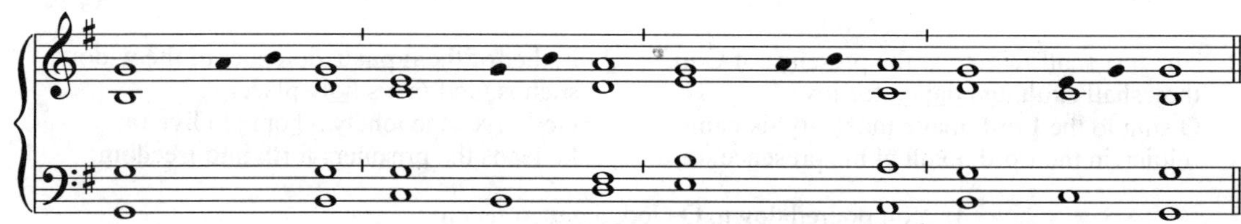

K.D.

1. You turn us back into dust
   and say: 'Go back, children of the earth!
   To your eyes a thousand years are like
   yesterday, come and gone,
   no more than a watch in the night.

2. You sweep us away like a dream,
   like grass which springs up in the morning.
   In the morning it springs up and flowers:
   by evening it withers and fades.

3. Make us know the shortness of our life
   that we may gain wisdom of heart.
   Lord, relent! Is your anger for ever?
   Show pity to your servants.

4. In the morning, fill us with your love.
   we shall exult and rejoice all our days.
   Let the favour of the Lord be upon us:
   give success to the work of our hands.

Gospel Acclamation John 15:15

Alleluia.
I call you friends, says the Lord,
because I have made known to you everything
I have learnt from my Father.
Alleluia.

or Psalm 118:135

Alleluia.
Let your face shine on your servant,
and teach me your decrees.
Alleluia.

C Instrument

B♭ Instrument

Twenty-Fourth Sunday in Ordinary Time

Responsorial Psalm Psalm 50:3-4, 12-13, 17, 19. Response Luke 15:18 YEAR C

Simon Lesley

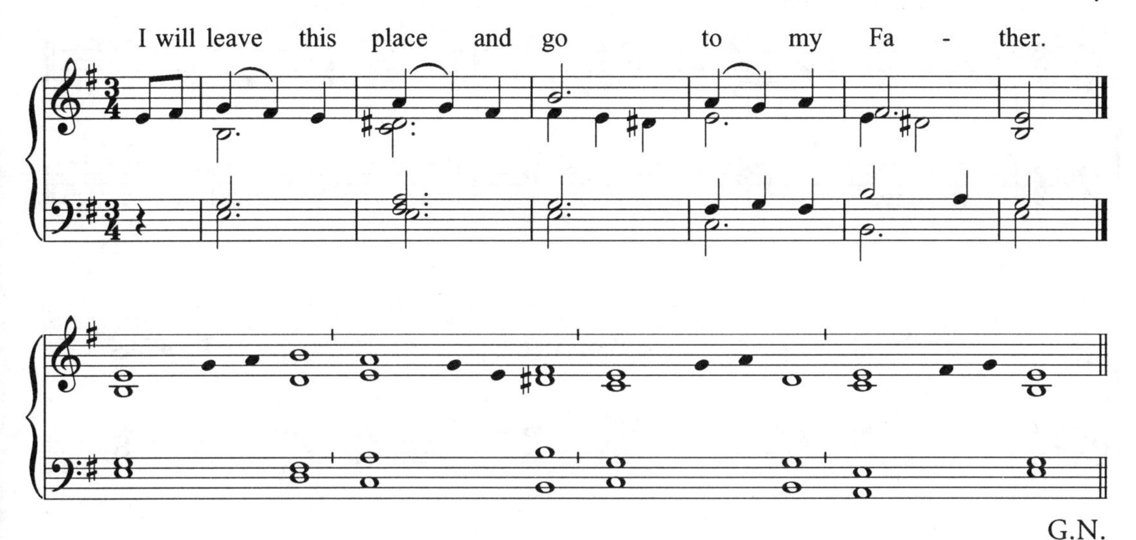

1. Have mercy on me, God, in your kindness.
   In your compassion blot out my offence.
   O wash me more and more from my guilt
   and cleanse me from my sin.

2. A pure heart create for me, O God,
   put a steadfast spirit within me.
   Do not cast me away from your presence,
   nor deprive me of your holy spirit.

3. O Lord, open my lips
   and my mouth shall declare your praise.
   My sacrifice is a contrite spirit;
   a humbled, contrite heart you will not spurn.

Gospel Acclamation cf. Ephesians 1:17, 18

Alleluia.
May the Father of our Lord Jesus Christ enlighten the eyes of our mind,
so that we can see what hope his call holds for us.
Alleluia.

or 2 Corinthians 5:19

Alleluia.
God in Christ was reconciling the world to himself,
and he has entrusted to us the news that they are reconciled.
Alleluia.

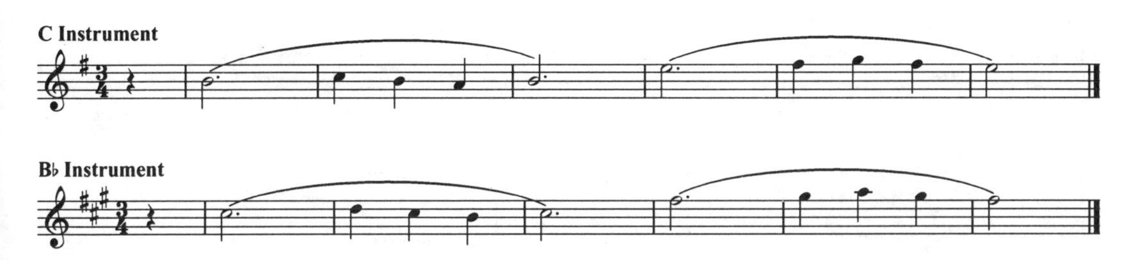

Twenty-Fifth Sunday in Ordinary Time YEAR C

Responsorial Psalm Psalm 112:1-2, 4-8. Response cf. vv.1, 7

Colin Mawby

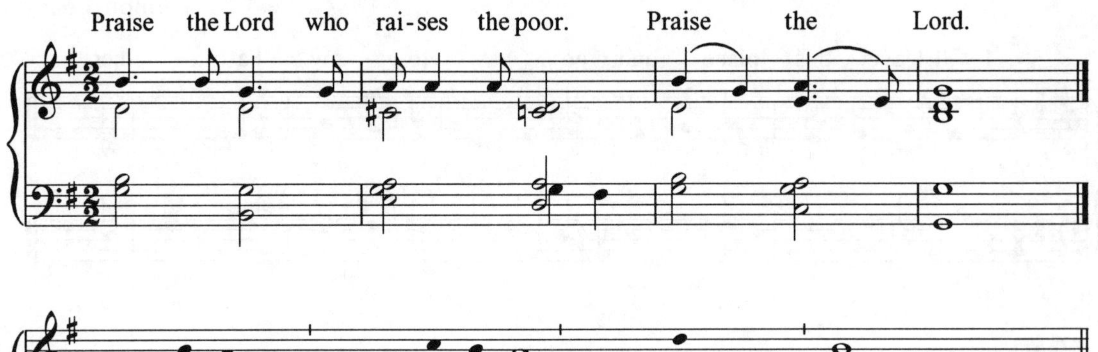

Praise the Lord who rai-ses the poor. Praise the Lord.

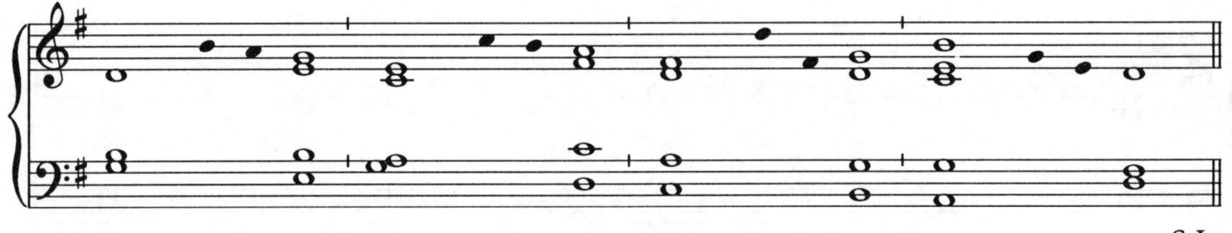

S.L.

1. Praise, O servants of the Lord,
   praise the name of the Lord!
   May the name of the Lord be blessed
   both now and for evermore.

2. Who is like the Lord, our God,
   who has risen on high to his throne
   yet stoops from the heights to look down,
   to look down upon heaven and earth?

3. From the dust he lifts up the lowly,
   from the dungheap he raises the poor
   to set them in the company of rulers,
   yes, with the rulers of his people.

Gospel Acclamation cf. Acts 16:14

Alleluia.
Open our heart, O Lord,
to accept the words of your Son.
Alleluia.

or 2 Corinthians 8:9

Alleluia.
Jesus Christ was rich,
but he became poor for your sake, to make you rich out of his poverty.
Alleluia.

C Instrument
B♭ Instrument

Twenty-Sixth Sunday in Ordinary Time

Responsorial Psalm Psalm 145:6-10. Response v.2 YEAR C

Andrew Wright

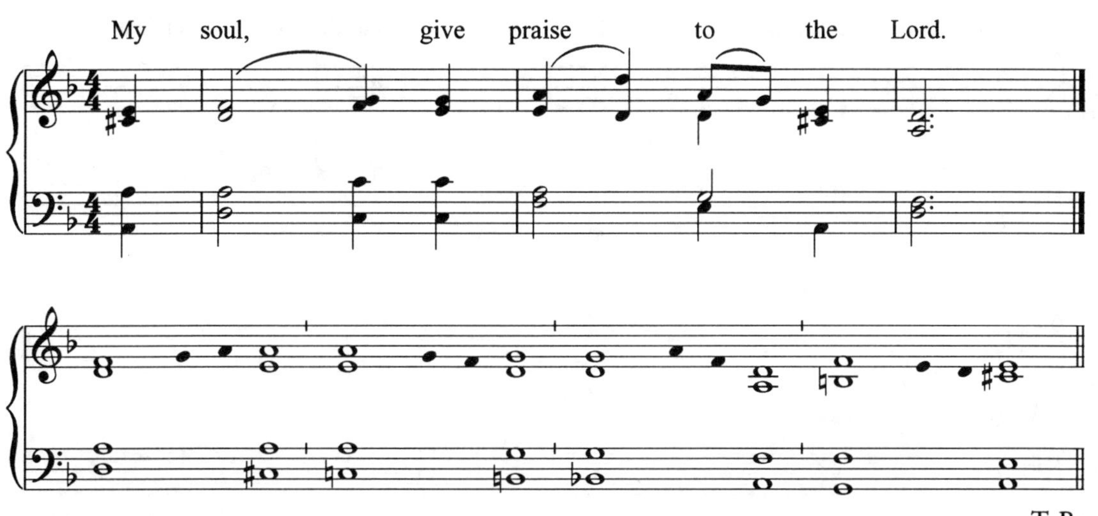
My soul, give praise to the Lord.
T.B.

1. It is the Lord who keeps faith for ever,
   who is just to those who are oppressed.
   It is he who gives bread to the hungry,
   the Lord, who sets prisoners free.

2. It is the Lord who gives sight to the blind,
   who raises up those who are bowed down.
   It is the Lord who loves the just,
   the Lord, who protects the stranger.

3. He upholds the widow and orphan
   but thwarts the path of the wicked.
   The Lord will reign for ever,
   Zion's God, from age to age.

Gospel Acclamation John 10:27

Alleluia, alleluia!
The sheep that belong to me listen to my voice, says the Lord,
I know them and they follow me.
Alleluia!

or 2 Corinthians 8:9

Alleluia.
Jesus Christ was rich,
but he became poor for your sake, to make you rich out of his poverty.
Alleluia.

C Instrument
B♭ Instrument

Twenty-Seventh Sunday in Ordinary Time

Responsorial Psalm Psalm 94:1-2, 6-9. Response v.9 YEAR C

Simon Lesley

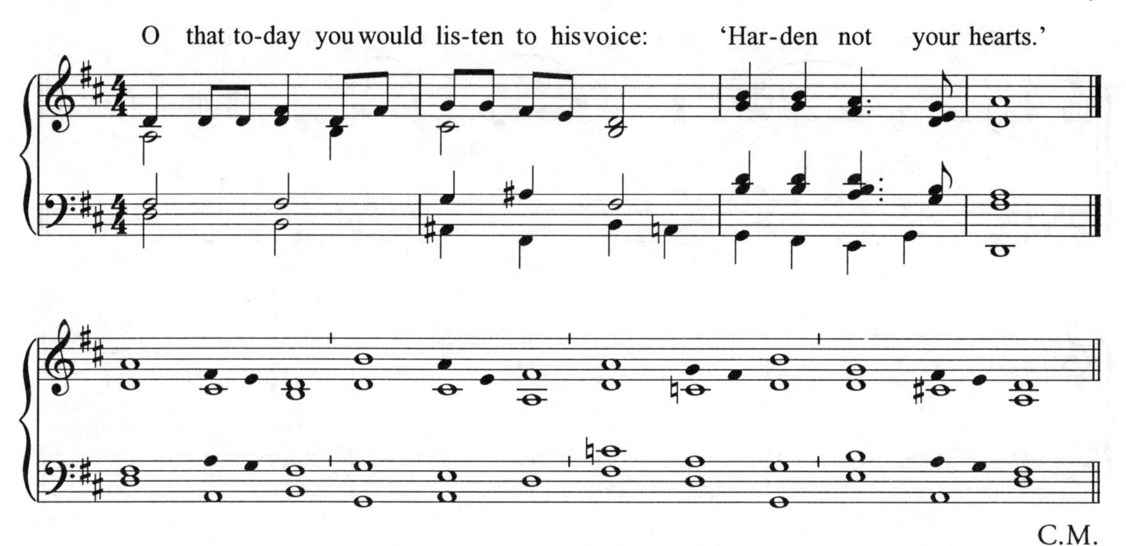

1. Come, ring out our joy to the Lord;
   hail the rock who saves us.
   Let us come before him, giving thanks,
   with songs let us hail the Lord.

2. Come in; let us bow and bend low;
   let us kneel before the God who made us
   for he is our God, and we the people who
   belong to his pasture,
   the flock that is led by his hand.

3. O that today you would listen to his voice!
   'Harden not your hearts as at Meribah,
   as on that day at Massah in the desert, when
   your fathers put me to the test;
   when they tried me, though they saw my work.'

Gospel Acclamation 1 Samuel 3:9; John 6:68

Alleluia.
Speak, Lord, your servant is listening:
you have the message of eternal life.
Alleluia.

or 1 Peter 1:25

Alleluia.
The word of the Lord remains for ever:
What is this word? It is the Good News that has been brought to you.
Alleluia.

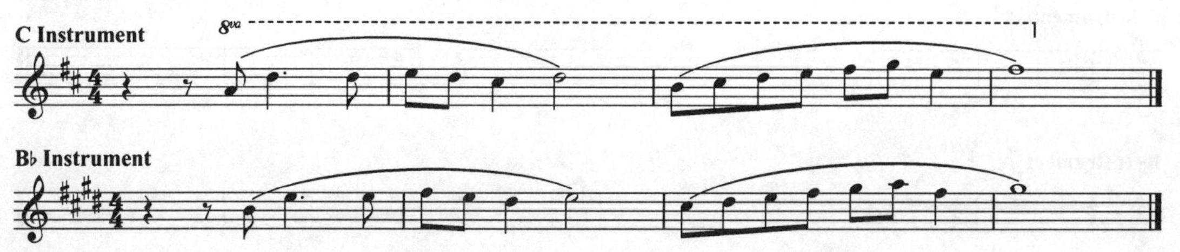

Twenty-Eighth Sunday in Ordinary Time

Responsorial Psalm Psalm 97:1-4. Response cf. v.2

YEAR C

Richard Lloyd

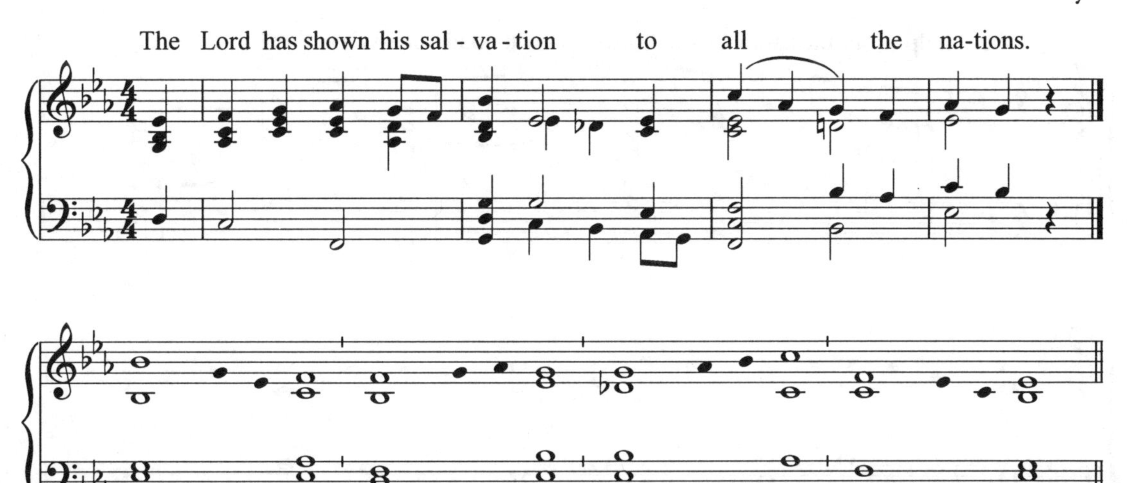

G.N.

1. Sing a new song to the Lord
   for he has worked wonders.
   His right hand and his holy arm
   have brought salvation.

2. The Lord has made known his salvation;
   has shown his justice to the nations.
   He has remembered his truth and love
   for the house of Israel.

3. All the ends of the earth have seen
   the salvation of our God.
   Shout to the Lord all the earth,
   ring out your joy.

Gospel Acclamation cf. John 6:63, 68

Alleluia.
Your words are spirit, Lord, and they are life;
you have the message of eternal life.
Alleluia.

or 1 Thessalonians 5:18

Alleluia.
For all things give thanks,
because this is what God expects you to do in Christ Jesus.
Alleluia.

Twenty-Ninth Sunday in Ordinary Time

Responsorial Psalm Psalm 120. Response cf. v.2

YEAR C

John McCann

K.D.

1. I lift up my eyes to the mountains:
   from where shall come my help?
   My help shall come from the Lord
   who made heaven and earth.

2. May he never allow you to stumble!
   Let him sleep not, your guard.
   No, he sleeps not nor slumbers,
   Israel's guard.

3. The Lord is your guard and your shade;
   at your right side he stands.
   By day the sun shall not smite you
   nor the moon in the night.

4. The Lord will guard you from evil,
   he will guard your soul.
   The Lord will guard your going and coming
   both now and for ever.

Gospel Acclamation cf. Ephesians 1:17, 18

Alleluia.
May the Father of our Lord Jesus Christ enlighten the eyes of our mind,
so that we can see what hope his call holds for us.
Alleluia.

or Hebrews 4:12

Alleluia.
The word of God is something alive and active;
it can judge secret emotions and thoughts.
Alleluia.

Thirtieth Sunday in Ordinary Time YEAR C

Responsorial Psalm Psalm 32:2-3, 17-19, 23. Response v.7

Andrew Moore

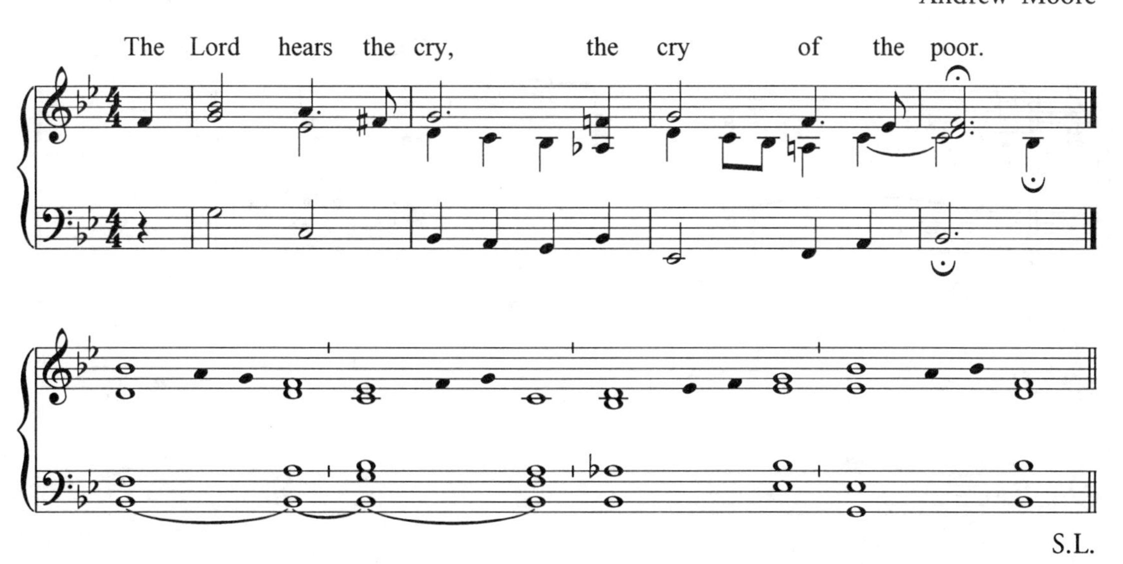

The Lord hears the cry, the cry of the poor.
S.L.

1. I will bless the Lord at all times,
   his praise always on my lips;
   in the Lord my soul shall make its boast.
   The humble shall hear and be glad.

2. The Lord turns his face against the wicked
   to destroy their remembrance from the earth.
   The just call and the Lord hears
   and rescues them in all their distress.

3. The Lord is close to the broken-hearted;
   those whose spirit is crushed he will save.
   The Lord ransoms the souls of his servants.
   Those who hide in him shall not be condemned.

Gospel Acclamation cf. Matthew 11:25

Alleluia.
Blessed are you, Father, Lord of heaven and earth,
for revealing the mysteries of the kingdom to mere children.
Alleluia.

or 2 Corinthians 5:19

Alleluia.
God in Christ was reconciling the world to himself,
and he has entrusted to us the news that they are reconciled.
Alleluia.

Thirty-First Sunday in Ordinary Time YEAR C

Responsorial Psalm Psalm 144:1-2, 8-11, 13-14. Response cf. v.1

Colin Mawby

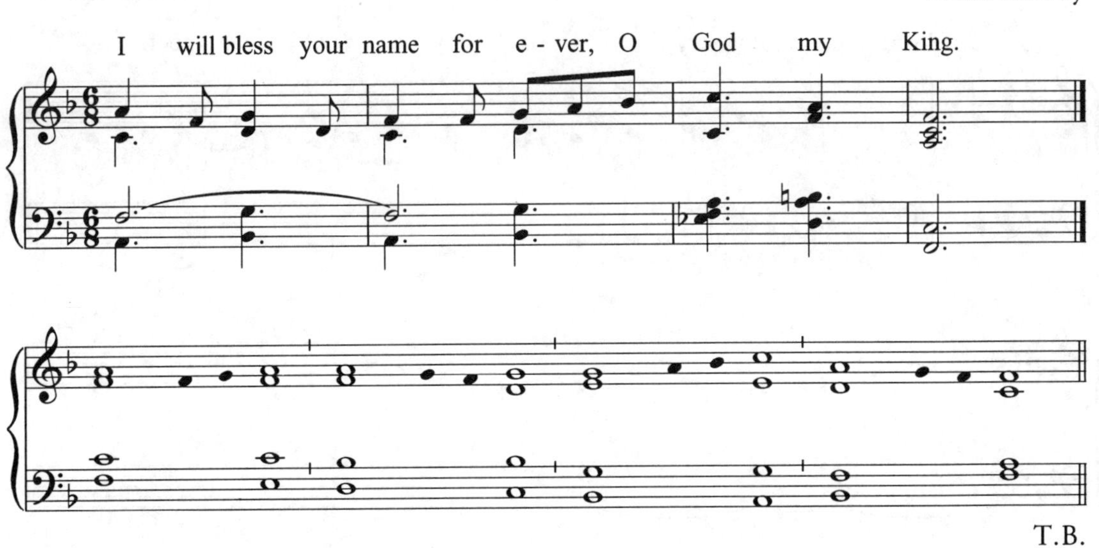
I will bless your name for e - ver, O God my King.
T.B.

1. I will give you glory, O God my King,
   I will bless your name for ever.
   I will bless you day after day
   and praise your name for ever.

2. The Lord is kind and full of compassion,
   slow to anger, abounding in love.
   How good is the Lord to all,
   compassionate to all his creatures.

3. All your creatures shall thank you, O Lord,
   and your friends shall repeat their blessing.
   They shall speak of the glory of your reign
   and declare your might, O God.

4. The Lord is faithful in all his words
   and loving in all his deeds.
   The Lord supports all who fall
   and raises all who are bowed down.

Gospel Acclamation Luke 19:38

Alleluia.
Blessings on the King who comes in the name of the Lord!
Peace in heaven and glory in the highest heavens!
Alleluia.

or John 3:16

Alleluia.
God loved the world so much that he gave his only Son,
so that everyone who believes in him may have eternal life.
Alleluia.

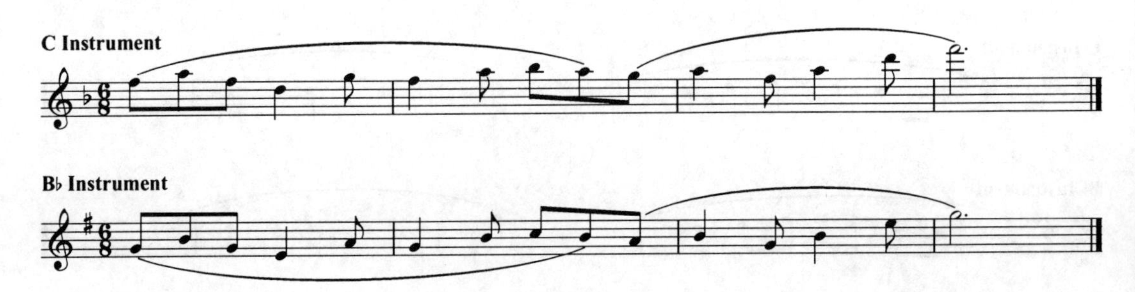
C Instrument
B♭ Instrument

Thirty-Second Sunday in Ordinary Time

Responsorial Psalm Psalm 16:1, 5-6, 8, 15. Response v.15

YEAR C

Keith Duke

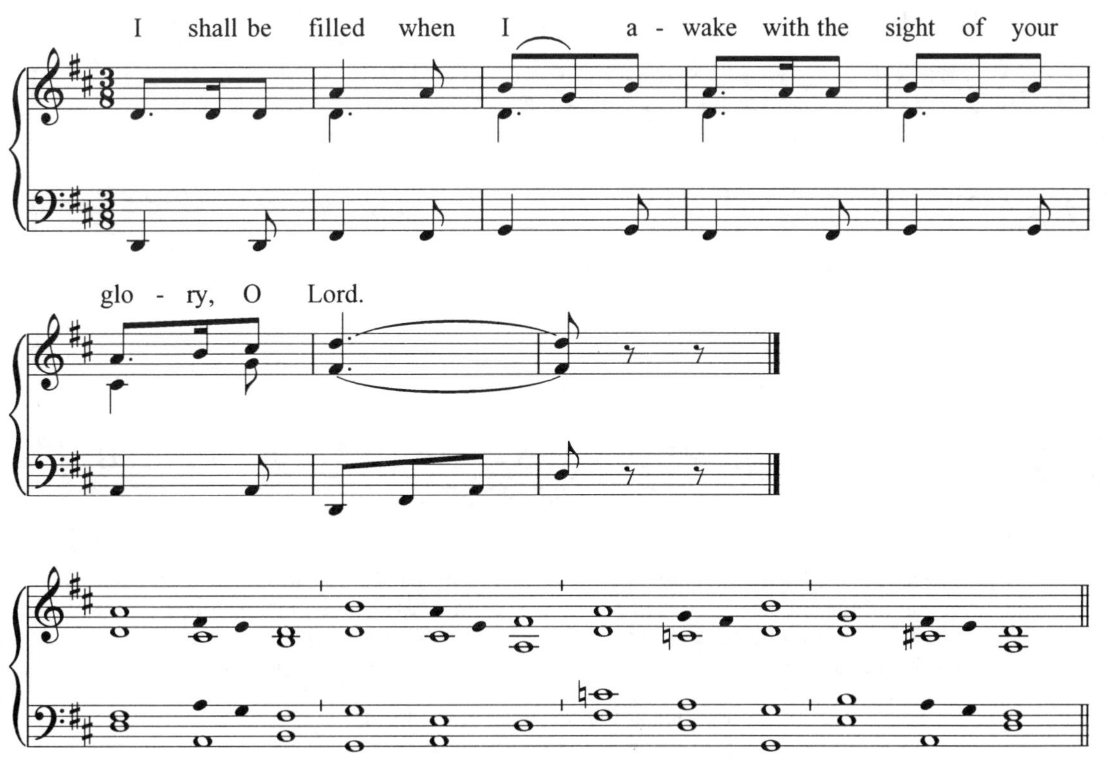
I shall be filled when I a - wake with the sight of your
glo - ry, O Lord.
C.M.

1. Lord, hear a cause that is just,
   pay heed to my cry.
   Turn your ear to my prayer:
   no deceit is on my lips.

2. I kept my feet firmly in your paths;
   there was no faltering in my steps.
   I am here and I call, you will hear me, O God.
   Turn your ear to me; hear my words.

3. Guard me as the apple of your eye.
   Hide me in the shadow of your wings.
   As for me, in my justice I shall see your face
   and be filled, when I awake, with the sight of your glory.

Gospel Acclamation Luke 21:36

Alleluia.
Stay awake, praying at all times
for the strength to stand with confidence
before the Son of Man.
Alleluia.

or Revelation 1:5, 6

Alleluia.
Jesus Christ is the First-born from the dead;
to him be glory and power for ever and ever.
Alleluia.

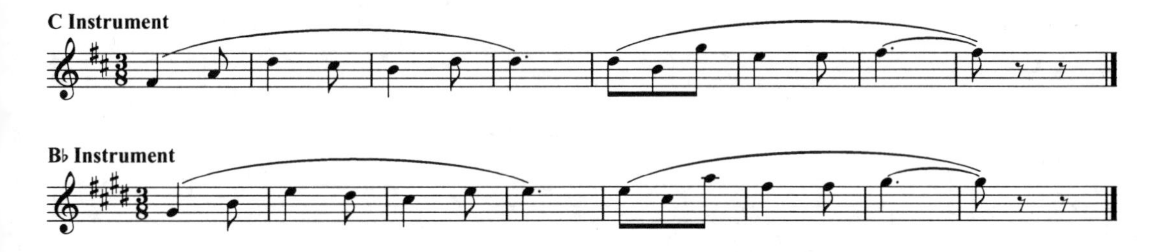
C Instrument
B♭ Instrument

Thirty-Third Sunday in Ordinary Time YEAR C

Responsorial Psalm Psalm 97:5-9. Response cf. v.9

Geoff Nobes

1. Sing psalms to the Lord with the harp
   with the sound of music.
   With trumpets and the sound of the horn
   acclaim the King, the Lord.

2. Let the sea and all within it, thunder;
   the world, and all its peoples.
   Let the rivers clap their hands
   and the hills ring out their joy.

3. Rejoice at the presence of the Lord,
   for he comes to rule the earth.
   He will rule the world with justice
   and the peoples with fairness.

Gospel Acclamation Luke 21:36

Alleluia.
Stay awake, praying at all times
for the strength to stand with confidence before the Son of Man.
Alleluia.

or Luke 21:28

Alleluia.
Stand erect, hold your heads high,
because your liberation is near at hand.
Alleluia.

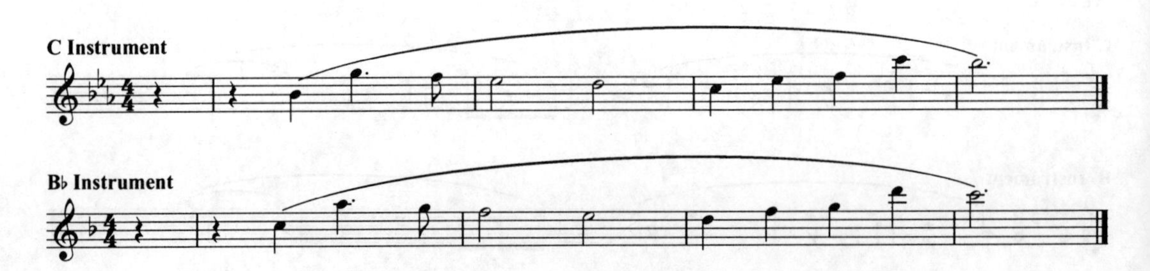

Last Sunday in Ordinary Time

YEAR C

Our Lord Jesus Christ, Universal King

Responsorial Psalm Psalm 121:1-5. Response cf. v.2

John McCann

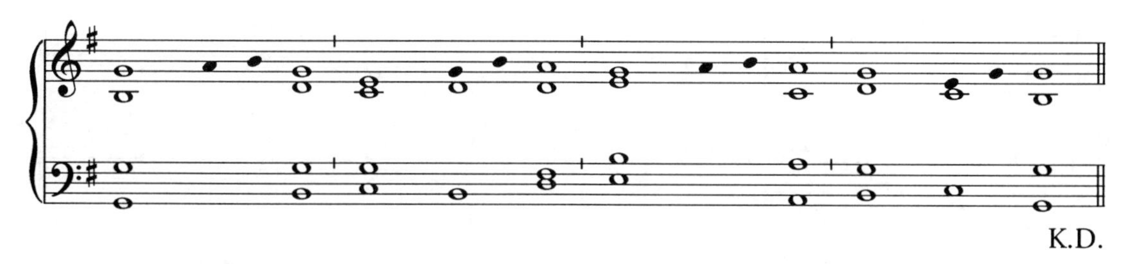

1. I rejoiced when I heard them say:
   'Let us go to God's house.'
   And now our feet are standing
   within your gates, O Jerusalem.

2. Jerusalem is built as a city
   strongly compact.
   It is there that the tribes go up,
   the tribes of the Lord.

3. For Israel's law it is,
   there to praise the Lord's name.
   There were set the thrones of judgement
   of the house of David.

Gospel Acclamation Mark 11:9, 10

Alleluia.
Blessings on him who comes in the name of the Lord!
Blessings on the coming kingdom of our father David!
Alleluia.

2 February

The Presentation of the Lord

YEARS A, B AND C

Responsorial Psalm Psalm 23:7-10. Response v.8

Keith Duke

S.L.

1. O gates, lift up your heads;
   grow higher, ancient doors.
   Let him enter, the King of Glory!

2. Who is the King of Glory?
   The Lord, the mighty, the valiant,
   the Lord, the valiant in war.

3. O gates, lift high your heads;
   grow higher, ancient doors.
   Let him enter, the King of Glory!

4. Who is he, the King of Glory?
   He, the Lord of armies,
   he is the King of Glory.

Gospel Acclamation Luke 2:32

Alleluia.
The light to enlighten the Gentiles
and give glory to Israel, your people.
Alleluia.

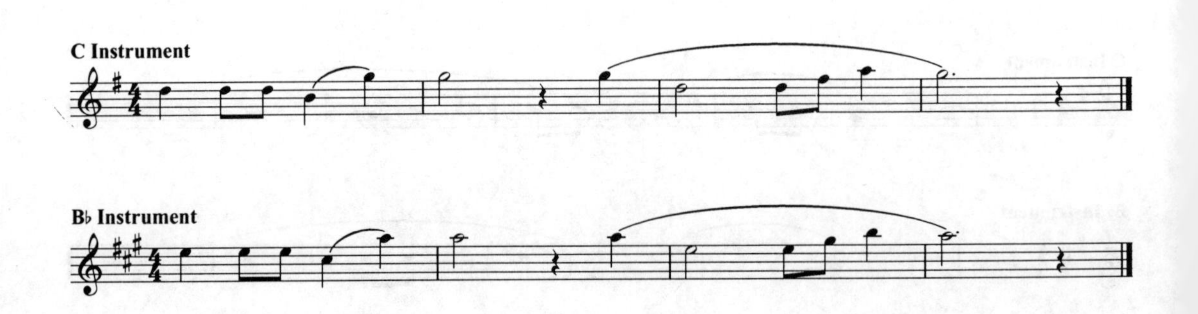

24 June

The Birth of St John the Baptist

YEARS A, B AND C

Responsorial Psalm Psalm 138:1-3, 13-15. Response v.14

Andrew Wright

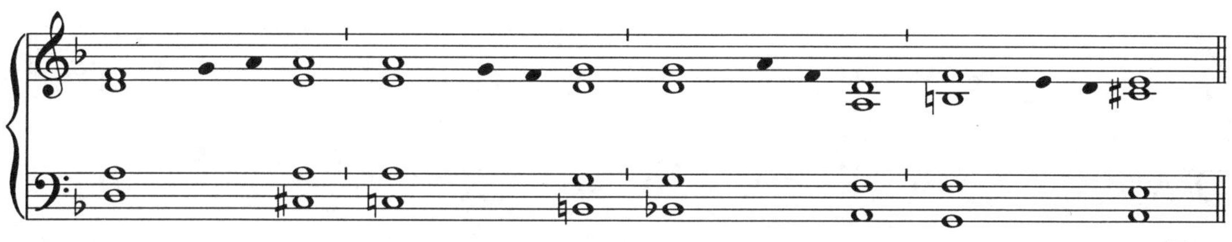

T.B.

1. O Lord, you search me and you know me,
   you know my resting and my rising,
   you discern my purpose from afar.
   You mark when I walk or lie down,
   all my ways lie open to you.

2. For it was you who created my being,
   knit me together in my mother's womb.
   I thank you for the wonder of my being,
   for the wonders of all your creation.

3. Already you knew my soul,
   my body held no secret from you
   when I was being fashioned in secret
   and moulded in the depths of the earth.

Gospel Acclamation cf. Luke 1:76

Alleluia.
As for you, little child, you shall be called a prophet of God, the Most High.
You shall go ahead of the Lord to prepare his ways before him.
Alleluia.

29 June

YEARS A, B AND C

SS Peter and Paul, Apostles

Responsorial Psalm Psalm 33:2-9. Response v.5. Alt. Response v.8

Keith Duke

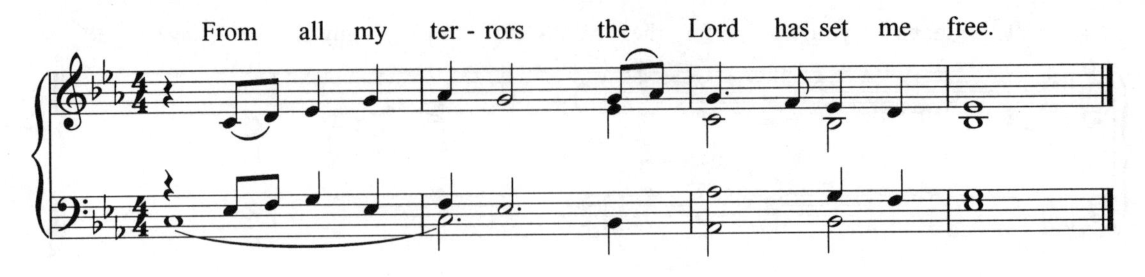

From all my ter - rors the Lord has set me free.

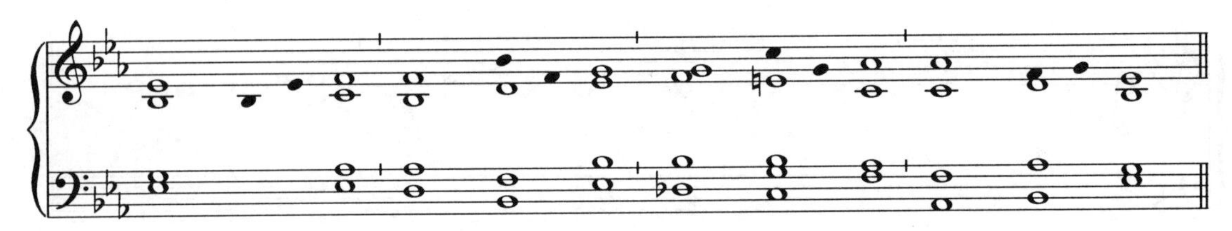

C.M.

1. I will bless the Lord at all times,
   his praise always on my lips;
   in the Lord my soul shall make its boast.
   The humble shall hear and be glad.

2. Glorify the Lord with me.
   Together let us praise his name.
   I sought the Lord and he answered me;
   from all my terrors he set me free.

3. Look towards him and be radiant;
   let your faces not be abashed.
   When the poor cry out the Lord hears them,
   and rescues them from all their distress.

4. The angel of the Lord is encamped
   around those who revere him, to rescue them.
   Taste and see that the Lord is good.
   They are happy who seek refuge in him.

Gospel Acclamation Matthew 16:18

Alleluia.
You are Peter and on this rock I will build my church.
And the gates of the underworld can never hold out against it.
Alleluia.

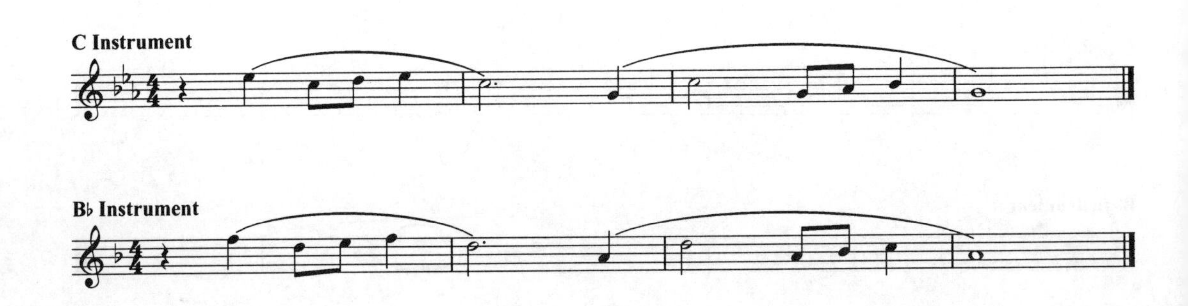

6 August

YEARS A, B AND C

The Transfiguration of the Lord

Responsorial Psalm Psalm 96:1-2, 5-6, 9. Response vv.1, 9

John McCann

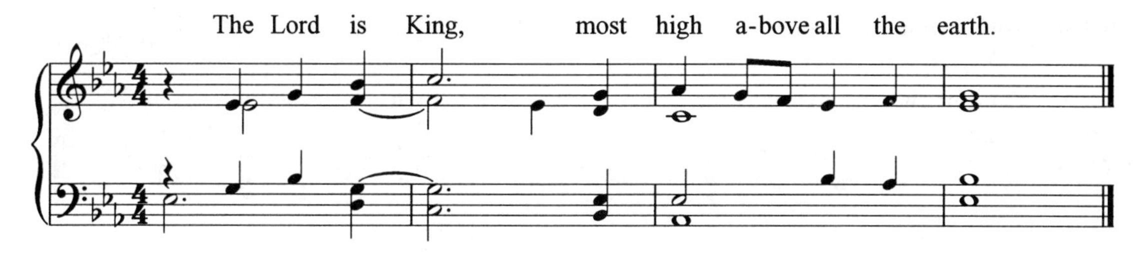
The Lord is King, most high a-bove all the earth.

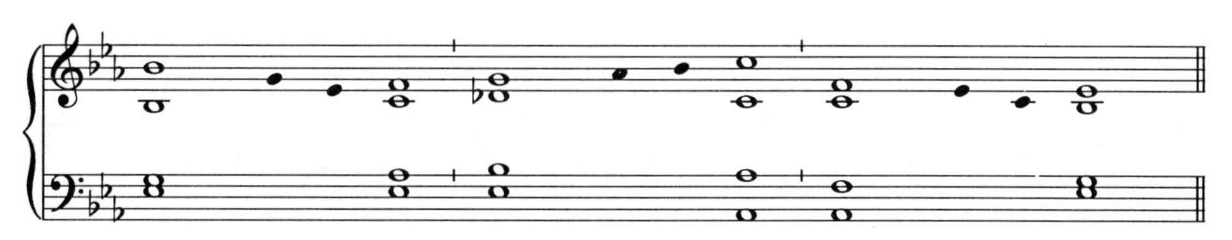

G.N.

1. The Lord is king, let earth rejoice,
   let all the coastlands be glad.
   His throne, justice and right.

2. The mountains melt like wax
   before the Lord of all the earth.
   All peoples see his glory.

3. For you indeed are the Lord
   most high above all the earth
   exalted far above all spirits.

Gospel Acclamation Matthew 17:5

Alleluia.
This is my Son, the Beloved,
he enjoys my favour; listen to him.
Alleluia.

C Instrument
B♭ Instrument

15 August

YEARS A, B AND C

The Assumption of the Blessed Virgin Mary

Responsorial Psalm Psalm 44:10-12, 16. Response v.10

Geoff Nobes

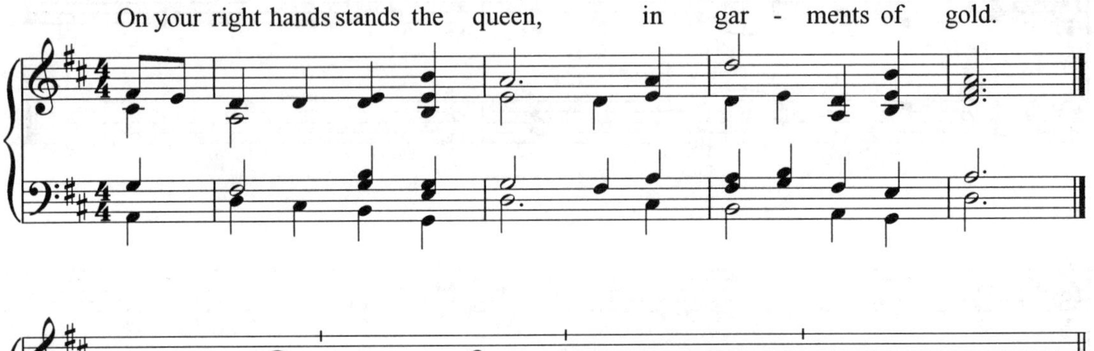

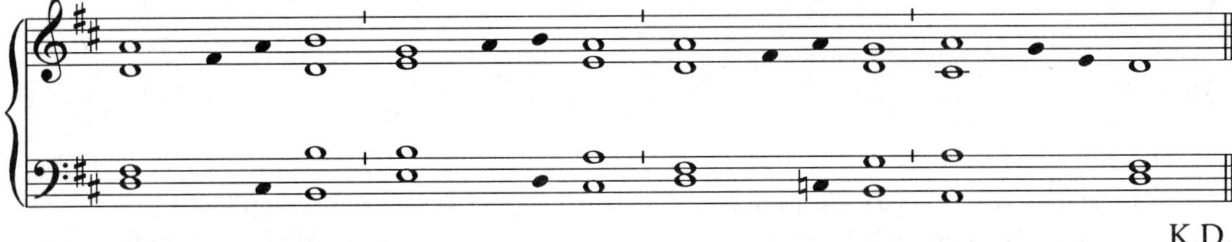

1. The daughters of kings are among your loved ones.
   On your right stands the queen in gold of Ophir.
   Listen, O daughter, give ear to my words:
   forget your own people and your father's house.

2. So will the king desire your beauty.
   He is your lord, pay homage to him.
   They are escorted amid gladness and joy;
   they pass within the palace of the king.

Gospel Acclamation

Alleluia.
Mary has been taken up into heaven;
all the choirs of angels are rejoicing.
Alleluia.

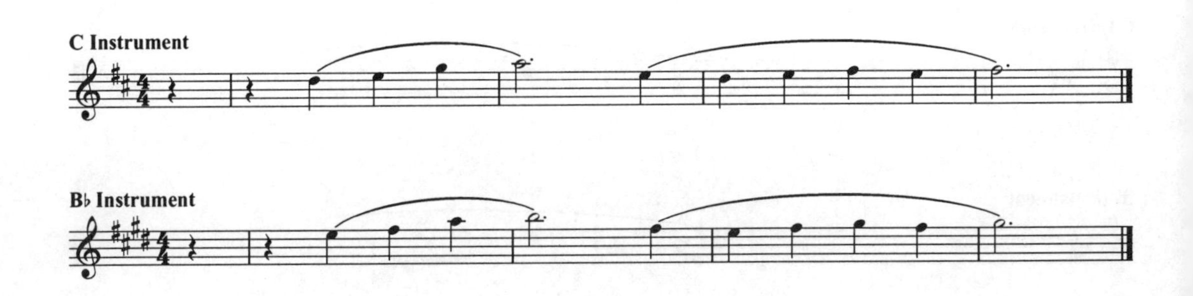

14 September

YEARS A, B AND C

The Triumph of the Cross

Responsorial Psalm Psalm 77:1-2, 34-38. Response v.7

Geoff Nobes

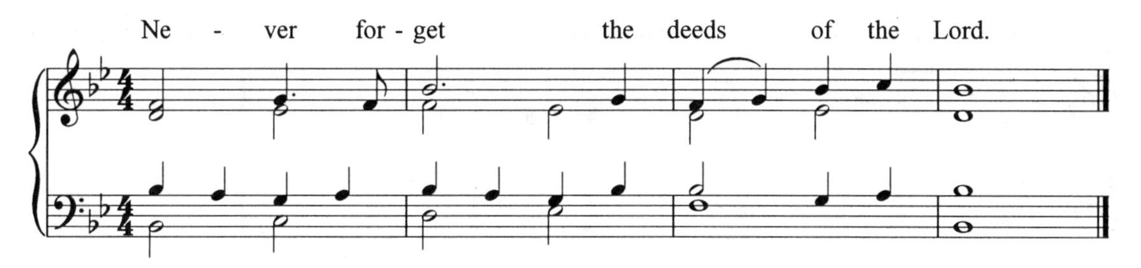

Ne - ver for - get the deeds of the Lord.

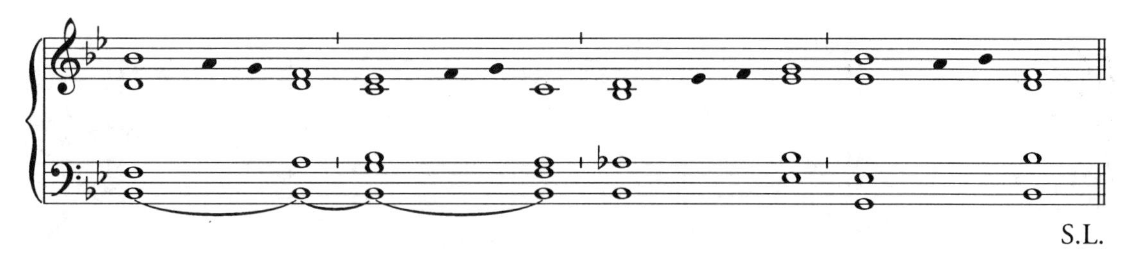

S.L.

1. Give heed, my people, to my teaching;
   turn your ear to the words of my mouth.
   I will open my mouth in a parable
   and reveal hidden lessons of the past.

2. When he slew them then they would seek him,
   return and seek him in earnest.
   They would remember that God was their rock,
   God the Most High their redeemer.

3. But the words they spoke were mere flattery
   they lied to him with their lips.
   For their hearts were not truly with him;
   they were not faithful to his covenant.

4. Yet he who is full of compassion
   forgave their sin and spared them.
   So often he held back his anger
   when he might have stirred up his rage.

Gospel Acclamation

Alleluia.
We adore you, O Christ, and we bless you;
because by your cross you have redeemed the world.
Alleluia.

1 November YEARS A, B AND C

All Saints

Responsorial Psalm Psalm 23:1-6. Response cf. v.6

Keith Duke

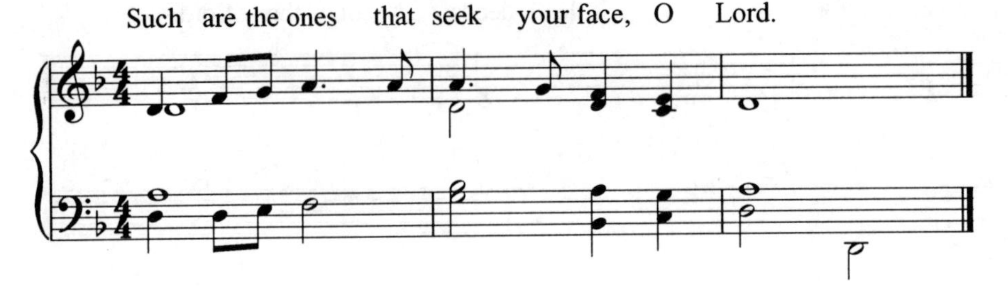

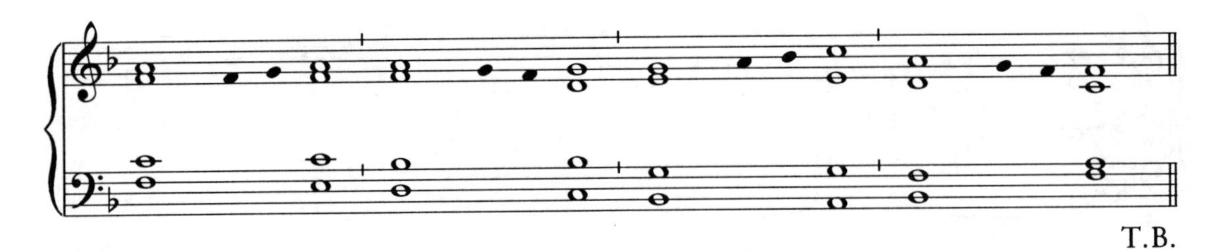

1. The Lord's is the earth and its fullness,
   the world and all its peoples.
   It is he who set it on the seas;
   on the waters he made it firm.

2. Who shall climb the mountain of the Lord?
   Who shall stand in his holy place?
   Those with clean hands and pure heart,
   who desire not worthless things.

3. They shall receive blessings from the Lord
   and reward from the God who saves them.
   Such are the ones who seek him,
   seek the face of the God of Jacob.

Gospel Acclamation Matthew 11:28

Alleluia.
Come to me, all you who labour and are overburdened,
and I will give you rest, says the Lord.
Alleluia.

C Instrument

B♭ Instrument

2 November

YEARS A, B AND C

The Commemoration of all the Faithful Departed

Responsorial Psalm Psalm 26:1, 4, 7-9, 13-14. Response v.1. Alt. Response v.13

Geoff Nobes

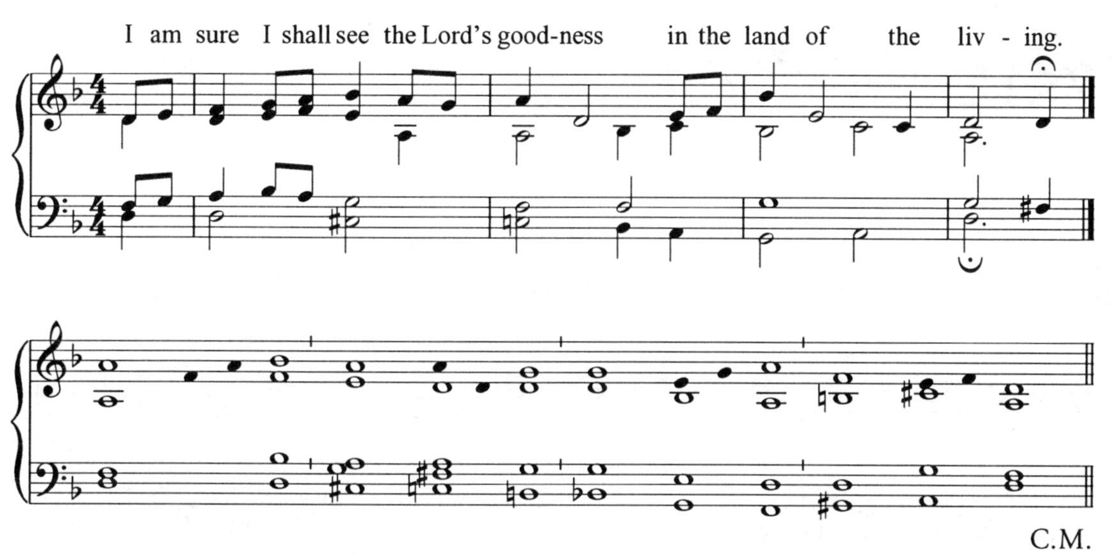

1. The Lord is my light and my help;
   whom shall I fear?
   The Lord is the stronghold of my life;
   before whom shall I shrink?

2. There is one thing I ask of the Lord,
   for this I long,
   to live in the house of the Lord,
   all the days of my life.

3. O Lord, hear my voice when I call;
   have mercy and answer.
   It is your face, O Lord, that I seek;
   hide not your face.

4. I am sure I shall see the Lord's goodness
   in the land of the living.
   Hope in him, hold firm and take heart.
   Hope in the Lord!

Gospel Acclamation John 6:39

Alleluia.
It is my Father's will, says the Lord, that I should lose nothing of all that he has given me,
and that I should raise it up on the last day.
Alleluia.

The Dedication of a Church

Responsorial Psalm Psalm 45:2-3, 5-6, 8-9. Response v.5

Geoff Nobes

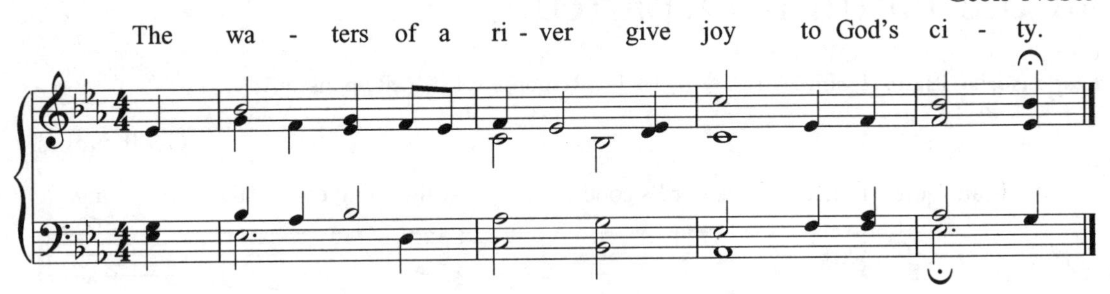

1. God is for us a refuge and strength,
   a helper close at hand, in time of distress:
   so we shall not fear though the earth should rock,
   though the mountains fall into the depths of the sea.

2. The waters of a river give joy to God's city,
   the holy place where the Most High dwells.
   God is within, it cannot be shaken;
   God will help it at the dawning of the day.

3. The Lord of hosts is with us:
   the God of Jacob is our stronghold.
   Come, consider the works of the Lord
   the redoubtable deeds he has done on the earth.

Gospel Acclamation 2 Chronicles 7:16

Alleluia.
I have chosen and consecrated this house, says the Lord,
for my name to be there for ever.
Alleluia.

Psalms suitable for funerals

Psalm 121 I rejoiced when I heard them say:
'Let us go to God's house.'

First Sunday of Advent, Year A – page 11

Psalm 114 I will walk in the presence of the Lord
in the land of the living.

Second Sunday of Lent, Year B – page 40

Psalm 26 The Lord is my light and my help.

Second Sunday of Lent, Year C – page 41

Psalm 102 The Lord is compassion and love.

Third Sunday of Lent, Year C – page 44

Psalm 22 The Lord is my shepherd;
there is nothing I shall want.

Christ the King, Year A – page 125

Psalm 129 With the Lord there is mercy
and fullness of redemption.

Fifth Sunday of Lent, Year A – page 48

Psalm 62 For you my soul is thirsting, O Lord my God.

Twenty-Second Sunday in Ordinary Time, Year A – page 111

Psalm 41 Like the deer that yearns for running streams,
so my soul is yearning for you, my God.

The Easter Vigil (after the seventh Reading) – page 60

Psalms suitable for weddings

Psalm 127 O blessed are those who fear the Lord.

The Holy Family – page 25

Psalm 33 Taste and see that the Lord is good.

Fourth Sunday of Lent, Year C – page 47

Psalm 32 May your love be upon us, O Lord,
as we place all our hope in you.

Second Sunday of Lent, Year A – page 39

Psalm 22 The Lord is my shepherd;
there is nothing I shall want.

Christ the King, Year A – page 125

Psalm 127 May the Lord bless us all the days of our life.

Twenty-Seventh Sunday in Ordinary Time, Year B – page 152

Music for Gospel Acclamations

Throughout the year 1

Fintan O'Carroll

Al - le - lu - ia, al - le - lu - ia,
al - le - lu - ia, al - le - lu - ia.
K.D.
C Instrument
B♭ Instrument

Colin Mawby

Throughout the year 2

Jacques Berthier

G.N.

Colin Mawby

C Instrument

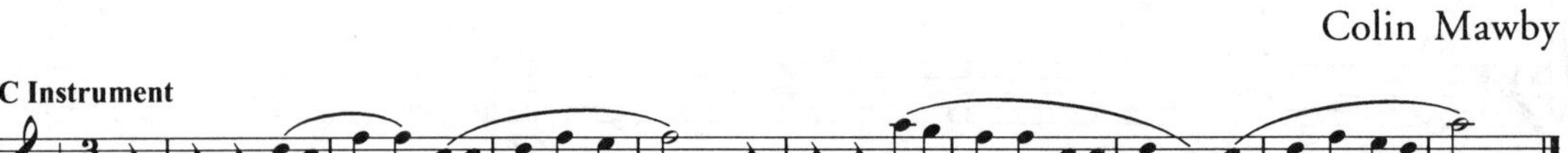

B♭ Instrument

Throughout the year 3

Richard Lloyd

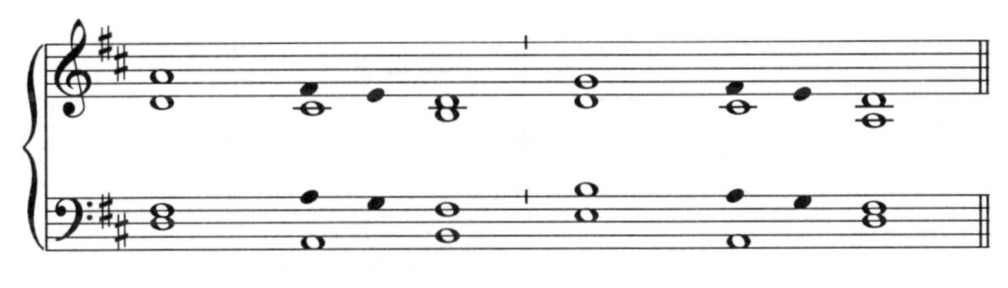

C.M.

C Instrument
B♭ Instrument

Throughout the year 4

Plainsong arr. Andrew Moore

Al - le - lu - ia, al - le - lu - ia, al - le - lu - ia.

S.L.

C Instrument

B♭ Instrument

Throughout the year 5

Gerry Fitzpatrick

Al - le - lu - ia, al - le - lu - ia, al - le - lu - ia.

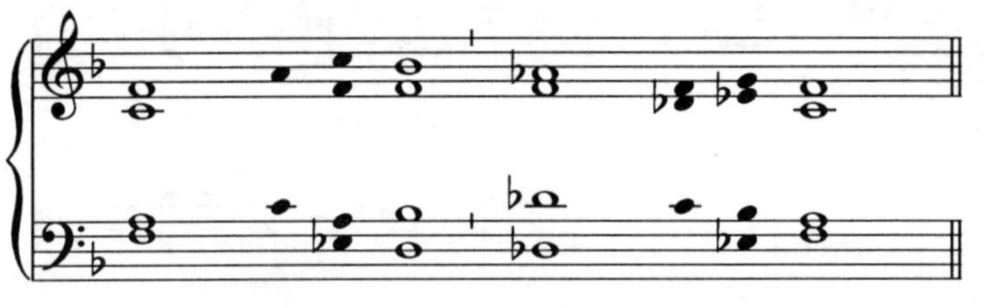

K.D.

C Instrument

B♭ Instrument

Throughout the year 6

Geoff Nobes

Al - le - lu - ia, al - le -
lu - ia, al - le - lu - ia.

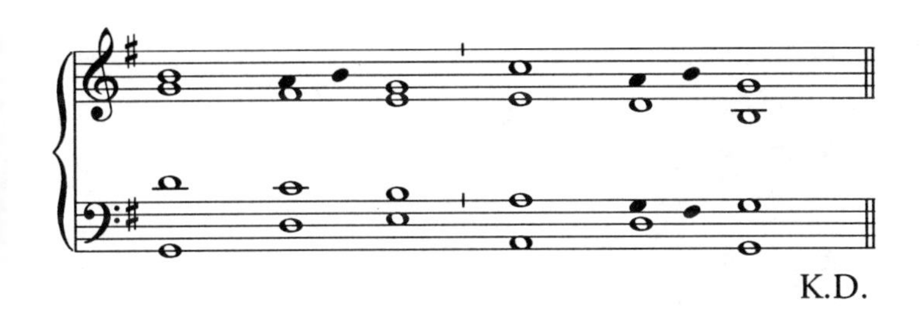

K.D.

C Instrument
B♭ Instrument

Throughout the year 7

Keith Duke

Al - le - lu - ia, al - le - lu - ia; al - le - lu - ia, al - le - lu - ia!

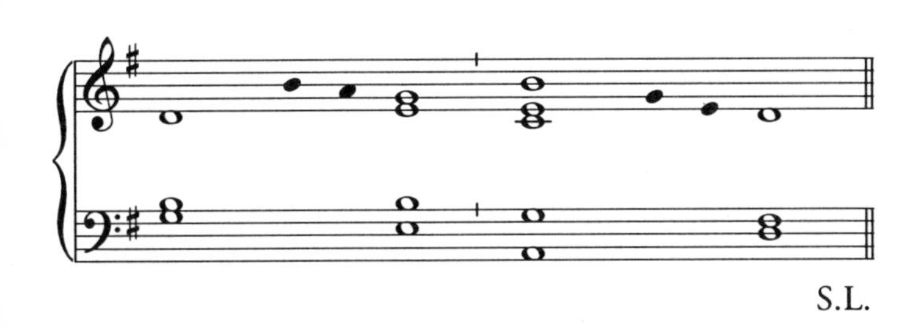

S.L.

C Instrument
B♭ Instrument

Throughout the year 8

Simon Lesley

Al - le - lu - ia!

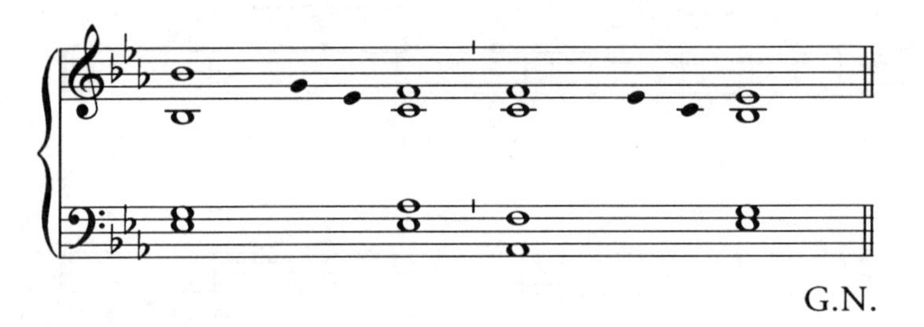

G.N.

C Instrument
8va

B♭ Instrument

Throughout the year 9

John McCann

Al - le - lu - ia.

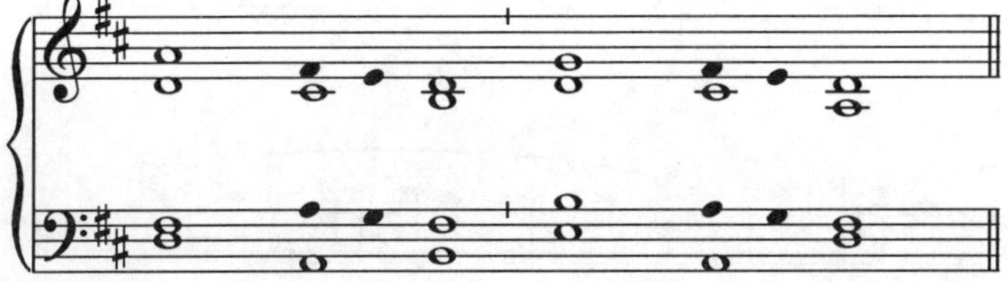

C.M.

C Instrument

B♭ Instrument

During Lent and Holy Week 1

Colin Mawby

Praise to you, O Christ, King of e - ter - nal glo - ry.

K.D.

C Instrument

B♭ Instrument

During Lent and Holy Week 2
Colin Mawby
Glo - ry and praise to you, O Christ! Glo - ry and praise to you, O Christ!
K.D.
C Instrument
B♭ Instrument
During the Easter Season
Plainsong arr. Andrew Moore
Al - le - lu - ia, al - le - lu - ia, al - le - lu - ia.
A.G.M.
C Instrument
B♭ Instrument